ORIGINS OF MODERN PSYCHIATRY

ORIGINS OF MODERN PSYCHIATRY

By

ERNEST HARMS, Ph.D.

Editor-in-Chief of the Journal ADOLESCENCE

With a Foreword by

FRANCIS J. BRACELAND, M.D.

Senior Consultant, Institute of Living
Editor, AMERICAN JOURNAL OF PSYCHIATRY
Clinical Professor of Psychiatry, Yale University
Lecturer on Psychiatry, Harvard University
Cambridge, Massachusetts

CHARLES C THOMAS · PUBLISHER
Springfield · Illinois · U.S.A.

Published and Distributed Throughout the World by
CHARLES C THOMAS • PUBLISHER
BANNERSTONE HOUSE
301-327 East Lawrence Avenue, Springfield, Illinois, U.S.A.
NATCHEZ PLANTATION HOUSE
735 North Atlantic Boulevard, Fort Lauderdale, Florida, U.S.A.

With THOMAS BOOKS *careful attention is given to all details of manufacturing and design. It is the Publisher's desire to present books that are satisfactory as to their physical qualities and artistic possibilities and appropriate for their particular use.* THOMAS BOOKS *will be true to those laws of quality that assure a good name and good will.*

Printed in the United States of America
C-1

FOREWORD

THIS volume is the record of the culmination of half a century of the research and experience of Ernest Harms; it covers the period from the time of Paracelsus—the works of whom continue to fascinate Dr. Harms—to the present and about which he is a keen commentator. He has been a close observer of the works of Freud, Jung, Adler, and their contemporaries, and for almost a decade he helped Jung collect material for his works on alchemy.

His insights should be extremely interesting to the reader today. He has been occupied in tracing original documents. He is distressed that solidity and sureness of thinking are not everywhere apparent in current psychiatric thought. He believes that if he can inspire in some of us the feeling that one cannot be a good psychiatrist without definite knowledge of the origins of his field, he will have justified his efforts.

The first chapter of this work is entitled "A New Approach to a History of Psychiatry." Dr. Harms here announces his intention "to study the various periods of Psychism and somatophysiology with a view to finding a unifying line." This unifying line is what he designates *the humanitarian approach,* which rests mainly on basic socioethical concepts that have been at issue at one period or another. He predicts that the future for existentialism is promising, but uncertainty still hovers over it.

The author is not at all happy about Friedreich's book published in 1830 because he feels that the contents were plagiarized from Heinroth. He is unhappy about many of the histories of psychiatry published in the past twenty-five years, for he believes them to be full of errors. Also he regrets exceedingly "fanatic rejection of previously expressed ideas by propagators of new theories."

Laehr, he points out, summarized the work of 8,500 authors from 1459 to 1799, but he believes he is justified in saying there was no real psychiatric historical information prior to 1800. He attributes the first real history of psychiatry to Heinroth (1818) and believes it can be demonstrated that Friedreich's work is a rehash of that first volume. Friedreich's second book was published in 1836, and for forty years thereafter there was no extensive textbook on the history of psychiatry until Lentz' volume appeared in 1876. It was basically a book on socioethical care of the mentally ill, and that approach is humanitarianism.

It is not possible to comment upon each of the chapters of this work, much as one might desire to do so. The chapter on Paracelsus as seen through the eyes of Heinrich Damerow (1798-1869) puts Paracelsus in a new light. Damerow had to read all of his works in order to understand him, for many approximations of Paracelsus were unfair. Paracelsus had to fight against the approach of his contemporaries, for they led in some instances to astrological alchemy, yet he had to use the terminology of the alchemists in so doing, for it was with this that people were familiar. Also, although it has been nearly forgotten, Paracelsus classified mental diseases. Most important, however, was the "sense of causality" which imbued him to find causes and even causes of causes. Damerow believed that it was the work of Paracelsus which enabled later psychiatric concepts to come to flower. Paracelsus himself summarized his method by saying that "the task is to find in the insane traces of still sound consciousness and to use them on the basis for a psychointellectual attempt at cure."

There are chapters on Felix Plater, under whom the change to the medical and psychological view of man began; Georg Ernst Stahl, about whom few have heard, yet who the author feels should be recognized as one of the four great fathers of psychiatry; and Friederich C. G. Scheidemantel, who wrote the first systematic textbook of psychosomatic medicine in 1787. There is a wealth of fascinating material in each of these chapters. The author finds evidences of social psychiatry, mental hygiene and electroshock therapy in the Eighteenth Century! Not all of the origins are as plainly demonstrated as are some, but to those of us who believed that all of these concepts were of recent origin, they are a revelation.

Simon Andree Tissot the author designates as "the Freudian

before Freud." He also gives a high place to Vincenzo Chiarugi, who deserves this position as the first organizer and thorough surveyor of psychological history. He decries Pinel's devaluation of Chiarugi, which caused him to be almost forgotten.

Dr. Harms holds Heinroth in quite high regard, for he made an attempt to establish an actual clinical system of psychotherapy. He described what it meant and what it could achieve according to the psychiatric knowledge of the time. Heinroth even divided the work of the clergyman and the psychiatrist, a problem which is still very much under scrutiny today.

Previous historians had not viewed psychiatric work with children within the frame of reference of the general field of psychiatry, the author notes, but Dr. Harms offers a short presentation of a total view of the history of nervous and mental diseases of childhood. He had mentioned earlier that child psychiatry had a history dating back almost two hundred years.

The writer was personally acquainted with Janet and Jung; he traces Janet's influence on the development of modern psychotherapy and outlines his teachings and writings. He gives Freud credit where credit is due but feels that most biographical studies of him appear to the historian as "subjective, idealizing hero-worship rather than scientific biographies," and this includes Jones' work. He tries to correct some of these misapprehensions.

Dr. Harms defends Jung with spirit. He knew him and worked for the firm which published Jung's works. Dr. Harms was sent by them to Jung on an interesting mission. He makes a valiant and, I believe, successful attempt to dispel the charges of antisemitism against Jung by examining all of his writings and going into detail about the circumstances which led to the accusations being made against him in the first place. He traces the origins of Jung's thought to the Zurich school and denies that he was a "pupil" of Freud, though he admired his work greatly. Jung for a while was his heir apparent. This writer was a Rockefeller Fellow in Zurich in 1935 and can attest to the veracity of many of Dr. Harms' statements, having talked to Jung about them personally.

Jung's major contribution, Harms believes, was his attempt to establish "a scientific, autonomous psychology based on a concept of the psyche as a dynamic, self-contained energy system." Yet despite the brilliance of his ideas and his skill as a clinician and an educator, his work was incomplete; he never drew together the major aspects of his teaching. As a matter of fact, he told Dr. Harms personally that to do it would take another lifetime.

The final chapter concerns William Alanson White, whom he terms "The Forgotten Giant of American Psychiatry." He questions why Sullivan's presentations of White's ideas became popular and have lasted while the originator's books were forgotten. He calls attention to White's middle-of-the-road attitude and prophesies that future generations will rediscover his writings.

While forewords should not sound like reviews, this one must of necessity do so, for there is no other way to do justice to the volume. The work is scholarly, painstaking and thorough, and one can only indicate this by quotations from chapters and an overall survey. The author makes individuals some of us have never heard of come alive. It is a chastening experience to read the book, for one becomes humble in the lack of knowledge about his forebears. Though the doctor gets a bit wroth at times at some ancients and even a few contemporaries, his observations and complaints must be given careful consideration. One need not, and probably will not, agree with all of the author's opinions, and may find some of the comments a bit acerbic in spots; he will nonetheless have a great respect for the overall result which represents a lifetime of work and experience. This book will have to be considered in all subsequent historical examinations of psychiatry, for being multilingual, the author has gone to original sources to back up his opinions.

FRANCIS J. BRACELAND, M.D.

INTRODUCTION

THE historical study of the achievements of the art of mental healing has been an integral part of my work in psychiatry for almost fifty years. When I entered the university, P. J. Mobius' cultural and historical inroads into academic psychiatry held great interest for me. The problem of "Genius and Insanity" formulated by him and Lombroso, has continued to fascinate me far more deeply than any cold intellectual interest. As a result I have written numerous biographies of creative individuals impaired by mental ailments.

Through my contact with C. G. Jung, a wider perspective was opened to me. Jung made me aware of the wealth of knowledge of ancient and primitive peoples in the art of mental healing. In their own languages and ways they had methods of preserving mental health more far-reaching than the information about the human psyche offered to us by the modern scientific approach. This was the basic thesis of Jung's psychotherapeutic teaching. It was not only a fascinating revelation to me, but the essential key to a more accurate and sure feeling about the mental growth of mankind. My contact with Jung since the early twenties has greatly enriched my understanding of the actual inner dynamics of mental and cultural behavior, for his thesis touches the vital pulse of mankind.

Our contact was also not without fruits for his own work. For almost a decade I have helped him to collect demonstrative and illustration material for his books, for example, his *Alchemy*.

A third and major phase of my interest in the problems of psychiatric history arose when, almost in self-defense, I had to survey, sift and evaluate the relationships of various contemporary schools of psychiatry to each other, and genetically to previous trends of thought. It is hardly necessary to point out that this revived impulse to historical study was ignited in me by Sigmund Freud's pretentious paper entitled "The History of the Psychoanalytical Movement." With its programlike title—speaking of a movement where from a genuine historical point of view, no movement was yet in existence—it compelled me to seek the way through to the real truth regarding the connections and basic sources of the so-called French and Zurich schools. This made of me a real historical scholar, as it must make of everyone. This research necessarily led me to Kraepelin's classical *One Hundred Years of Psychiatry*. Once caught in the net of the amazing farsightedness and clarity of this work, there was no more escaping the investigations and follow-up studies which have shaped the general operational basis of my mind even when interrupted for longer or shorter periods of time and which I will not easily give up again.

I had, however, made only a small number of contributions toward the writing of this history of psychiatry when a major American foundation offered me several years of support for broader research in the field of psychiatry. From its first to its present days the historical study of psychiatry has been tragically stigmatized by improper historical recording and unchecked copying. I found it an unpleasant task to point out that the so-called "first" history of psychiatry, Friedreich's famous book, was nothing more than an enlarged plagiarization of Heinroth, whose name it had attempted, violently but vainly, to erase from pages of history.

Another book the size of the present one would be required, unfortunately, to correct page by page the mistakes and false quotations to be found in some major historical books published during the past quarter of a century. The author has felt, however, that this was not his task except in a few instances where he found it of the utmost importance. For the rest his guiding impulse has been to present an objective approach to historical reporting and to show that the solidity and sureness of thinking presently lacking in psychiatric speculation and in its application in everyday practice will reappear when historical perspectives support the mind in its searching tasks. If the author is able to inspire in some the feeling that a psychiatrist cannot be a good one without definite knowledge in the origins of the field, he considers his task achieved.

ACKNOWLEDGMENTS

A NUMBER of the chapters in this book are based on articles written by the author and previously published in psychiatric journals here and abroad. For enclosure in this book they have been revised and reorganized, and a number have been greatly enlarged.

These articles were carried in the following journals: *American Journal of Orthopsychiatry, American Journal of Psychiatry, Diseases of the Nervous System, Journal of Mental Science* (London), *Journal of Pastoral Care, Journal of Social Therapy, Psyche* (Stuttgart), *Psychiatric Quarterly* and *Studium Generale* (Berlin).

ERNEST HARMS

CONTENTS

                                                                  Page

Foreword—FRANCIS J. BRACELAND   v

Introduction   ix

Acknowledgments   xi

Chapter

1. A New Approach to a History of Psychiatry   3
2. Early Historians of Psychiatry   9
3. Heinrich Damerow's Interpretation of the Psychiatric Ideas
   of Theophrastus Paracelsus   15
4. Felix Plater: At the Threshold of Scientific Psychiatry . .   28
5. Georg Ernst Stahl: The Seventeenth Century Psychiatrist .   41
6. Alexander Monro II: An Early Neurodrug Experimenter .   44
7. F. C. G. Scheidemantel: The First Systematic Test in Psychosomatic Medicine   46
8. Social Psychiatry and Mental Hygiene in the Eighteenth Century   58
9. The Origin and Early History of Electroshock Therapy . .   67
10. Simon Andree Tissot: The Freudian Before Freud . . .   70
11. Vincenzo Chiarugi: The First Great Systematic Psychiatry .   75
12. The General Importance of Johann Christian Reil . . .   86
13. The Forgotten Systematic Psychiatry of Johann Christian
    Reil   97
14. J. C. A. Heinroth's Attempt to Formulate a System of Psycho-
    therapy 106
15. J. C. A. Heinroth's Concept of the Psychiatrist's Task . . . 121
16. How Heinroth Divided the Tasks of the Clergyman and the
    Psychiatrist 126
17. Benjamin Rush: American Ambassador to Europe . . . 131
18. A Pre-Freudian Complex Theory 134
19. F. E. Beneke's First Phenomenological Psychiatry 136
20. Karl Kahlbaum, Terminologist 154
21. At the Cradle of Child Psychiatry 168

Chapter   *Page*

22. Predecessors of Morton Prince's Dissociation Concept . . 182
23. Pierre Janet: The Psychological Psychiatrist 186
24. An Ideological Interpretation of Freud's Development Versus
    the Freud Mythologies 190
25. Carl Gustav Jung: Defender of Freud and the Jews . . . 200
26. Carl Gustav Jung and American Academic Psychology . . 234
27. The Fragment of a Gigantic Psychology 237
28. William Alanson White: The Forgotten Giant of American
    Psychiatry   246

    Name Index   249
    Subject Index   253

ORIGINS OF MODERN PSYCHIATRY

Chapter 1

A NEW APPROACH TO A HISTORY
OF PSYCHIATRY*

WE might expect psychology, normal as well as abnormal, to be—as the science of human inner life—autonomous, with its own self-governing principles and scientific postulates. However, it has been forced to conform to the scientific conditionings of the two worlds which come together in human existence and experience: the outer, natural world, and what we call the cultural world, which is composed of the multiplicity of things that constitute man's creations and the expressions of man's desires and ambitions. There has been much speculation about the innate principles that govern the natural and cultural sciences and the contradiction between them.

In the case of psychology, we find that certain individuals and certain periods have tried to annex the specialty to either natural or cultural science. The contention that the choice depends on the point of view and character or temperament of the individual scholar has not held its ground. Historians in the field of psychology and psychiatry have made little headway, however, in demonstrating innate developmental trends and concepts which would show a definite pattern of growth in this field of science. What stands out most impressively for anyone seeking insight, especially in regard to abnormal psychology or psychiatry, is the almost fanatical rejection of all previously expressed ideas by each advocate of a new theory, and the presentation of the new theory as representing the first truly scientific approach.

We all know (not only as a matter of history, but also professionally) what occurred in the early part of this century when "a certain Dr. Sigmund Freud" started his "psychoanalytic movement" in Vienna. Before then, however, things were not much better.

---

* In somewhat different form, this chapter was presented before the Tenth Congress on History of Science at Cornell University in August, 1962.

The man who is supposed to have written the first objective book on the history of psychiatry, J. B. Friedreich (1830), was the most fanatical pamphleteer the field has ever known.

Because of the strong tendency to reject the psychiatry of the earlier periods and presentation of the new ideas as almost prophetic—which, of course, is also found in other scientific fields—early historical concepts are overlooked or forgotten. As an example, we have heard it maintained in recent decades that the specialty of child psychiatry was not born until the second decade of this century. I have shown elsewhere in this book that child psychiatry has a history of almost two hundred years. Although psychiatrists maintain that they are the wisest and most tolerant representatives of the medical profession, it has apparently required the more rational and cool-headed historian to show them out of what scientific background they have come and by what deeper impulses they are driven.

In a paper published in 1957 I pointed to the fact that the two basic scientific concepts mentioned above—that of the natural sciences and that of psychological-cultural life—do not appear only in connection with personal theoretical ambitions, but have existed as general trends of schools and periods. When one concept developed into an extreme and radical form, it induced a trend to and development of an opposing concept; when the latter in turn developed into a radical form, it induced a swing back into the direction of the first concept.

Historians will readily recognize here the dialectical principle of history formulated by Hegel. It is this swinging from one extreme position or trend to another that is represented by the concepts capable of theoretical formulation. This dialectic, as it appears in the history of psychiatry, is well known from two early major representations: the so-called "Psychism" of the psychiatry of the period called classical (the period of Reil, Heinroth and Beneke); and the somatic and physiological psychiatry of the period that followed it.

It was Friedreich's "Somatism" that represented the first dialectical swing, but it did not prevail in its fanaticism and radicalism any longer than did the Psychism it was opposing. Little more than twenty years later there was a swing away from Somatism to the ego psychiatry of Griesinger and a similar movement in England connected with the name of Maudsley. Ego psychiatry was in turn replaced by a new neurophysiological psychology and the "psychology without a soul" of the third quarter of the Nineteenth Century.

Then came a new swing, probably induced by Semon's Mnemonism and academically represented by Kraepelin and Bleuler, but carried to its crest by the great wave of depth psychology and depth psychiatry of the psychoanalytic movement. No one can be unaware of the new swing towards the physiological side which we have seen in the past ten years in the mass application of chemotherapy and the rapid loss of ground held by the concepts of depth psychiatry.

None of the described movements shows any open indication of relating itself to a similar earlier movement; nevertheless, a definite dependency can at times be seen. For example, I have pointed in a later chapter of this book to the fact that Freud was more influenced in the development of his theoretical concepts of ego psychology by his reading of Griesinger than, as is generally believed (especially by his dogmatic followers), by his personal relationship to Charcot.

Three years after my above-mentioned historical paper appeared, a younger psychiatric writer took up my concept of the history of psychiatry. He changed the dialectical formulation from "psychologic and physiologic" to "psychologic and organic," but he did not understand nor did he penetrate into the deeper meaning of these historical swings by recognizing them as a concrete expression of the Hegelian dialectic. In its aboriginal philosophical form, Hegel's dialectic states that out of the contradiction between being *(sein)* and nonbeing *(nicht sein)* rises the developmental progressive dynamic activity of the becoming *(werden)* which pushes the developmental growth forward step by step.

In practical circumstances, however, things may not always go that way. I remember, for example, that Heinrich Damerow, probably the greatest psychiatric institutionalist and organizer up to the middle of the Nineteenth Century, suggested that the Psychists and Somatists stop quarreling, because he believed that each could make a valuable contribution to progress in the field.

As a good method for the historical study of psychiatry I suggest the approach I have myself adopted, namely to study the various periods of Psychism and the various periods of somatophysiology with a view to finding a unifying line. A comparison of the conceptional contents of each brings the astonishing discovery that there is indeed a concrete, unifying trend of development. This trend is, as I emphasized in my introductory sentence, in a direction outside the sphere of the natural and cultural sciences. It constitutes a unity in itself, a unity concerned with human inner life. This makes it apparent that the unifying line is not to be found in constant attempts to assimilate or make use of the prevailing concepts of natural or cultural science. That no unifying line has been found is due to the lack of such a definite approach before now.

I see the unifying line in what I like to call *the humanitarian approach*. This rests mainly on basic socioethical concepts that have been at issue at one period or another. It was not the concepts of the speculative psychology and philosophy of the late Eighteenth Century that provided the basic scientific and practical impulse to the psychiatrists of the so-called Classical period. The impulse came from the same socioethical concepts that inspired Kant's practical reason and ethical concepts as well as Hegel's social philosophy. It was a basically socioethical conceptionalism that made the psychiatrists of Germany, Italy, France and the United States voice the demand for a new approach to insanity. In one form or another, they all asked that the mentally deranged be looked at, not as criminals, but as sick persons to be treated by means of psychological medicine.

It was not this humanitarian impulse that was destroyed when the fury of Friedreich's Somatism broke over the Psychist school. In our view, Somatism actually brought an inner consolidation of the totality of psychiatric speculation. When in the middle of the Nineteenth Century Darwin started and Haeckel concluded the formulation of general onto- and philogenetic concepts, psychiatrists were ready to formulate their own psychological autonomic geneticism of the psyche as being separate from body and nerves. This was presented by Griesinger in his ego psychiatry and by Maudsley in his psychiatric autonomism.

I refrain from arguing with the representatives of normative ethics, who will deny for reasons of principle that psychological autonomism can have something to do with the normative or practical side of their field, but looked at psychologically, an ethical point of view and ethical progress are represented, and with this there is a general humanitarian concept established, expressed in an acknowledgment of ourselves as autonomous, self-determining and self-directed egos. Of course we could go back to Kant's categorical imperative and elaborate a little on historical determinism, but we must consider the validity of a self-directed (in contrast to a nonself-directed) action in its ethical aspect. We must consider what it means in regard to self-control as the psychotherapeutic factor in all of modern psychiatry. Unfortunately, we do not have a fully worked-out set of psychiatric principles so far, because the things I point out here have not yet been actually developed.

I am compelled, in connection with the ethical humanitarian principle, to think of the psychologist Harold Höffding and his contribution to the concept of the birth and death of categories of thinking, which he illustrated in his writings on the concept of totality. Totality was still an unknown concept around 1875, but the influence it exerted during the following three decades in the form of Gestalt psychology and biological and historical holism is known to everyone. Conventional and theoretical speculation might lead us to assume that the Griesinger and Maudsley influence died when the neurophysiological period began; in our view it did not. It continued in methodological form and came to be known as the clinical method of psychiatry. This method became established everywhere during the neurophysiological period and was unjustly considered a new but now academic approach. It became the generally acknowledged practical scientific method in the field of psychiatry for which Reil and Damerow had been fighting at least fifty years earlier.

Taking the next step, we arrive at the beginning of this century at the great impact of social speculation and the slow disintegration of the autocratic social pattern. In psychiatry we find the parallel in the psychoanalytic social acknowledgment of pathological subconscious channels of sex and defective thinking and acting. Unfortunately, I am unable in such a short survey to go into the necessary detail regarding the most recent and most challenging events. If I could do so, I would be able to show that the actual line of historical development in psychiatry is not contained in neurological and other discoveries nor in meritorious new methods of experimentation, but in the new psychological human approach. If we permit ourselves to remove the blinkers placed on us by our narrow view of our special field and our special theoretical concepts and accept a wider view of the most imminent driving element of medicine, of the social and natural sciences and of the techniques for life improvement, we come to the revelation that this element (in normal as well as abnormal psychology and psychiatry), properly conducted and viewed, demonstrates this humanitarian principle more than any other discipline.

If I attempt to answer the question as to any prediction of a future development of psychiatry, I am pressed into a conflict. Modern science has as its basic principle to establish only facts, not to predict. However, in earlier times the meaning of most study of the past as well as of the course of the stars was to predict man's future. I would like for once to make in this respect a little compromise in pointing not at someone's lucky day or at the good and bad in the future of mankind, but simply at certain valid facts which are near in the range of evidence.

Regarding the above-mentioned pharmacological development as the next period in the history of psychiatry, some of us who like to look into the future point at the still nuclear development of an existentialism in the field of psychiatry. I must confess that these things have greatly interested me personally. The emerging existentialist concept of psychiatry seems to me to be an extremely promising step toward the categoric confirmation of what I have found as the basic impulse of psychiatry. How this will unfold in detail and how far this new swing towards a psychic pattern of psychiatry will lead to its autonomous completion I feel would go beyond what I have the right to predict.

Chapter 2

THE EARLY HISTORIANS OF PSYCHIATRY

IN 1955 German psychiatry celebrated with great emphasis the fiftieth anniversary of the death of B. Heinrich Laehr, who, during his eighty-five year lifetime, contributed considerably to the development of institutional methods in middle Europe. As early as 1850 Laehr had started a private mental institution, where, with characteristic definiteness and intensity, he began his experiments. Many later developments were based on his progressive institutional method.

While Laehr is known mostly for this work, he made an equal and perhaps even greater contribution which has been almost entirely forgotten. In 1895, ten years before his death, he published a large study, *Die Literatur der Psychiatrie, Neurologie und Psychologie im 18. Jahrhundert,* a two thousand page, three-volume work which covers the period from 1459 to 1799, listing sixteen thousand works by 8,500 authors. Summarizing all the most important material, this bibliography is, up to now, the most important contribution extant to the history of psychiatry. The reason it has been completely overlooked or ignored is a hard question for the historian to answer. The contradictory development of psychiatry to which we have referred no doubt contributed to this neglect. A just acknowledgment and evaluation of a man like Laehr can be achieved only through objectively viewing the early historical writings about psychiatry in the way I shall attempt here.

Until the Seventeenth Century most medical and other scientific authors used to refer to ancient authors or mythological and religious documents for their proof. These quotations were a main source for antique and early ideas on mental ailments and their cure. They are not completely reliable as source material, however, because of much misquotation and still more false interpretation. In searching through early medical literature one finds no

9

trace of real psychiatric historical information before 1800. The earliest even limited historical summaries are given by the ingenious Kurt Sprengel in his *Versuch einer pragmatischen Geschichte der Arzeneikunde (Attempt at a Pragmatic History of Medicine)*, published between 1801 and 1803. Here we find a few pages on neurology and the physiological aspects of psychiatry.

The first real history of psychiatry, however, is actually almost completely unknown, although its author, Johann Christian A. Heinroth, is considered not only one of the foremost early psychiatrists but also one of the greatest humanists of all times. He ranks with Wilhelm von Humboldt in having written basic works in almost every field of the humanities, including his famous two-volume psychiatric work published in 1818, *Lehrbuch der Stoerungen des Seelenlebens oder der Seelenstoerungen und ihrer Behandlung vom rationalen Standpunkt aus betrachtet (Textbook of the Disturbances of the Psyche)*. Actually this is the first large survey of previous psychiatric achievements. A chapter on earliest times is followed by the "Treatment of Psychic Disturbances According to the Writings of the Great Physicians of the Ancient World," including a detailed presentation of the Hippocratic writings. The next chapter treats the intermediary period between old and new, while the last division is devoted to modern times and reports the various "national schools," as the author terms them.

In his basic viewpoint, Heinroth was the first symptomatologist in psychiatry; this is, of course, applied to the way he reports psychiatric history. He emphasizes that he does not believe psychopathology can be explained physiologically, as through autopsy. Heinroth therefore saw many early authors as mistaken in searching the liver for the causes of melancholia instead of studying the actual psychological symptoms of the disease. He emphasizes that, accordingly, psychiatry up to his own time had not developed clear somatic pictures or systematizations of the various forms of psychopathology. Studying psychiatric history was for him a search for symptoms. In an incomparably brilliant way, Heinroth analyzed, for example, the Hippocratic writings by dividing his presentation into (1) symptoms of the developing mental sickness, (2) symptoms of the sickness process, and (3) symptoms of cure. The further contents of his two volumes are based on this historical presentation; he repeatedly refers to material from those writers he considers his scientific ancestors.

In 1830, twelve years after Heinroth's textbook appeared, a book was published which is still acknowledged to be the first real history of psychiatry. This book not only overshadowed the entire Nineteenth Century, but was considered so valid in even this century that major portions were translated by Smith Ely Jelliffe and published in a set of papers. The author was J. B. Friedreich; the title of his work, *Versuch einer Literaturgeschichte der Pathologie und Therapie der psychischen Krankheiten (Attempt at a History of the Literature of Pathology and Therapy of Psychic Illnesses)*. If one examines this book with Heinroth's history in mind, one makes the astonishing discovery that Friedreich's book is more or less a revised edition of Heinroth. Not only does he use the same structure (and in parts, the same contents), he also quotes Heinroth constantly—but only in order to reject and contradict the earlier writer. Additions in Friedreich's volume are mainly detailed résumés of Fifteenth, Sixteenth and Seventeenth Century writers, in whose views Heinroth was less interested.

Heinroth had called his a "history from the rational point of view." A pupil of Fichte, Hegel and Schelling, he was strongly under the influence of the objective idealism of his time. He was head of the psychiatric department of his university and at the same time was a member of the philosophical and theological departments. In addition to medicine, he taught anthropology, biology, philosophy and criminology.

Heinroth was as much a medical man as he was a brilliant thinker and writer. Friedreich, on the other hand, wanted to be a member of the vanguard in natural science. Undoubtedly he started out brilliantly—at the age of twenty-four he taught on the medical faculty of Wuerzburg—but because he was seemingly a disagreeable radical and fanatic, after not more than ten years he was demoted and given the job of court physician in a small Bavarian town. He made a short academic comeback at the secondary Bavarian university of Erlangen, but soon retired to devote himself to psychiatric writing, where his role was undisputed.

Six years after the large historical text had appeared (1836),

Friedreich published another historical study. In this he openly targeted Heinroth as the major representative of the psychological school of psychiatry to which belonged leading Nineteenth Century workers such as Carus, Reil and Neuman. Friedreich's book, *Historische-kritische Darstellung der Theorien uber das Wesen und den Sitz der psychischen Krankheiten (Historical Critical Presentation of the Theories Regarding the Nature and Origin of Psychic Diseases)*, is a lengthy and rather ironical presentation of psychological psychiatry. He calls Heinroth's concepts "a psychiatric comedy of the devil," which he "hopes will be the last of its kind."

Friedreich tries to establish what he calls the "Somatical Theory of Psychiatry," which he formulates as follows: "All psychic diseases are the result of somatic abnormalities; only the body can become sick, and not the psyche as such." In other words, Friedreich is the first prominent exponent of "psychology without a psyche" along medical lines, and started the neurophysiological psychiatry which led the field for the following seventy-five years. Friedreich had learned and accepted from Heinroth the view for differential and systematic consideration. He was indeed fortunate in standing at the beginning of neurophysiological psychiatry, for if those theories which he subsequently elaborated in his own *Textbook of Pathology* had been presented some decades later, neurophysiology as it developed during the second half of the century would have considered them more mystical than anything Heinroth had represented. Friedreich was an excellent abstracter and summarizer who, if he so desired, was able to present most objectively any other writer's work. When it came, however, to presenting theories which he rejected, he deviated considerably from the path of objectivity.

It is hard to say whether it was a result of the popularity of the Friedreich book or of the antihistorical tendencies of the new physiological psychiatry which developed in the mid-Nineteenth Century that no new extensive textbook on the history of psychiatry appeared for almost fifty years. If we examine leading works on the general history of medicine, such as those of Emil Isensee (1845), Heinrich Haeser (1875) or August Hirsch (1893), or actual textbooks of psychiatry, such as those of Feuchtersleben (1845), Flemming (1859) or Schuele (1878), we find each depending on Friedreich as their major source.

The first notable history of psychiatry deviating from this pattern came from a Belgian with a German name, F. Lentz; *Histoire des Progress de la Medicine Mentale depuis le Commencement du 19ieme siecle jusqu'a nos Jours (History of the Progress of Psychic Medicine from the Beginning of the Nineteenth Century to Our Own Day)* was published in Paris in 1876. This book sums up the two tendencies which had developed in previous decades.

Although any interest in earlier centuries' psychopathological views was killed by the new neurophysiological tendencies, alienists still had to treat their patients (especially since institutions were springing up by the dozen). These workers had a certain interest in knowing about earlier attempts at institutional and personal treatment, and quite a number of books appeared which reported earlier treatments and institutional care. The most intensive of these studies came in 1851 from Heinrich Neuman: *Ueber die oeffentliche Irrenpflege im 18 und 19 Jahrhundert (On the Public Care of the Insane during the Eighteenth and Nineteenth Centuries)*. This book was widely used, even though its author belonged to the disregarded psychological school. The earliest of these studies came from a Frenchman, Ch. Laseque: *Etudes Historiques sur L'Alienation Mentale (Historical Studies of Mental Insanity)*, 1845. The crowning work was Th. Kirchhoff's *Grundriss einer Geschichte der deutschen Irrenpflege (Outline of a History of the Care of the Insane in Germany)*.

It must be pointed out that the English-speaking world took considerable interest in this same field. Much material on alienation was contained in the famous memoirs of John Conolly, which appeared in London in 1869. Some historical studies on mental illness also came to the fore during the last century out of the growing historical interest in the antique world, which was especially strong in France. Here we may note one of the more prominent: Semelaigne's *Etudes Historiques sur L' Alienation Mental dans L' Antiquite (Historical Studies on the Institutional Care of the Insane in Ancient Times)*, published in 1870. These new interests—in both recent and ancient treatment—had given Lentz enough material for an entirely new perspective on the history of psychiatry. He attempted to see these radical changes in a light considerably more objective than Friedreich's.

By 1885, B. Heinrich Laehr had already presented a completely different historical approach to the field of psychiatry. In that year he published a rather strange book entitled *Gedenktage der Psychiatrie (Memorable Dates in the History of Psychiatry)*, which covered the period from 1655 to 1883. Here he reported, year by year, dates from the lives and work of professionals, as well as special cases and institutional and legal events. For the first time a pragmatic chronology was advanced.

Laehr must have been already considerably far into his bibliography of psychiatry when he published his *Gedenktage*, for both are undertaken in the same spirit. The bibliography is also as uneven and in many ways as uncritical a work as the history. This is especially true for works listed for the first 150 years. Writings on witchcraft, theology and herbatology are mixed in with subject matter which later became important. In the coverage of the later period we find that material which originated in the psychological school is left out, because these concepts were not acceptable to Laehr's own theoretical point of view. The added abstracts were made, it seems, without any specific methodological principle; they are partly tables of contents, or emphasize some part of the contents which interested him. They have, therefore, sometimes only a secondary value. In spite of all we may wish to say against Laehr's bibliography, however, it remains the most important source book for the period it covers. None of those who after the beginning of the Twentieth Century increasingly interested themselves in the genetic growth of psychiatric work have, so far as we can see, taken much advantage of the Laehr bibliography. The clearest evidence of this was its being forgotten in the memorial which the leading German periodical, *Der Nervenarzt*, devoted to B. H. Laehr.

Chapter 3

HEINRICH DAMEROW'S INTERPRETATION OF THE PSYCHIATRIC IDEAS OF THEOPHRASTUS PARACELSUS

SHALL we ever be able to understand the world of ideas of Theophrastus von Hohenheim better than we do today? The major part of Paracelsus' scientific ideas moves in the realm of hemireligious and alchemical concepts of the late medieval world which we will never be able to lift out of the fog of nonunderstandability. It is doubtful that any future insight will be able to pierce this fog. From the vantage point of our current modes of thought, we seem not nearer but farther away from the ways of thinking of the Middle Ages, yet in spite of the dim understanding of our scientific world-view when confronted with Paracelsus' ideas, his thought strikes us as extremely important and profound. Disdained and banished by his contemporaries, able to print his books only with immense difficulty, this wandering medical rebel has been named by present-day historians "one of the greatest physicians of the history of mankind" and "one of the most distinctive men of all times and peoples."

Since Sudhoff's excellent complete edition of Paracelsus' works and Aschner's usable German translation of them, repeated attempts have been made to lift the veil of mystery that seemed to cover all of Paracelsus' life and work and to open an access to his wisdom for the understanding of our modern scientific mentality. Psychology and psychiatry, being such important instruments in the orchestra of the modern sciences, have naturally made various attempts to utilize Paracelsus' concepts for an understanding of the healthy as well as the diseased psyche. Unfortunately, most of these attempts have borne little fruit.

The only extensive study of this kind, C. G. Jung's *Paracelsica,* treats the matter only in connection with a rather widely framed historical conceptionalism. The same must be said of Jolande Jacobi's sensitive introduction to his valuable selections from

15

Paracelsus. In such an introduction he could not make it his task to give a detailed presentation of the master's psychology or of its relationship to the theories of modern psychology. The few attempts of research which have been made during this century are all more or less wordy attempts to prove that Paracelsus is unintelligible. This is true of the presentation of the unreliable medical journalist Galdson.

The few who have concerned themselves seriously with a historical consideration (Kornfeld, Ackerknecht, Beyerholm) devote to Paracelsus only a few paragraphs, quite out of proportion to his actual importance. The dean of the history of psychiatry, Kirchhoff, begins his uniquely important *Deutsche Irrenärzte* with Paracelsus, but devotes to him a mere three pages. He confesses that Theophrastus is dark and unintelligible to him because he is still under the influence of prescientific thinking.

The meager results of our survey provide no useful and sound basis for an understanding and appreciation of Paracelsus' psychiatric thought. Astonishingly enough, however, there exists one rather large and intensive study of the psychiatry of Paracelsus which has remained unobserved by all the historians mentioned and of which no trace can be found in all the Paracelsus literature. It is a thirty-eight page treatise by Heinrich Ph. A. Damerow, *"Paracelsus über psychische Krankheiten"* ("Paracelsus on Psychic Diseases"), issued in 1834.

Heinrich Damerow (1798-1866) holds a place of honor in the history of psychiatry as the founder of the first larger periodical in the field, *Allgemeine Zeitschrift für Psychiatrie* and as an eager vanguard in the advancement of care for the insane. In his day he attempted a mediating role in the hot fight between Heinroth's school of Psychists and the Somatists of the Friedreich type. In his writings and as editor of his journal, he tried to make peace by revealing the one sidedness of each view and assimilating the valuable of both into a universal concept of psychiatry.

This sensitive objectivity enabled him to treat Paracelsus seriously as a psychiatrist and to patiently elaborate his concepts, making what he felt was valuable for his time understandable and applicable. Damerow lived during the flowering of the Romantic school of literature and philosophy, whose ideal was to develop empathy and understanding for cultures and ethnological worlds of the distant past. With this attitude, Damerow developed a much deeper understanding of Paracelsus than had anyone else.

Trying to find a position for an objective evaluation of Paracelsus, Damerow found himself in nearly the same situation we are in today. Both the leading writers of his time rejected Paracelsus for the same reason as do our contemporaries—nonunderstandability. Heinroth designated him indigestible, yet Damerow maintained that Heinroth's "direct psychotherapeutic method" was nearer to Paracelsus than anyone else had ever come. He says, ironically, that neither Heinroth nor any other of his contemporaries could have really read Paracelsus. In fact, he discovered the plagiarizing by Friedreich, all of whose statements about Paracelsus were copied from other authors.

For any real understanding of Paracelsus, Damerow insisted, one must seriously study his many writings. Reading a few pages of the one often-cited tractate, "Diseases which Rob Man of His Sanity," was totally inadequate. He lists three other short works which ought to be read and demands that other writings which contain various passages on normal and abnormal psychic life should also be studied.

Damerow urges that it is essential for a genuine understanding of Paracelsus to avoid viewing him as "a man of his time," for instance an alchemist. It was the most characteristic trait of Paracelsus' mental striving that he actually fought against the basic impulses of his time, including astrological alchemy. He sought to redirect the thinking of his time toward the budding natural sciences, but in order to be understood by his contemporaries he had to use the terminology of the alchemists with which they were familiar. To irritate these astrological alchemists, however, he maintained that a winegrower who makes wine from grapes and a weaver who knows how to weave cloth are alchemists as accomplished as a medicus who mixes his medicines. This unastrological concept of alchemy he expressed in his own terms: "Alchemy teaches the highest that is in nature. Nature as such does not manifest itself in completed form. Man first brings it to completion, and this completion is alchemy." In our words, Paracelsus meant, "The discovery and application of the laws of nature—that is alchemy."

For an understanding of Paracelsus, Damerow employs a principle of historical evaluation which Hegel had also used. To understand Paracelsus, he points out, we must not try to revive his theories from their historical grave and imitate their meaning. This would be a regress and not an advance. Many of his concepts are out of date, but we can learn from him how he conceived and developed his scientific concepts. Damerow showed that Paracelsus had in this respect insights and methods which were as little exhausted in their applicability and importance then as they are today, three hundred years later. Damerow emphasizes Paracelsus' methodological views and his farsightedness, which make him a teacher also for our times, which have seen the development of a too-scientific mode of inductive studying of details.

The first main point in which Damerow sees the lasting importance of Paracelsus is his view for the totality, which, as he has again and again emphasized, reaches from the microcosmos to the macrocosmos. In psychiatry this means seeing body and psyche together in their interrelated unity. If one has an empathy for Paracelsus' language, one will find what three hundred years later Heinroth designated as psychological totality concepts and what, in our century, Jung postulated as, "The psyche as a totalistically closed and self-sufficient energetic system." One will find, moreover, the relationship factors of modern psychosomatic and somatopsychologic considerations in evidence throughout Theophrastus' writings, which proves them to be not at all new.

The second point Damerow underlines as a basic principle of Paracelsus' psychiatry is his clear method of differentiating mental diseases (what we today call classification and type separation). Anyone who would pretend that no understanding of this problem existed before the start of the Twentieth Century cannot have even superficially looked over Paracelsus' major psychiatric treatises. He differentiated five forms of mental illness: *Lanatici, Insani, Vesani, Melancholici* and *Obscessi*. Damerow shows that Paracelsus appears so dark and unclear in this classification because his typology has grown in combination with that of the four temperaments. However, if one trains oneself to follow his thoughts, one can only admire how he develops the forms as variations in a separation and combination process.

A further element in Paracelsus' methodology is his clear vision of the total system and simultaneous elaboration of varied and interrelated details. This is especially important in Paracelsus' psychotherapy, with which we shall deal a little later.

As the most important point in all his scientific thinking, Damerow underlined the sense of causality which Paracelsus possessed. Everywhere Paracelsus' main concern is to find the cause and even the cause of the cause. This means that in his establishment of a pathology, Paracelsus also established a pathogenetic approach. He concentrated on the development of the disease and on the disease as a process. It was a most important step in the progress of psychiatric when C. G. Jung established the so-called dynamic concept, but it was actually not new, already having been present in the process view of Paracelsus. To view illness as a total process with a beginning and an end was new for psychiatry at the start of this century. It was not completely new for Damerow one hundred years earlier, since he was faced with it in nuclear form in Paracelsus. Indeed, wherever one opens his psychiatric treatises one meets this causal point of view. Although he does not try to give, in our modern manner, a detailed symptomatological picture, it is his principle to ask the origin of the illness and its cause.

Just as Paracelsus' diagnosis is causalistic, his therapy is finalistic. Our present therapy is mainly improvement therapy. For us healing means primarily an improvement of the pathological conditions of the patient. Not so for Paracelsus. His basic definition of illness was "being not healthy." Disease was for him degeneration of or deviation from a normal, healthy status of body and psyche. In the same sense, therapy was for him a return to health, humanness, spirituality and deistic experience. He approached therapy with a definite and clear view of an end to sickness. The aim of any therapy was a cured and healthy individual. Today, with our phenomenological approach, we see our only therapeutic task in making the pathological symptoms vanish and disappear.

Another important point Damerow underlines is Paracelsus

contribution to the formation of psychiatric terminology. Hardly any one of the terms he formulated himself has survived, only those few, like mania and melancholia, which he himself adopted from previous times. The distinct way in which he formulated his concepts doubtlessly has had great influence upon his successors, however, and in turn, upon the entire development of the field. Although Damerow does not, in the limited space of his paper, follow this problem through in detail, he is convinced that it was Paracelsus' influence which made to flower the psychiatric concepts of the centuries after him.

Lastly, Damerow turns to his pluralistic mode of thinking. Medicine is for Paracelsus not a simple and one-sided matter, nor is psychiatry. The doctor of the psyche must be also a doctor of the body. Without understanding the physical functions, he never could cure psychopathology. Furthermore, he must be a philosopher in regard to general medical knowledge. He must be an artist in the art of healing, and he must be a religious person, a Christian and deeply humane. In short, all the important qualities of a truly human life must be united in him.

Damerow is confined to a short characterization of Paracelsus' psychopathology and psychotherapy. We will here limit ourselves to a brief abstract of his presentation.

The basic element of his psychiatry, explains Damerow, is his clear differentiation of bodily, psychic and mental functions which, by their own specific character and interrelationships, cause the various psychopathologies. Some psychopathologies are solely of bodily origin, others derive entirely from the mind, but one must always keep an eye on both. With incomparable precision Paracelsus has described individual pathologies. At the start of his major treatise, for example, he presents what he calls the falling sickness *(hinfallende Krankheiten)*, those pathologies we today designate as epilepsies and seizures. He maintains that these diseases do not affect the actual health of the body nor alter any physical conditions. However, he distinguished five different forms of these diseases which depend on the part of the body in which they are centered. Each of them has a special root which results from the spirit of life *(Lebensgeist)*, and the sickness appears wherever this root is located. For the spirit of life itself, such a disease means a poisoning. The root of a falling sickness (its origin) comes into existence in the prenatal period. Attacks are due to special circumstances in the life of the individual and the pathogenic experience which the spirit of life undergoes.

Another important point Damerow underlines is Paracelsus' of mania. Mania is for Paracelsus a deterioration of the power of reasoning; it is not caused by our senses. There are two kinds of mania: One which appears in the healthy body, and a second which is caused by other diseases. One attacks above and the other below the diaphragm. A variety of the second type appears only in the extremities. This certainly does not sound like alchemy. Damerow is quite right when he points out the psychological and psychopathological sensitivity expressed in this kind of diagnostic procedure. Stated in the language of Paracelsus' time, it is not easy for us to understand, and it often needs a kind of theoretical and conceptual translation. In place of Damerow's own translation into the scientific language of his own time, I would like to offer here a sample of Paracelsus' writing, a quotation from Aschner's translation, which most nearly enables us to understand the original meaning: "Mania kindles rarely shown attitudes and abilities of man, which, until then, have never come into the open. Sometimes mania shows not only the natural behavior of man, but his struggles against his own illness. One must very carefully observe manic behavior, therefore, since helping the sick means supporting him in his own fight against the illness. Besides, in such a situation one can get insight into the natural and healthy forces in man and not only his sickness. In any case one must always remain aware that mania not only shows the outer nature of man, but often the inner, how he really is." One cannot but admire the amazing perception contained in such sentences.

Of special interest to Damerow was a special somatic description which Paracelsus called deafness *(Taubsucht)*. Some have translated this by leaving one vowel out: *Tobsucht,* or delirium. However, Paracelsus wants concretely to designate something else, namely deafness in regard to reason. In his own words he says, "If a healthy person loses his power of reasoning or gives it up and does not utilize this power for its proper purpose, but rages and romps furiously and uncontrollably, this state I understand to be *Taubsucht*. *Taubsucht* is a real disease, whereas he does not consider possession, drunkenness, foolishness and tyranny as such. *Taubsucht* is the highest degree of mania. The cause of this condition, Paracelsus says, is an overexertion of reasoning. To explain this he uses one of his remarkable imaginative interpretations, which very much impress the modern reader, regardless of whether he understands his theories or not.

"As the human eye is blinded when it looks at the sun, which is the eye of heaven, so our power of reasoning is paralyzed if it is applied to things which cannot be understood and which, therefore, are like the sun in regard to our physical eye. If one seeks to reach higher with reasoning than is possible, it may lead to a breakdown of our power of reason. Some persons have more strength than others. In the same way, one person can go further with his power of reasoning than another. Each one must learn to know the limits of his ability so that he does not fail with his power of reasoning against problems of reasoning he cannot comprehend, as the human eye stands against the blinding power of the sunlight, this eye of heaven."

Paracelsus has applied this concept of weakness of the mind to various spheres of psychic experience. We see this concept in contemporary form in Pierre Janet's *force et faiblesse psychiques*. It is especially the concept of psychic weakness which Paracelsus expounded again and again. Important for this idea, according to Damerow, is the contention of the master that *Taubsucht* is not only a psychic element, but has its foundation in a general state of weakness which, in the bodily aspect of human existence, reveals itself as the cause of ulcers. On this point Paracelsus gives a theoretical description which heads in the direction of the modern energetic theories, of which one may justly consider Paracelsus an early representative.

Those suffering the most severe form of mental disease **Paracelsus** called the "really insane." These are the real lunatics. They are not occasionally or acutely sick, but chronically. Damerow had already singled out this type in his introduction, but here he tries a more detailed description of the fundamental traits of Paracelsus' psychopathology. In his formulation of the five types of insanity, Paracelsus departed more than anywhere else from the thinking of modern psychiatry, and not only because these types are formulated causally. In the first, the *lunatici*—which he attributes to the influence of the moon—he seems still near to the alchemy of his time. The influence of the moon is, however, aside from the very real effect of the sun, the only one to which Paracelsus still attributes some reality.

Whatever position one may take in regard to this about Paracelsus or in general, we have been forced during the past decades to be considerably more tolerant regarding the possibility of influences from the cosmos upon existence and life on earth. It has, for instance, become almost a fashion to consider very real the influence of sun spots upon happenings on earth. Certain experiments have actually registered with most modern technical means specific planetary influences upon the atmosphere of our globe. Being moonstruck is no longer a nursery tale, but is a serious psychopathology, an hysterical supersensitivity, and is registered as such in most textbooks of psychiatry.

There is only a small step between what Paracelsus describes as moonstruckness and what modern psychiatric books tell us about it. Concretely, it is a state of being conditioned to the influence of certain emanations coming from the moon, and it is a serious mental pathology. If we want to apply a classification in our modern sense, we could register the insanity of these *lunatici* as one due to extraterrestrial influences. Paracelsus' second type of insanity, that of the *insani*, he considered to be caused by prenatal influences. From our present psychiatric position we can say nothing against the establishment of this type.

The third type of insanity, the *vesani*, he considers due to eating, drinking and similar causes. In our modern language we could say that certain psychopathologies are due to metabolic conditions.

The fourth type of classification is the *melancholici*. This is one of the conceptions he has taken over from ancient times. However, Paracelsus' melancholia is a more serious form of insanity than Hippocrates, Galenus and their successors considered it to be. Melancholia, for Paracelsus, is a very deep-seated sickness. He says that melancholia is a disease of the actual nature of man (by which he doubtlessly means the self of man). It seems to me of utmost importance that he distinguished four forms of melancholia which connect themselves with the four temperaments. This permits us to assume that melancholia is for Paracelsus a general pathology of the self, varying according to the temperaments. Dynamically, he characterizes melancholia as a turning away of man's true nature from reason to ignorance. In contrast to many of the melancholia definitions we find in the history of medicine, this one is a purely psychopathological one.

His fifth and last type of insanity, Paracelsus called *obscessi*. This form is especially significant because Paracelsus amalgamated in it the religious and medicopsychological concepts of his time. Man is constituted by an animal (or beastly) and a human (or spiritual) nature. If someone is so overpowered by the animal nature that he is possessed by it continually, this state is insanity.

This dualistic constitution of man can also be given a religious interpretation which expresses itself in the contradiction of God and Christ on the one hand and the devil and the demons on the other. All his life Paracelsus tried to remain in the frame of the Christian world-view of his time. However, he continually battled to bring this religious concept into an agreement with his totalistic, natural, scientific and psychological thinking. Belief belonged for him to human nature, but there is also a false belief which can become cause for serious illness. Mental illness due to false religion can be as little cured by religious practices as can physical disease. In such very direct and discreet judgments of true and false Paracelsus shows his wise nearness to life and spiritual realities.

Damerow was indeed very justified to point out the great importance of Paracelsus' psychotherapy. It contains the essence of his psychiatric views. In his large paper, Damerow has presented these psychotherapeutic thoughts in a somewhat scattered way. I would like to try to present this psychotherapy of Paracelsus here in a little more comprehensive way.

Paracelsus' pathological thinking we must designate as causalistic. His psychotherapeutic thinking we find predominantly prophylactic and preventive. For every somatic picture he describes, he offers his preventive prescription. In his actual physical and psychological measures he makes a very definite separation of the two modes. Of course, his physical medicine is in many respects very different from ours. No one would accept as legitimate a medicine that made incisions into hands and feet and kept the wounds open to drain bad juices out of the body. Also, bloodletting, aside from its use in transfusions, is today considered outside acceptable medical practices, especially regarding therapy for the insane.

On the other hand, Paracelsus' hydrotherapeutic and thermotherapeutic prescriptions are hardly different from our own. His chemotherapy recommends tranquilizers as well as vitalizers, laxatives, vomiting and blood-purifying medicines. Ischuretic medicines seem especially important to him. Sleeping cures play a very important role in Paracelsus' psychotherapy. Sleepwalking he calls *mania somnii*, for which he also recommends sleeping cures.

It is astonishing how farsighted he is regarding sexual and nutritional psychotherapy. In his actual psychotherapeutic practises, Damerow cannot but concede that Paracelsus went far beyond what was customary within the horizon of the Nineteenth Century, and we cannot but still feel very much the same today. Paracelsus had clear views regarding the highly sensitive means to be used in the treatment of melancholia and depressive states, which according to him should be mainly cheering attempts. He also gave clear indications for restraining therapy in hyperactivity. He had an unusual insight into the deeper dynamics of almost all psychotherapeutic effects and the necessity for a clear differentiation of the various stimulations applied.

I would like to offer here a quotation from Paracelsus which Damerow considered important enough to quote himself: "The right way of help is to prove to the sick person that besides the unsane way there exists also a sane one. One must show the insane what he can do in order to use the sound power of reasoning that still exists to clean out his brain and to see the sickness of his behavior."

Paracelsus also recommended the preservative method. He believed most insane people can understand very well where and when they do wrong, but they are too sick to realize the consequences. It is our task to teach them to overcome this. Paracelsus suggested that such preservative cure should be started as early as possible, when the nature of the sick is still more receptive. In later stages of insanity, the nature of man is more and more hardened, and it is more difficult to give him relief from the sickness. Paracelsus summarizes his method as follows: "The task is to find in the insane traces of still sound consciousness and to use them as the basis for a psycho-intellectual attempt at cure."

Indeed, this is the most important principle of any genuinely rational psychiatry. Its purpose is not to influence the patient from outside, but from inside the diseased psyche with the help of still-present healthy elements. With them the patient must overcome the *aggritude* and the *morbus* of his ailment. This is a genuine Socratic method, healing the psyche by means of its own forces. It utilizes the awakening and supporting of its own innate abilities. The doctor of the psyche, in this Socratic sense, is only the midwife of the innate psychic health. These are thoughts on which the psychiatrist of today does well to reflect. Similar to the modern method of "patient-centered psychotherapy," they even reach beyond the frame of such currently accepted techniques.

Most impressive, however, are the basic concepts of Paracelsus' psychiatry. With a boistrous pride, the start of the Nineteenth Century maintained that it had finally freed the insane from the chains of being treated like criminals and applied to them a humanitarian medical care. Those who maintain this today, I advise to read Paracelsus' small treatise, *"De Lunaticis et De Daemoniacis et Obsessis,"* written in 1533. Nevertheless it had not been possible for this hated and persecuted progressive and wandering medicus to create an institution for the insane as he had envisioned it. From the following quotation it is evident that he demanded that each and every insane person should receive medical and humane treatment.

> Therefore no one should be coined a nut or a fool, who has been betrayed by nature, into which we have been born. Neither Adam nor Eve should be a deciding factor in our relationship to one another in

this world. . . . Anyone should be aware that our human knowledge means nothing before God. In all our earthly wisdom we equal the fool and whatever and how much we try and are able to contrive and speculate with our animal reasoning, it does not differ from that which fools do. It is Christ alone who can be our helper. As we all are friends and of one blood, we are the same with our wisdom before God. He who has salvaged the wise will also salvage the foolish. In Christ we all are brothers, the foolish and the wise. . . . Crazyness becomes insanity when consciousness can no longer be awakened. According to the law of charity we should remind ourselves of such unfortunate ones and pray to God our Savior to free them. Since there is no difference between the various ones who are possessed and afflicted. . . .

Such a conviction would certainly end the practice of placing the insane in jails to be kept as prisoners, and would place them in a medically cared-for environment. However, Paracelsus' spirit required three hundred years of occidental history to come near to its realization, and there are other psychiatric theories in Paracelsus that will require a thousand years before men's insight will ripen enough to recognize and put them into practice.

Chapter 4

FELIX PLATER: AT THE THRESHOLD
TO SCIENTIFIC PSYCHIATRY

NO one would dare to deny that Theophrastus Paracelsus originated the nontheological, scientific impulse which started
the history of modern scientific man, but if, viewing Paracelsus
in the totality of his world-view, one tries to place him in the line
of development of the centuries that followed him, one realizes
that we have every reason to admire the cosmocentric (macro-
microcosmic) concept. In this concept he was able to coordinate,
in his amazingly intuitive and truthful way, the finer structural
factors and tendencies to pathology that exist in human nature.
Such a cosmocentric viewpoint has, as any other, its limits. This
view was mainly the result of the impulses of historical mental
development which expressed itself in the quest for empirical
natural-scientific certainty experience. It was precisely this demand
for certainty experience that emerged as the basic problematic
factor in all modern approaches to reality. This is indeed still the
case in our time.

History develops in steps that lead from one problematic insight
to another, from one empirical discovery to the next. There was
to be taken a next step after Paracelsus toward a modern approach
to understanding man's normal and abnormal existence, both
physical and mental. This step was to change from a cosmocentric
to an anthropological, or if one prefers, an anthropomorphic point
of view. Man should no longer be viewed primarily as within and
part of the world or worlds around him, but as an existence in
himself, viewed from himself and in regard to his own nature.
More specifically, he should be viewed in terms of a medical and
psychological concept which bases itself upon an empirical description of the facts of his bodily and mental existence. The first
man to attempt this new approach was frequently mentioned in
historical writings, but hardly ever recognized in his specific importance. This was Felix Plater, the Swiss physician.

In contrast to the gigantic and controversial Theophrastus, who had to flee by night from Switzerland's major city of that time (Basel), Felix Plater lived a settled life there for decades. He was a highly esteemed practitioner, and as an academic teacher, he rose to the presidency of Basel University. He wrote a certain number of medical treatises in the Paracelsan style which he combined into a sturdy volume, *The Practice of Medicine*. After it first appeared in 1602, it stood its ground as a major text for 130 years and had about half a dozen reprintings. In contrast to Paracelsus, Plater wrote in Latin modified by the medical equilogism of his time, but in a most careful and thoughtful way, attempting to express clearly his thoughts about the facts of human existence.

There can be no doubt that Plater's two major publications, his *Practice of Medicine* and his *Observations of Diseases Injurious to Body and Mind,* were intended to be general texts covering the entire medical field. Nevertheless, those who have been most interested in him and who have extensively written about him have been impressed by the amount of space Plater devotes to what we today designate as nervous and mental disease. They are also struck by the fact that he begins his books—definitely designated to treat of general medicine—with a section on the treatment of mental ills. No one until now has tried to answer *why* he has proceeded in this way. Viewing the situation of medicine in our days, it would be considered rather strange if an author would start his text with chapters devoted to the neurological and psychiatric fields.

There cannot be any doubt that Plater had good reason for beginning his presentation of the total field of medicine with psychiatry. Twenty years earlier, Plater's first major publication had been a textbook on anatomy. This indicates that one could not consider him as a psychiatrist or a mental scientist. I wish also to point out here that his placing so many psychiatric facts at the start of his text on general medicine must be for another reason than simply a desire to advance or give the first place to the field of mental diseases. This emphasis by most of the previous writers about Plater's work apparently results from some kind of misconception. This misconception seems to me to be caused by the fact that Plater's actual general approach to medicine was not properly seen and understood at its root. To give the reader the right focus at the outset, it could be said that Plater looked actually less psychiatrically than psychologically upon his patients. He tried to describe the field of human ailments with such a psychologically viewing eye. The result was that certain psychiatric factors and somatic pictures appeared as the first in his view.

To describe this view I would like to quote a few sentences from the first pages of the *Observations* in the somewhat condensed translation made by Culpepper and Cole in 1664. This first chapter is entitled "Observations on the Weakness of the Mind."

> It is not necessary to show that many of those who are naturally without wit are without any apparent disease. . . . When children begin to learn to read, it is easily perceived; for some cannot learn their letters or spell without great difficulty; nor afterwards being older learn any languages, arts or sciences; as do others who are ingenious. This comes from the diversities constitution and nature, which makes some more ingenious than others for arts and actions; and so it is in other creatures of the same kind. . . .
>
> We see many born fools, who declare themselves such in their infancy by their carriage, laughter, and reluctance to be taught anything that is industrious, but make sport by trifling and doing all things crossly, fit to please great men, who give them their education.

These sentences contain an almost phenomenological, psychological description of the kind we are familiar with in Nineteenth and Twentieth Century terminology. All Plater's books are written in this way, expressing a point of view which cannot but be called psychological. It is the application of this psychological view to all of medicine which characterizes Plater's entire concept, but we must point out that earlier he had written a text, or better a student's instruction book, on anatomy which shows nothing different from the customary physiological views of his time. However, from a medical point of view, he presented human existence in its totality. In doing so he applied a psychological anthropomorphism which was basically different from Paracelsus' conception and very different from the physiological view characteristic for the medical conceptionalism of the Seventeenth and Eighteenth Centuries.

Although this psychological approach of Plater has never yet been properly emphasized, some may now feel justified to consider him a progressivist in advance of the two following centuries. I feel, however, that this would not be quite accurate. The Swiss scholar Hans Christoffel, who has doubtlessly contributed the best that has been written about Plater during the past few decades, designates him as a spiritualist. This is indeed true if one, following Plater himself, includes the human psyche in its major and most elementary existence in the spiritual sphere. Because of this, Plater is much nearer Paracelsus than to the medical physiologists who dominated medical thinking during the time when the last editions of his *Practice of Medicine* were printed.

This spiritual psychology, as we may now call it, expresses itself further in a religious acknowledgement of a higher theistic sphere from which negative influences may impart sickness just as an actual mistreatment of the body may. There was still no division established between the medical and clerical spheres of thinking as was later urged by Heinroth in regard to mental behavior and the treatment of mental diseases. Living in this intellectual atmosphere, Plater still acknowledged a possessedness for which only "the servants of Christ" may have a remedy. If this was vain, he agreed to the extermination method of his days in the form of witch burning. Later writers have condemned Plater because of this attitude; however, we cannot completely agree to this. Plater lived in the tense religious atmosphere of Switzerland and was part of it. He was attempting to draw a strict line between that atmosphere and his medical task. Witch burning was not actually a procedure he subscribed to, nor was exorcism, which was still common in the Roman Church of those days. He saw in them social hygienic measures which eliminated dangerous elements against which he, with his medicines, was unable to undertake anything constructively. However, he fought intensively to uproot the most commonly accepted superstitions of his day.

In his *Observations* we find the delightful story of his curing a physician who for years believed he had a live frog in his belly. We feel we can best illustrate Plater's impressive mode of thinking by quoting from this frog cure.

The argument by which I cured him was this, that frogs are but short-lived and could not live above two years, but are bred every year of the spawn they leave, and that he made himself ridiculous by saying that he had a live frog in his belly seven years old. I said further that frogs, if in water long and lacking air cannot live. I proved this by laboring to take a drunkard from the love of wine, by suffocating a frog in the wine he was to drink. I bid him try the same, to put a frog in such a place, and he would find him dead in a short time. And I wondered that he, being a doctor, should be of so childish a judgment. By these arguments he was overcome, confessed his folly, gave me thanks, and went away cured of his phantasies.

In this argumentation there certainly speaks a mind of natural scientific thought: Such was Plater's wherever we probe his writing. Plater indeed still belonged to what some have called the spiritualism of his time, but if one takes this timely basic concept and applies it in conjunction with Plater's struggle for a scientific rationalization, one arrives at the kind of psychological approach that we find in him. Viewing the psychological functions as they appear in the nature of man was the most realistic method to be found, but it was at the same time a spiritualistic one. This was Plater's approach to the reality of human nature, and it must be our approach to understanding him.

If we today start a description of what we prefer to call a system of psychiatry—not to speak of one of general medicine—we expect to start with the physiological (or at least the neurological) basis of man's mental life. This means we start from below and move towards the higher functions. In general psychology we have a similar scientific trend. We start from outside, from a psychology of the senses, and move inside and upward to the psychology of the functions of thought.

In Plater we see the reverse in the way he lays out the general description of medical practice. He actually starts from above and inside and moves from there to the physiological part of human existence. This is the practical execution of his new point of view, and it is characteristic for him. Indeed, we see him starting his systematic description of medical practice with what he calls *mentis laesiones,* which we may translate as *mental injuries,* or in our terminology, *mental abnormalities.* Here again, characteristically, he starts with abnormalities of what appear to him to be the major higher functions: imagination, reasoning and memory. Afterward he comes to the pathology of the actual sense perception. Here again we see the line of progression from above and inside towards below and outside.

Let us now consider the contents of Plater's entire medical system as it is laid down in the table of contents of his *Praxis Medica*. There are distinguished three parts which have the Latin titles: *De Functionum Laesionibus, De Doloribus* and *De Vitiis*. It is, of course, actually not too easy to translate these titles in a simple, verbal way. *Functiones Laesiones* would mean *injured junctions*. This, however, would be too general a concept to have any concrete meaning for our present way of thinking. A translation such as *injured dynamics* would come nearer. Even this comes only part of the way toward expressing what Plater seems to have meant. It appears to me that one best grasps his meaning by studying carefully the sentence from the first chapter I have reproduced above. This sentence expresses most characteristically how much Plater aims at presenting an observation of the processes he concerns himself with, and how anxious he is to distinguish the inner from any other element of such observation. This means in a more general sense that he aims at a description of his "experience." Actually wherever we open the *Praxis Medica* we find not so much the presentation of simple facts as such, but the experience of the way and the function by which these facts of human abnormal life present themselves.

In other words, the method of Plater is to present the variety of forms and the function of experience in which human illness and injuries come to awareness. Since the first and basic modes of our experience are our inner sense perceptions of the world as well as of ourselves, Plater starts with them his presentation of the entire system of medicine. As we have already pointed out, Plater does not, as we would do today according to our scientific conception, start with the treatment of the lower and outside function even where he deals with human inner abnormal experience. He does not follow the famous formulation of Fechner, to present a *Psychologie von unten* (a psychology from below), but he basically pursues the progression from above.

In describing these *functiones laesionibus* in the first part of the

Praxis Medica, Plater divided the field of immediate abnormal human experiences into two sections. He names them *Sensuum Laesiones* and *Motuum Laesiones.* This is only logical according to his consequential method, which also leads him to begin the *Sensuum Laesiones* with what he calls the *Mentis Laesiones.* Only after these does he treat the actual sense perceptions and the illnesses which may arise from them.

Mentis Laesiones are the actual mental illnesses of our days. We have the full right to translate *mens* to *mental,* since mental functions, as Plater wishes to discuss them here, are for him imagination, reasoning and memory.

The chapter on the *Mentis Laesiones* is actually Plater's presentation of the field of psychiatry. There are distinguished four forms of *Mentis Laesiones: Imbecilitas Mentis, Consternatio Mentis, Alienatio Mentis* and *Defatigatio Mentis.* As always, we must study the contents of what is presented to gain an understanding of the title. For example, in many instances the meaning is different from what we may understand by the words and titles according to our modern conceptions.

Imbecilitas Mentis, for instance, is not identical with our present concept of imbecility. Plater's concept is much broader. It means all those mental states which result from a constitutional weakness, to which he counts *imprudentia,* which is one of the lighter forms and may be translated *mental retardedness.* Our imbecility is one of the more severe forms.

As we have pointed out earlier, Plater views all pathological states as experienced in their dynamic character. Therefore we should not be surprised to find that in his two further concepts of *consternatio* and *alienatio* he presents a division in mental abnormality according to weakness and strength, or under- and over-stimulation of the consciousness. This kind of thinking and classification appears to be quite characteristic for Plater.

Consternatio, which is the state of lack or loss, starts with numbness and giddiness, and progresses via lethargy and stupor to apoplexy, and epilepsy and convulsions.

Alienatio, which is a too-strong and therefore pathological mental state, starts with excitedness, drunkenness and psychopathic forms of love and ends with madness, mania, obsessions, hydrophobia and corea.

It may appear dubious to find Plater enlist *Melancholia* under these mental diseases of the *alienatio* group. In his long and differentiating discussion of *Melancholia,* however, Plater emphasizes that *melancholia* is always a state of disturbedness. This seems to justify his counting it among the types of excitement.

As a fourth kind of mental illness, Plater delineates what he has called *Defatigatio Mentis.* Here again we have a concept enlarged beyond our present conventional meaning. Plater includes here all the states ranging from simple tiredness to complete exhaustion. There are a great variety of mental illnesses which we know today and for which most are reluctant to formulate or to accept any organized classification. These we find here classified etiologically by Plater in an amazingly clear and simple way as constitutional weakness, dynamic loss or dynamic overstimulation and weakness by exhaustive abuse. Whether we may be willing to accept this classification today or not, we cannot help but acknowledge it as an amazing scientific achievement of the Seventeenth Century.

In a second division of the *Sensuum Laesiones* we find a short description of the actual pathology of the senses: *Tactus, Gustus, Visus, Auditus* and *Olfactus Laesiones.* This is far from what specialized medical disciplines of today, such as ophthalmology, have as contents. We deal here far more with a short psychopathology of those senses differentially viewed. Of course what Plater presents here has the limitation of the knowledge of the physiology of his time.

Those who have made it their task to study Plater's psychopathology or psychiatry or believe they have done so have stopped here with no further study of the *Praxis Medica.* They have indeed been able to point out this amazing early observer of abnormal human mental life, but none has actually seen the basic underlying concept and the range with which Plater applied his fundamentally psychological view through the whole of his medical perceptions. This actually comes first to the fore when one sees the *Praxis Medica* as a whole and studies the whole of its contents.

Following the *Sensuum Laesiones,* the first part of *De Functionum Laesionibus,* comes a second which has the title *Motuum Laesiones.* Separating such *moti* from the senses must have, of course, a meaning to Plater. We do not go wrong in assuming that we deal here with functions of human nature which, also still in the actual sphere of specific experience, are on a lower, more organic level. We find these *moti* divided into two kinds, *volentari* and *involentari.* These terms make it evident that again the psychological functionality is the essential and discriminatory element.

Three *Motus Voluntarii Laesiones* are enumerated. They are *Motus Debilitas, Motus Impotentia* and *Motus Depraviatio,* terms which, according to the contents to which they are referred, we may translate as *unmanageable, powerless* and *inverted.* As *moti debiliti* Plater lists, among others, drunkenness pathologies and exhaustions. As the *moti impotentia* he lists paralysis, spasms, strabismus and bone fractures. The *moti depravatii* are tremors, restlessness and various local cramps.

As involuntary *moti* Plater lists defective respiration, defective appetite, sickish sweating, hemorrhoids, faulty blood circulation and digestion, and finally defective conception and lactations. Actually we cannot differentiate the meanings of voluntary and involuntary by what today we relate to something more or less will-controlled. We come nearer to the meaning given by Plater if we apply the concept of activity diseases. For some of the voluntary types of *moti* one could also apply a classification designating them as spontaneity illnesses. Meanwhile, for some of the involuntary types of *moti,* one could apply the designation of congenital dysfunctions.

However, the most specific of all the classifications of Plater appears only when we compare all that he designates as *Laesiones* with what is contained in the second major part of the entire work, which carries the title *De Doloribus,* a term which we best translate as "Painful Diseases." For our modern medical and physiological concepts, it would appear almost ridiculous to separate pain or painful diseases from all others as a specific kind of illness. To our thinking, pain cannot be singled out as a disease. Pain is a symptom, a reaction of the nervous system upon all major injuries to the human body. For Plater, however, pain was a most basic and multiform disease. Actually, no other opinion than this is more characteristic for the specific type of medical thinking we find in Plater. We designated this a psychological one, and to present it properly, we can do no better than to report Plater's own introductory presentation to *De Doloribus.*

Plater is himself quite aware of the unusual character of his concept, even for his own time. He therefore presents a careful deduction. Pain, he emphasizes, is a sickness which can appear all over and in all parts of the human body. It is not a symptom of any other illness, but is itself an illness. Pain is an injury to any part of the body which we, of course, must perceive with our organs of sense. It is actually not to be identified with any particular sense perception, although it may appear as if it were a sickness of the perception of touch. Pains have a different form of appearance from the perceptions of sense.

Study of the classification of the various forms in which pain appears in the body brings us nearer to its actual meaning. There are four kinds of pain: (1) fever; (2) pains observed through the actual senses, to which are referred pleuritis, pneumonia, and among others, pains of the genitals; (3) *Dolores Habitus Corpus,* which are, among others, rheumatism, podagra and pains in the bones; and (4) *Dolores Superficei,* which are pains from skin diseases and from wounds. Most revealing for this entire pain concept is the fact that fever is one of its major forms. Again we must from our modern point of view point out that we could not agree that basically fever is or produces pain.

If we now analyze more exactly Plater's pain concept, we do best to designate it first of all as a kind of quasi-feeling which is separate from all sense perceptions. The scope from which it is conceived and viewed seems to be a psychological inner standpoint which we usually consider the area of emotions and feelings. Also today, if we speak of pain, we view it mainly as an emotionally negatively colored sense perception, for instance if we have hurt ourselves in a fall or have received a bruise or a bleeding wound in an accident. We know that here, in some respect, an emotional element is everywhere involved. However, we also know that there are special forms of pain which are entirely and strictly emotions, as for instance sorrow and grief. Generally speaking, pain as Plater has perceived it is primarily a psychological experience occurring below the sense perceptions. It is the first time in the mental development of modern man that such a purely inner psychological experience (independent of the sense perceptions) has been pointed at and described. This is the importance of Plater's pain concept. This insight was—and I am here coming back to my previous contention—possible for Plater only because of his basic concept, which we have designated as psychological or psychiatric and which Christophel had called spiritualistic. The latter designation we feel, after our previous presentation, should be discarded.

This basic psychological aspect finds application again in Plater's enumeration of the four forms in which pain apparently does occur. Again he applies the methodological point of view we found previously in the enumeration from upward-down and from inward-out. First we have his sensitive, all-comprising and probably most inwardly perceived sphere of fever as pain. Next come all the pains connected with the perceptions of the sense organs, and added to them, as of the same category, are those pains connected with the most sensitive spheres of the human body: the nervous system (pleuritis), pains in the respiratory system (connected with pneumonia) and finally, pains in the sex organs. As a third kind of pain, Plater enumerates those of the actual physical constitution of the body, pains in the muscles and bones (rheumatism, podagra or what he calls *ossium dolores*—pains in the bones). Finally Plater comes to the outermost part of the body—its surface. Here a fourth kind of pain is established, that of broken skin or wounds. In this fourfold classification every part of the body is covered again in an admirably totalistic way.

Not until the third and last part of the *Praxis Medica* does Felix Plater become physiological in our modern sense. This last part is given the title *Vitiis*. Here Plater actually deals with the physiological pathology of the human body and the injuries which can occur to it. Plater applies an interesting division: *Vitia Corporis* and *Vitia Excretorum*. From our point of view it appears important to point out this division since it reflects in a limited way the specific psychological basis which we have emphasized in Plater. It is expressed in the dynamism or functionalism which is applied. In *Vitiis Corporis* we deal with the intercorporal, the inner functions of the body and in the eliminatory functions, those which are always directed towards the outside. Such a dynamic view always comes to the fore where the physiology is viewed from a psychological point of view.

As in the other section of the work, we find here the tendency toward a total coverage and integrated survey of all the important phases involved. The inner functional pathologies are covered from the diseases of growth and deformation to the actual digressive diseases, such as tabes, phthisis and atrophy.

As I pointed out above, it was rather unfortunate that those who tried to make Plater's contribution to psychiatry known have missed the special psychological character of his writings, except for the actual chapters devoted to mental abnormality. If one views Plater's psychiatry chapters alone, one sees, on the background of modern psychiatry, that his contribution may not be too great and not of major importance for the development of this special field. However, if one takes into the picture the total work of Plater with its underlying basic concept, his importance grows by the minute. He proves to be the first who has sized up the field of psychiatry totalistically and placed it rightly in the leading role in the total study of human nature. He has besides, more than anyone else yet, organized the field of mental pathology in a meaningful way with respect to the whole field of medicine. Even today few dare to tackle this problem. He finally has seen the underlying psychology where it is active in all of medicine and where psychology itself gives the background for the correct view on the actual psychopathology. It was one of the major achievements of modern psychiatry that it demanded that the proper approach to psychopathology was its determination as deviation from normal functions and not merely the description of abnormal phenomena. It was actually Plater who indicated and applied this point of view.

Plater is frequently pointed out in the general history of medicine as a stepping stone in the development from alchemistic medicine to medical realism. Nobody would deny this acknowledgement, but we wish to add here his importance for the realism of early psychiatry as well as for an integrated view for the psychiatric field in that of general medicine.

Chapter 5

GEORG ERNST STAHL:
THE SEVENTEENTH CENTURY PSYCHIATRIST

L IKE Paracelsus, Georg Ernst Stahl is better known for what his contemporaries and later medical writers said against him than for what he himself represented. However, he was undoubtedly one of the most influential medical theorists of his time, and as is usual, he was attacked as an enemy of the point of view of his attacker. To the materialist of his day he was a pietist; to the spiritualist, a materialist. Actually he was neither. He was a most radical realist with an amazingly discrete sensitivity, which placed him on a new, higher level between the two major camps. True, he was difficult to understand. He wrote a baroque Latin mingled with contemporary German expressions. If we did not have the admirable translation of his *Theoria Medica Vera* (by the psychiatrist Karl Wilhelm Ideler) in the beautiful and lucid German of a Romantic essayist, we would be hopelessly lost in trying to understand him. In this remarkable Germanization, the brilliance of Stahl's basic deductions becomes wonderfully clear.

As Paracelsus fought against the alchemist metaphysicians and cleared the air for the formulation of natural scientific laws, Stahl courageously opposed the "man—a machine" notions of the flowering materialistic and mechanistic thinking in his time. In his lifelong struggle, full of bitter polemic, he declared himself a vitalist and psychist. He applied his clear reasoning powers to the distinction between matter and organism: A living organism cannot be only mechanically functioning matter; it begins to disintegrate at the moment of death; life must be a quality added to matter. This unique quality Stahl designates as *animus,* which is not a deistic spiritual element but a *motus,* as he calls it in his Latin, a movement, a dynamic element—which was, in the following century, designated as *psyche.*

The German medical historian Kirchhoff believed that it was identical with Hippocrates' *physis.* The placing of the human

41

psyche "between heaven (not spiritual) and earth (not a physiological element)," as he puts it, is the great achievement of Stahl.
Despite the claims that the psychoanalytic concepts of this century
were the first to have developed the dynamic aspect of psychology,
its real discoverer and first representative was G. E. Stahl. Stahl's
starting point was the need for a clear teleological concept as the
basis of human existence. The final result is what, in its most
modern form, C. G. Jung has formulated as the human psyche, a
closed unit of a dynamic system. It is especially this clear and
systematic thinking that accounts for Stahl's great influence, which
during his time extended all over Europe.

To be historically objective, one must hand to Paracelsus the
palm for having initiated psychotherapy by his demand that the
insane be viewed, not as persons possessed by the devil and pun-
ished by God, but simply as sick human individuals. However,
Stahl's influence on the development of psychiatry was no less
great, since he was the first to demand concrete psychological treatment. Although hardly a practitioner in the care of the insane, one
of his most important writings, his *De Animi Morbis* (1708), was
devoted to psychiatric treatment methods. He clearly distinguished
between mental diseases resulting from actual bad behavior and
those physiologically conditioned, among which delirium was for
him the most characteristic. He also clearly differentiated between
psychosomatic and somatopsychological influences.

The latter, normal functions he described in great detail in his
more scientific version of the old concept of the four temperaments. He saw *animus* functions as influencing the body psycho-
somatically in a dual way, by contracting and extending—a concept that attained its classical form in Goethe's "systole and dia-
stole." Abnormal functioning of the *animus* he considered the
major cause of insanity.

Kirchhoff correctly pointed out that the first clear psychiatric
differentiation—Langermann's diopathic and sympathic mental
ailment—goes back to this concept of Stahl's. There can be no
doubt that the great psychiatrists of the past century—Reil, Heinroth and Griesinger—were profoundly influenced by Stahl, who
was their major source of thought. He foresaw not only the basic

theory of modern vitalism and holism, but envisioned the libido theory as well, more in its Jungian than its Freudian form. In a clear form he later prefigured conditioned reflex theories.

One of his most astonishing insights was his description of allergy. The following passage was written in 1706. It is a translation taken from one of his shorter polemic writings, *Disquisition de Mechanismi et Organismi Diversitate* (Discussion of the Difference between Mechanical and Organic Reality).

There are people who are born with a certain sensitivity because of which, when entering a room in which a cat is present, an irritation starts on the surface of their body which makes them rather uncomfortable. They are at first not aware of the cause of this condition and only repeated occurrence—with the aid of memory—makes them realize the object that creates the disturbance.

I can report such a condition: It occurred to a young lady, very intelligent and free from feelings of social insecurity and fear, who for many years enjoyed undisturbed health. Once, while away from home, she felt quite comfortable until she had to sleep in a bed made of eiderdown. She spent a sleepless night, tortured by a strange restlessness and irritation, the cause of which she felt unable to determine. In the morning she complained of a heaviness and emptiness of the head, but not of headaches, assuming this condition to be due to the unusual sleeplessness. She remained this way until after lunch. Overpowered by tiredness and without bias against the resting place of the previous night, she decided to rest in the same bed. Experiencing the same discomfort in an increasing way, she feared the start of an illness. This she attributed to the difficult journey, until she examined the bed and found its fillings consisted of eiderdown. She suddenly remembered that this material had always caused her similar troubles.

When the history of psychiatry matures to become an objective survey and not merely the history of this or that school of psychiatric thought, it will have to recognize Georg Ernst Stahl as one of the four great fathers of psychiatry.

Chapter 6

ALEXANDER MONRO II:
AN EARLY NEURODRUG EXPERIMENTER

ALMOST two hundred years ago, in an amazingly modern way, a neurodrug experimenter approached the problem of the influence of drugs upon the nervous system. Modern experimenters will be interested to learn about one of their ancestors, the astonishing, polyphonically inclined "professor of surgery" at Edinburgh, Alexander Monro II (1733-1817). Medical historians have credited him with several important, original discoveries about the lymphatic system and anatomic structures. His name is linked with the discovery of the "foramen of Monro."

Monro's experiments on the influence of drugs upon the nervous system have been completely ignored by history. Monro first reported his attempts through the application of opium injections on various animals in 1771. They seem to have occupied him fairly continuously for about twenty-five years. In 1793, he published "Experiments on the Nervous System with Opium and Metalline Substances." Here he surveys his own attempts so impressively that we can sum them up best by quoting his major sentences:

> I cut one hole in the fore and upper part of the cranium and dura mater of a frog and another in the back part of the lower-most vertebrae, and then injected, from the one hole to the other, a small syringe full of water, in five ounces of which one ounce of opium had been infused for three days. The infusion, by this means brought into contact with the whole surface of the encephalon and spinal marrow, produced almost instantly universal convulsions; and, in less than two minutes thereafter, the animal was incapable of moving its body from the place where it was laid. A quarter of an hour thereafter, I found the heart beating twenty-five times only in the minute; and so feebly, that it could not entirely expel the blood. When half an hour thereafter, the sciatic nerves were pinched, a slight tremor only was excited in the muscles of the leg; and animal electricity produced but feeble twitchings of the muscles.
>
> The infusion of opium injected in the same manner in rabbits and in a pig, produced similar effects.

Continuing this report, Monro discusses the theories of Felice Fontana, whose book on the effect of poisons was receiving much attention at that time. In his book Fontana maintained that poisoning occurs by way of the bloodstream. Monro doubted the correctness of this thesis, and after reporting a set of experiments disproving that the vascular system had the primary role in carrying the toxic influence, he presents his case in the following climaxing statements.

Many years ago, I found, after cutting the venae cavae and aorta of a frog, that a watery solution of opium poured into the heart, occasioned, in a few minutes, convulsions in its legs; and, after cutting out the heart, that the opium poured into the cavity of the abdomen affected the legs in like manner; although, in these experiments, the circulation was not only interrupted, but the greater part of the blood evacuated. I therefore then concluded, and now conclude, that opium and other poisons, even after they are mixed with the mass of blood, produced their fatal effects, chiefly and almost solely, by acting on the nerves of the heart and vascular system, and through these, affecting the whole of the nervous system.

In connection with the active experimental work of today in neurophysiology it seems worthwhile to recall Monro's experiments of two hundred years ago.

Chapter 7

F. C. G. SCHEIDEMANTEL:
THE FIRST SYSTEMATIC TEXT IN
PSYCHOSOMATIC MEDICINE

A YOUNG Hessian physician, born in 1735, who had hoped for an academic career, had to return home after his graduation in 1762 because of the death of his physician father and a fire which destroyed the major part of his home town, including his paternal home and property. He put aside his original plans for research and became a general practitioner in his small town. His practice also encompassed the neighboring spa at Brückenau and the court of the local prince. The medical biographies list him as an able and sage practitioner and credit him with several writings which were frequently used in his time for reference regarding the usefulness of spas for various diseases. The least recognized of his works, however, is a book published in 1787, nine years before his early death. In the introduction, he designates this work as the "red thread" of his scientific occupation, but one which he was only able to produce slowly because of the lack of physical and scientific means. This book, *Die Leidenschaften als Heilmittel (The Passions as a Means of Cure),* is the first systematic presentation of what we today call psychosomatic medicine.

Friederich Christian Gottlieb Scheidemantel lived during the period which saw the dawn of German objective idealism, a philosophy which extended itself into the field of psychology as psychological romanticism and into the fields of medicine and science in a number of broad deductive systems. Scheidemantel stood with one foot in the strongly biogenetic medicine of his century and with the other he spanned the first decades of the new century with its psychological objectivism which considered *die Seele* (the psyche) a real part of the total of man's existence. The psyche was that part to which man owed his capacity to think, but this psyche was also considered the seat of virtue and vice which, together, Scheidemantel designates as the passions, and which we

46

today consider emotions and affects. This dual role of the psyche attracted Scheidemantel's scientific interest, and it became his mission to investigate from a medical viewpoint the influence of the psychic forces upon the body. In accordance with the scientific concepts of his time, he went to work systematizing and deductively organizing his observations. The results offer us an impressive presentation of the concepts of the mind-body relationship as they existed during his time.

The Passions as a Means of Cure is divided into two parts. The first gives an account of the ways in which passions cause bodily illnesses, including, at the end of the individual accounts, a description of the natural healing influence of each passion. In the second part he traces the actual therapeutic applications and effects of all the passions.

Both of the major sections begin with a chapter on general therapeutic considerations. Scheidemantel, in his introduction, rejects both one-sided physiological materialism and one-sided spiritualism, but "changes in the body caused by influences from the psyche" are basically evident for him. He is a strict empiricist and starts his argument almost phenomenologically by pointing to psychic manifestations in facial expressions, in the frown, smile and tears. For pathological indications he refers to the expressions caused by excessive pleasure, desires and dislikes. From this point it is a short distance to the manifest organic changes due to emotional expression, be they good or bad, such as changes in breathing, palpitations of the heart and changes in blood circulation. These are known areas which can be influenced by emotional upsets. For Scheidemantel the whole vascular motor system, skin temperature, excessive elimination of body fluids, voluntary or involuntary muscular contractions and changes in the nerves (*Nervensaft* or *nerve-fluid* in the terminology of his time) belong to the sphere of symptomatology—of direct actions of the psyche on the functions of the body. The basis of Scheidemantel's whole approach is this insight that the primary channel through which the psyche influences the body is the vascular motor system. It is worked out in great detail, however, with regard to his qualitative and quantitative values. He discusses in detail the relationship between the momentary intensity and the length of time of a passion's influence with regard to the more or less resistant or vulnerable bodily constitution and the conditions it influences.

His analysis of the effect of combinations of passions is elaborate; for instance, when a momentary scare strikes a fearful person or when fear follows a violent scare or several scare attacks follow one another. Similarly, he investigates the combination of rage and sorrow. The influence of environment is also a combination factor; for instance, the greater impact of scare in exposure to frost and of rage in hot weather. He also discusses the combination of passions with acute or chronic illnesses such as pregnancy, menses and convalescence. It is here that one realizes the sensitive understanding the author has for psychosomatic conditions.

Scheidemantel proves to be primarily a functional thinker regarding actual pathological elements. The pathogenic influence of the passions are mainly carried by a contraction, expansion or enlargement of the vascular system. All further effects are a consequence of this.

To emphasize the character of his thought and aims, I am quoting the following passage, which is so modern that it is astonishing to know it was written 125 years before the concepts of psychoanalysis and individual psychology appeared.

> Remembrances of events inducing scare which were imprinted upon the psyche in childhood, insecurity, superstition, the pressure of guilt feelings in the consciousness of having committed a bad deed, and a melancholic disposition make the temperament vulnerable to fear, and the start of its influence is facilitated by weakness of the nervous system.

In the first section of *The Passions as a Means of Cure,* Scheidemantel studies the major emotions and their effects: scare, fear, sorrow, bashfulness, rage, indignation, joy, hope, love, hate and envy, vanity and ambition, and longing.

The first and longest chapter is devoted to scare as a pathogenic factor. Following his well-organized pattern, Scheidemantel describes the experience of scare.

> The bewildered stages of the psyche expresses itself with great vehemence in the motions of our body. The moment a person becomes

scared his arms and legs tend to become rigid. Like lightning, a sensation strikes the pit of the heart; one has a feeling that the thorax is too tight. One gets pale and cold; a chill runs through the body. The skin of the entire body contracts and gooseflesh develops. The eyes seem paralysed and unable to move. The scared person is paralysed; he is unable to make a decision and therefore unable to escape. He remains immobile at the spot where the scare struck him. He has a rapid, short and irregular pulse. The heart trembles or beats so hard that one can hear it. The chest feels oppressed. The breath becomes slow and once in a while with a sigh one tries to gain relief. All limbs tremble and the word dies in one's mouth. Strength vanishes, the nerves becomes unreceptive, the psyche seems to want to leave the body which is threatened with a fainting spell. Such terrible episodes are caused by a scare, and a single word or a rustling leaf can bring the healthiest person into such a state.

This description is followed by a detailed presentation of the organic process. According to Scheidemantel, this organic process is basic to most physical pathology resulting from scare. As we pointed out before, it is the author's general theory that passions influence, at first, the vascular motor system, the heart and bloodstream, and all other effects result from the dynamic ramifications of this system. Disturbances explained in this way range from fainting and death due to scare shock to gooseflesh and hair-raising.

In describing the various disorders which can be caused by scare, Scheidemantel used a great many cases reported in medical literature. He read a great deal and abstracted an enormous amount of material. He proves to be acquainted not only with German literature, but with all European literature. For instance, he frequently quotes the French-Swiss neurologist, S. A. Tissot.

The diseases brought on by scare which he discusses first are various forms of febrile conditions. He then continues with hepatitis, menstrual irregularity, unusually strong bleeding, stillbirth, ruptures of the veins and finally, diseases of the respiratory system such as hiccoughs, lung bleeding and pneumonia.

All these disorders are connected with the vascular system, but he also reports conditions that go beyond this sensitive area. There are swellings and tumors of the female breast due to decomposition of the milk, and there are stomach ailments and colitis in which the reaction of the liquid release of the mucous membrane and the gland is the causal basis of scare. In the group of secondary effects, Scheidemantel records cases where the reaction to scare was enuresis or an unusually strong release of urine. In a nervous person, scare may cause chronic quivering and trembling as well as paralysis, convulsions, shock and severe spells of depression and melancholia. Finally, he points to cases of hernia and rupture caused by scare.

Scheidemantel also lists the positive effects of passions. With regard to scare attacks, he reports cases where severe bleeding or menstruation were stopped and fevers, gout, palsy and paralysis were alleviated by the momentary impulse. We today would speak of this as easing a hysterical spasm. He also enumerates cases where scare had a healing influence in mental ailments like hysteria, melancholia, depressions and delirious states. With intense interest Scheidemantel sets forth this healing function of passion in the second part of the book.

While scare has a momentary shocklike effect, fear, the second passion discussed, has a long-range influence. After delineating the actual process of fear and its organic effect, the author presents the actual pathologies caused by it. Fear has a basic tendency to cause chronic diseases because of its long-range influence. Again the vascular system stands in the foreground with chronic heart conditions, long-range irregularities of the pulse, congestions of the vascular system and the lungs as the areas attacked. However, an oversensitive nervous system attacked by fear may develop tremors, convulsions or lethargy. Bleeding, menstrual irregularity, diarrhea, colitis, the various forms of liver and gall bladder diseases, stomach and digestive disorders may also be due to exposure to fear over a length to time. Various types of mental diseases may also result from a long siege of fear, as well as language deficiencies like stammering and lesser effects like greying of the hair. Fear is emphasized as a serious secondary factor which would aggravate existing diseases. On the other hand, the author has observed cases where a sudden exposure to fear has improved stammering, dumbness, paralysis and chronic constipation.

Sorrow and its more intense sisters, grief and sadness, have similar organic effects. Most emphasized are a slow weakening of the functions of the heart, a toxic effect on the blood, a tendency towards malfunction of the glands and digestive processes due to the bad living habits of such sad and grief-stricken persons. It is pointed out that sadness induces a predisposition to strokes as well as to mental illnesses like depression and melancholia. Serious states of longlasting grief in a pregnant woman may have a serious effect upon her unborn child. Sorrow is the passion of the melancholic individual. Scheidemantel observed how much such melancholics "enjoy" their grief. There are no forms of illness which can be helped by sorrow or grief.

Bashfulness is explained as a mild form of fear. Its most common physical expression is blushing. It can cause mild physical discomfort of various kinds and is frequently the cause of stammering and other speech deviations.

Rage is almost always connected with hate and a desire to remove the irritating element. Rage has the most intense influence on the vascular system. The disturbances brought on by rage include acute, brief irregularities of the pulse as well as chronic irregularities and spastic conditions. There are certain physical dispositions which give some individuals a tendency towards rage. They are known as the choleric type, but hypochondriac and hysterical types also lean towards easy outbursts of rage.

In addition to disturbances of blood circulation and chemistry which can be traced to rage, there are also secondary effects of the intestinal and urinary system. These include liver, gall bladder and stomach diseases—more specifically colitis and other inflammations and ulcerous conditions. Fevers of various kinds, hemorrhages, lung tuberculosis, speech disturbances, convulsions and spells of dizziness, stillbirth and certain menstrual irregularities are also included here. Scheidemantel reports the folk belief that rage may drive bile into a nursing mother's milk and cause serious intestinal disturbances in the infant. On the healing side, rage can assist in overcoming hysterical paralysis, in bringing on menstruation which has stopped and in relieving gout and febrile conditions.

Indignation is described as a mixture of rage and grief. It is considered one of the most dangerous passions because of its lingering, penetrating effect. Some chronic conditions caused by indignation are dizzy spells, stomach and lung ailments, speech disturbances and mental diseases. Scheidemantel proves to be conscious of the basic Freudian postulation of suppression when he writes, "Indignation is most dangerous when it is intense and suppressed." There are also positive influences from indignation.

Joy is the passion with the greatest positive influence of all, and this is especially true when it finds its physical expression in laughter. Laughter revitalizes the vascular system and through this the entire body. It can help overcome many types of obstructions and constipation, and may even lead to the breaking of internal abscesses or may facilitate childbirth. However, excessive joy and laughter may have a serious negative effect. It can disrupt normal breathing and blood oxidation and cause hemorrhages and veins to burst. Quite a few cases were reported in history where overjoy even caused death.

Hope has effects similar to joy but not as strong. Hope is deeply involved with the total of human experience and is, in particular, the patient companion of the sick. It is the basis for confidence in the doctor. The author sees it as the real basis for all medical and pseudo-medical superstitions and miracle cures.

Love as conceived of by Scheidemantel is erotic and almost Freudian in its nature. He emphasizes the extent to which sound love improves physical and mental health. However, he also points out the consequences of too much erotic excitement or sexual excess. The consequences of unhappy and unfulfilled love and its extreme partner, jealousy, receive extensive treatment. Physiopathology caused by these passions range from hepatitis to insanity and death. Scheidemantel has also observed national characteristics pertaining to love and jealousy. He maintains that Turks, Italians and Spaniards have a greater tendency towards jealousy and its consequences than, for instance, the Germans. Love for other than human objects has similar but not such intense forms and effects. Hate is the passion diametrically opposed to love. In its psychological effects, its negative influences produce the same harmful, abnormal conditions in our body and mind.

Scheidemantel considers envy to be one of the most complex

passions. It is that passion with which one tends to be most preoccupied. Anyone who is seriously possessed by envy is difficult to help, and so are the chronic conditions it causes. The envious person is an atrophic individual who cannot properly enjoy life or food. He sleeps little, is deeply melancholic or expends himself in spells of choleric rage. He is predisposed towards lung and stomach sicknesses, but, strangely enough, he often lives a long life.

Arrogance, vanity and ambition belong to the same family. Arrogance is based on an unhealthy self-love and preoccupation with one's ego. Many believe it is actually a mental illness. Ambition is the son of arrogance with the addition of instability. Its negative organic effects are similar to those of indignation. Vanity, a member of the same family, is a passion with a strong propensity for mental illnesses.

Longing, the reverse of arrogance, is a desire not for oneself alone but for a foreign object. It tends to create a loss of appetite and sleeplessness, and if it lasts for any length of time it can be the basis for chronic diseases. Homesickness, a special type of longing which the author clearly depicts, is the most dangerous form of longing.

The most impressive part of the entire book, the general introductory chapter of the second part, deals with the passions as an actual means of treatment and cure. Scheidemantel emphasizes that here he is not referring to the natural positive influence passions may have by themselves, but to the actual use of passion as a therapeutic tool skillfully applied by the doctor. The author confesses that this is a completely new idea in medicine. Since he was able to find very little material in the literature, he had to rely mainly on his observations and experiments.

As the vascular system is the vehicle for the passions as agents of disorder, so it is their vehicle as therapeutic agents, and again their effect on the enlargement and contraction of the vascular system extends throughout the body. If such influence on the vascular system can assist in curing any disease, there is an opportunity to apply the passions as a remedy. Scheidemantel observes that there are certain illnesses for which there is no remedy in physical medicines. In these cases passions may become an important aid. Furthermore, there are diseases which are caused by passions, and the application of a correlated passion might help in their cure.

Before determining any practical applications, Scheidemantel points out the negative effects of each passion to make sure that these are ruled out in the planned use. As for the patient, he must be made aware of the role passions have, of the help he can receive when they are applied, and he must cooperate by following directions given with regard to these passion treatments. A prerequisite of all such treatment is that the patient learn to accept the disease as such, its length and the disagreeable factors the attempts at cure may involve.

We are without specific and detailed quantitative measurements in the practical application of passions. The only quantitative advice possible is such general specifications as weak, medium and strong. The doctor who wants to apply passions therapeutically must realize that simply prescribing them will not be of much help. Unlike physical medicine, the passions involve the innermost nature of the patient, requiring the doctor to work very closely with him. The basis for a judgment and evaluation in passion therapy is an intimate knowledge of the physical and mental nature of man. The doctor who wants to apply passion therapy must know much about the human temperament (psychology), the differentiation of the various stages of life, the educational and social background of his patient and the specific conditions of the ailment he is planning to treat. One cannot learn passion therapy from books, but only from long years of experience and a sensitive feeling for the very nature of passions.

Passions cannot be induced directly. They are carried through the memory and imagination. Therefore, the nature of the patient must be well known. Lacking a quantitative measure, the doctor must distinguish carefully between violent or negative passions and positive ones. Violent passions will prove helpful in certain conditions, but he must be more aware of the danger of using them than he need be with the milder passions.

After these general considerations, Scheidemantel again discusses the individual passions in the order used in the first part of the book. Scare is again given the longest consideration. He enumerates a number of disorders like sleepwalking, gout, epilepsy, malaria, paralysis, constipation and dropsy, which may be helped by scare therapy. In each case he advises when and how to apply it. He points out where the danger of harmful effects or regression lies. The underlying process in the specific sickness in connection with the effect of scare is carefully traced. Finally it is emphasized that scare should be used only where all other medical possibilities have failed.

Fear has basically the same pattern of therapeutic influence as scare. Again, scare has a momentary influence, whereas fear has a long-lasting one. Fear is believed to be especially valuable when intelligent and reasonable advice has failed to influence the patient. It seems to be extraordinarily important in ailments brought on by the patient's self-abuse, either from violent passions or vice and physical excess. Fear seems to influence all kinds of hemorrhages and menstrual irregularity, convulsions and chorea, tendencies toward fainting spells, digestive disorders and certain mental diseases. There is less danger from serious negative effects in the application of fear than exists with scare. However, serious consideration should be given when using fear to avoid harmful effects.

Grief has no therapeutic value because there are only negative effects. It may be useful only if one wants to prevent a patient from unadvisable actions. Bashfulness also has very little therapeutic value.

It would not be expected that rage has a therapeutic use; however, it proves to be a valuable factor in activating stagnant processes, giving a quick momentary impulse and warming up the body. Rage is a useful therapeutic means with phlegmatic types and with persons who, for one reason or another, refuse to move fast or at all. It has also proved helpful for obstructions of the liver and bile tract, sclerosis, rickets and to induce menstruation in certain types of women. Rage is also helpful in bringing about a catharsis in fevers, and as a result, it also effects smallpox, measles and chickenpox. As for mental diseases, rage may be used to break spells of depression and grief. However, Scheidemantel emphasizes most seriously that rage should always be used in a moderate form to avoid the danger of an uncontrolled rage, which may harm the patient.

Indignation is another passion which is discarded as unusable in therapy.

In contrast, joy is considered the most useful passion for healing purposes. By itself, it is a basic factor for all health and happiness, and it represents the best guarantee for reaching an old age. Joy cannot be underestimated as a strengthening factor in all health, and therefore it is a primary factor in advancing any cure and completing a convalescence. Scheidemantel lists thirty-four different disease patterns in which he sees joy as an active aid. Its basic influence is in the improvement of the general circulation. He lists children's and women's disorders, various fevers, colitis, diarrhea, lung ailments, colics, catalepsy, the various rheumatic conditions and many mental ailments, especially hypochondria. In each case, he gives detailed conditions for the application of joy. Special emphasis is placed upon its application as a basic factor in the cure of children's diseases.

Hope has a similar therapeutic effect to joy, but it is weaker and of a more long-ranged efficacy. Hope is an indispensable assistance to the doctor, and the author discusses its medical use thoroughly. He is very thoughtful in discussing the application of hope in incurable diseases and the effects of unfulfilled hope in recurrent disorders. For homesickness, hope is the only existing remedy.

Love, in the erotic sense Scheidemantel has discussed in the first part, has no therapeutic value which the medical doctor can apply. He doubtlessly differs greatly in this with the present Freudian psychoanalysis. However, love for nonhuman objects can be successfully utilized.

Finally, there is a group of passions which he lists as unusable for therapy. These are jealousy, arrogance, envy, vanity and empty longing.

There is much in Scheidemantel's thinking which is closely related to the scientific thought of his period. His psychology, although almost modern in some respects, is in other respects, especially the terminology, strongly within the pattern of the late

Eighteenth Century. The same must be said of his physiological thinking and especially of his basic concepts of neurology. In spite of this, his conception of the body as a whole and his differentiation of the internal systems and their coordination represent beliefs to which much of our recent physiological pragmatism has returned. However, his clear insight into the psyche-body relationship and his realistic insight into psychic functions in this sense is most astounding. In this respect he is certainly one of the great masters of psychosomatic medicine and practical psychology.

Chapter 8

SOCIAL PSYCHIATRY AND MENTAL HYGIENE IN THE EIGHTEENTH CENTURY

DEVOTED representatives of the mental hygiene movement who believe that the psychopathological conditions of our age are the worst in the history of mankind are hopeful that they have found a worthy ally in their struggle for the prevention and cure of these conditions in what they call social psychiatry—the study of environmental causes of mental abnormality. We are told that study in this field is still very much in its beginnings, since the concept is new and revolutionary. It appears, however, that there were some antecedents to our present-day social psychiatrists. The works of a number of writers on general health and mental hygiene in the first decades of the Eighteenth to the beginning of the Nineteenth Century indicate that in the northern part of the British Isles there was, at the time, a well-developed social-psychiatric insight.

The first of these writers was George Cheyne (1671-1743), who was born near Aberdeen. After receiving his medical education under Pitcairn in Edinburgh, he came to London where he was caught up in the gay life of the British metropolis. The indulgent life did not fit well with his Scotchman's nature, and he developed a liver ailment and grew overweight. Taking stock of himself, he set out on a cure by means of a stringent diet of milk and vegetables. To this self-invented and self-tested diet he attributed the health, wealth and and fame of his later life.

He established himself as a temperance doctor in London and at Bath, the famous English spa frequented by the nobility. He advocated diets consisting of vegetarian foods, meats naturally raised (that is, not coming from artificially fattened animals), and skim milk. He wrote a number of books on health subjects which were extremely popular in his time. In 1733 he published *English Malady*. The title has survived as a curiosity of historical and cultural literature, but the contents of this book have been totally forgotten.

Its subtitle suggests that it is a sort of psychiatric text: "A Treatise of Nervous Diseases of All Kinds, Spleens, Vapours, Lowness of Spirits, Hypochondriacal and Hysterical Distempers." In the preface we encounter what would today be considered the social-psychiatric approach: "The moisture of our air, the variableness of our weather, the rankness and heaviness of our food, the wealth and abundance of the inhabitants, the inactivity and sedentary occupations of the better sort, and the humour of living in great, populous and consequently unhealthy towns, have brought forth a class and set of distempers with atrocious and frightful symptoms, scarce known to our ancestors, and never raising to such fatal heights nor afflicting such numbers in any other known nation. These nervous disorders being computed to make up almost one third of the complaints of the people of condition in England."

Our belief that ours is the most "nervous" age meets impressive competition in Dr. Cheyne's evaluation of mental illness and its social causes during his time.

Cheyne's social-psychiatric approach was, one might say, conditioned by the social atmosphere of his time. Family relations and professional difficulties are not primarily stressed. The point of view is more strongly naturalistic, taking the human environment into its consideration. The environmental causes advanced by Cheyne, such as bad air and climate, would be the last to be considered today.

"If we add the present custom of living so much in great, populous, and over-grown cities; London—where nervous distempers are most frequent, outrageous and unnatural—is, so far as I know, the greatest, most capacious, close and populous city of the globe. The infinite number of fires, sulphurous and bituminous, the vast expanse of tallow and foetid oil in candles and lamps, under and above ground, the clouds of stinking breaths and perspiration, not to mention the ordure of so many diseased, both intelligent and unintelligent animals, the crowded churches, church-yards and burrying-places, with putrified bodies, the stinking butcherhouses, stables, dunghills, etc., and the necessary stagnation, fermentation, and mixture of such variety of all kinds of atoms are more than sufficient to putrefy, poison and infect the air for twenty miles round it. And which in time, must alter, weaken, destroy the healthiest constitutions of men and animals of all kinds; and accordingly it is in such-like cities, that these distempers are to be found in their highest and most astonishing symptoms; and seldom any lasting or solid cure is performed till the diseased be rusticated and purified from the infectious air and damps, transsubstantiated into their habits, by a great city, and till they have sucked in and incorporated the sweet, balmy, clear air of the country and driven the other out of their habit. For, by innumerable experiments it is certain, that nitre and acid of fresh, new air is as necessary towards life and health as fresh balmy food."

In the same way, Cheyne analysed food, excesses and luxury of living, along with other factors of the social life of the age. As cure and prophylaxis, he recommended strict diet, exercise and controlled activities. At one point he recommended strict abstinence from animal foods and alcohol, concerning which he says, "If the patient stands this shock with firmness and patience he may be assured of success and his perfect recovery is at hand."

Another social-psychiatric point of view was presented by Robert Whytt (1714-1766), who became President of the Royal College of Physicians of Edinburgh. Whytt was more a researcher, physiologist and neurologist than a practitioner, and his scope is accordingly wider than Cheyne's. In 1764, using the spelling "Whyte" in his name, he published a psychiatric text, *Observations on the Nature, Causes and Cure of those Diseases which have been commonly called Nervous, Hypochondriac or Hysteric.* Although his preface sounds different from Cheyne's, the two men were animated by very much the same spirit.

> The disorders which are the subject of the following observations, have been treated under the names of flatulent, spasmodic, hypochondriac, or hysteric. Of late, they have also got the name of nervous; which application having been commonly given to many symptoms seemingly different, and very obscure in their nature, has often made it to be said, that physicians have bestowed the character of nervous on all those disorders whose nature and cause they were ignorant of.

To wipe off this reproach, and at the same time to throw some light on nervous, hypochondriac and hysteric complaints, is the design of the following observations; which are also intended to show, how far the principles laid down in my essay on the vital and other involuntary motions of animals may be of use in explaining the nature of several diseases, and consequently, in leading to the most proper method of cure. Since, in almost every disease, the nerves suffer more or less, and there are very few disorders which may not in a large sense be called nervous, it might be thought that a treatise on nervous diseases should comprehend almost all the complaints to which the human body is liable.

In widening the scope of nervous suffering, however, Whytt did not look upon the outer world as the cause of such suffering, but rather on the totality of human nature itself.

As many of these complaints depend upon the sympathy which obtains between the various parts of the body, it seems necessary to begin with some observations on the sympathy of the nerves; a subject of the greatest importance in pathology.

This leads to what one might call an internal social psychiatry, a primary study of the relationship of the nervous system to the other organs of the body and the way in which these organs and the nervous system are influenced by the outer world. Whytt offers an early systematic somatopsychology and psychosomatology, which he explains below.

If it should be said, that to account for diseases from the sensibility or sympathy of the nerves, while we know not wherein these powers consist, is no better than referring them to a *facultas incognita,* or to the hypothetical motions and countermotions of the animal spirits; I shall only answer, that although we cannot explain why grief or joy should by means of the nerves, excite a greater motion than usual, in the vessels of the lachrymal glands, yet it is leading us to the truth, and advancing one step farther in our knowledge. We see that the increased secretion of tears, occasioned by those passions of the mind, proceeds from this cause, and not from any compression of the lachrymal glands or their ducts, by the neighboring muscles, as has been commonly imagined.

After distinguishing the borderline between general nervous pains and actual nervous and mental illness, Whytt proceeds to a study of the various forms of actual pathology. He develops a finely executed total and differential system of nervous impairments of the body, and finally, too, of their causes in the outer world. He refers here to his predecessor George Cheyne, whom he evidently considers competent. In his presentation of the actual outer social sphere, Whytt follows Cheyne. What is new in his presentation, however, is the detailed working out of the inner effect of those outside causes and the almost phenomenological presentation of the dynamism of the nervous functions as such. By uniting the organic with the social aspect, Whytt brought knowledge of abnormal nervous function to the point of a total picture—something that had not been attempted before.

How much Whytt's aim was a view of the total picture of human existence may be seen from quotations like the following from his book.

"A diminution of the moving power of the nerves, produces a debility of the whole body. A total want of this power, occasions either a partial or universal palsy, according as only a few of the nerves of the whole system are affected. When any of the muscles are deprived of the nervous influence, they are not only rendered paralytic, but soon after become smaller; because the circulation of the fluids cannot be carried on, as usual, through the very small vessels when they are deprived of the nervous power."

Certainly this is an amazing intuitive view of the reality of the function of the nerves!

To the historian, a further development of social-psychiatric thinking, that presented by the work of the Scottish physician Thomas Trotter (1760-1832), must appear a kind of synthesis. Trotter started his career as a medical orderly in the British Navy. After twenty years of medical service on the seven seas he set out to earn an M.D. He was a reformer at heart, and in his writings propagandized for the development and improvement of medical services in the British Navy. After finally settling down on dry land at Newcastle, he became a fierce fighter against alcoholism. It is reported that he went after inns and distillery vats with an axe. In 1807 he capped his writings with a book having the unusually long title of *View of the Nervous Temperament, Being a Practical Inquiry Into the Increasing Prevalence, Prevention and*

Treatment of those Diseases Commonly Called Nervous, Bilious, Stomach, and Liver Complaints, Indigestion, Low Spirits, Gout, etc."

Reading the Dedication and Introduction of this book, we cannot but recognize in Trotter the successor to Drs. Cheyne and Whytt, to whom he refers by name. He presents his thesis as follows.

> Mankind have seldom been delighted with a picture of their infirmities and the physician who warns his fellow mortals how to evade them, is liable to be considered rather an officious adviser, than a welcome monitor. But if it is true, as I have said, that nervous diseases make up two thirds of the whole with which civilized society is infected, and are tending fast to abridge the physical strength and mental capacities of the human race, it must be the duty of some person to sound the alarm and to announce the danger, however unprofitable the task.

No mental hygienist of our country has spoken with the vehemence of this Nineteenth Century writer. Nor was Trotter an impulsive fanatic.

> When I was a young man in the profession, no diseases puzzled me so much as those of the nervous kind. I was every day committing blunders: In vain I had recourse to books, for books could not supply the deficiency, and I was frequently mortified with seeing my patients get worse under my treatment. Time and much experience only, were capable of correcting my errors. What first gave my practice consistency, was the careful study of the nervous temperament; to mark what were its original peculiarities; what its propensities; and by what causes its diseases were drawn forth.

Now there speaks a real predecessor of our modern mental hygienists.

> Much of my animal versions on these disorders, is with a view to the prevention; and if parents and guardians will only interest themselves in the business, my trouble cannot be in vain. It is indeed a task, in the present stage of society, that well deserves the attention of every friend of his fellow-creatures, and his country. Great Britain has outstripped rival states in her commercial greatness; let us therefore endeavour to preserve that ascendancy which is so essential to our welfare in the convulsed condition of Europe, by the only means that can do it effectively. That is by recurring to simplicity of living and

manners. So as to check the increasing prevalence of nervous disorders which if not restrained soon, must evidently sap our physical strength of constitution; make us an easy conquest to our invaders, and ultimately convert us into a nation of slaves and idiots.

Nobody could speak more strongly in the cause of social-psychiatric therapy than did this English doctor a few pages later.

In the present day, this class of diseases form by far the largest proportion of the whole, which come under the treatment of the physician. Sydenham, at the conclusion of the Seventeenth Century, computed fevers to constitute two-thirds of the diseases of mankind. But, at the beginning of the Nineteenth Century, we do not hesitate of affirm, that nervous disorders have now taken the place of fevers, and may be justly reckoned two-thirds of the whole, with which civilized society is afflicted. Dr. Cheyne, who wrote about the year 1733, in his work entitled *English Malady*, makes nervous disorders almost one-third of the complaints of people of condition in England, from which we are led to believe they were then little known among the inferior orders. But from causes, to be hereafter investigated, we shall find that nervous ailments are no longer confined to the better ranks in life, but rapidly extending to the poorer classes. In this neighbourhood, as far as I am able to judge from my own experience, they are by no means limited to the rich.

We find here a most realistic and practical basis for a social-psychiatric approach, namely, an open eye for social conditions. Unlike the socialite Dr. Cheyne, Dr. Trotter saw not only the British nobility, but also the common man as afflicted with mental and emotional troubles. From this point of view, he arrives at a social framework in which to seek the causes of mental ailments.

He first points, in the manner of Cheyne, to general conditions in England: "It is the peculiar situation of Britain; insular variations of climate and atmosphere; its political institutions and free government and above all its vast wealth, so diffused among all ranks of people."

But then he becomes more concrete and enumerates ten "remote causes of nervous diseases": "Air, Exercise, Food, Clothing, Passions of the Mind, Intense Study, Lactation, Miscarriage and Premature Labour, Climate, and Medicine."

Although modern sociologists could construct a more detailed inventory of possible causes of mental disturbances in present-day life, Trotter's wide scope and clear insight into major factors of nervous disease at the start of the Nineteenth Century cannot but be considered astonishing. There are several factors, such as air, food, clothing and climate, which, as Trotter himself pointed out, had already been recognized as causative, especially by Cheyne. The acknowledgment of passion as a cause of mental disturbance goes back to ancient times, but, for his own time, Dr. Trotter's presentation was certainly novel.

Modern psychological geneticism of the analytical type may greet Dr. Trotter as a predecessor of their concept of childhood causes of mental abnormality and neurosis. Besides the dangers of unfortunate birth, Trotter considers lactation an important element affecting mental health, valid for both infant and mother.

Of special significance is Trotter's emphasis on the dangers of medication to mental health: "All nervous persons are uncommonly fond of drugs; and they are the chief consumers of advertised remedies, which they conceal from their medical friends. Among some well-meaning people this inordinate desire for medicine has frequently become of itself a disease."

This observation is followed by a forty-page description of the most common medicines of his time, in which he diagnoses the dangers each one may harbor for the mental health of the patient.

There is another fascinating aspect of Trotter's social psychiatry. It is not difficult to understand when one considers that he viewed the entire population in terms of mental illness, yet it is an aspect about which we at present lack satisfactory insight: The question of the relation of the forms of abnormal behavior to the various social groups. Indeed, one who did not have a good eye for society as a whole could not be aware of the distribution of the various mental abnormalities according to the social group. "Literary Men, Men of Business, the Idle and the Dissipated, the Artificer and Manufacturer, Those Employed in Drudgery, Persons Returning from the Colonies, and last but not least, The Female Sex; consisting of the higher, middle and lower Orders of Women." In short, detailed chapters on each of these groups, Trotter shows "how business, customs and manners influence health." Here is social psychiatry in a most specific form, if any form can be acknowledged.

Trotter and his British predecessors were not alone in believing that their own country harbored the most nervous ills. During Whytt's time Simon Andre Tissot was active. He was probably the most widely read medical writer of his time on the continent. In an eloquent and brilliant style he wrote little health books which, following a similar conviction as Trotter, were addressed to various social groups. There was one addressed to "Men of Letters," to "Men of the World," and one especially for "The Ladies," on the ways of life at the time of the French kings. One, which became internationally famous, was addressed to "Youth." Tissot thundered at the youth of his day "that they were about to become dangerously decadent, addicted to the mass neurosis of onanism by which mankind was in danger of perishing." Later in life he wrote, in the style of Trotter, a large book, *The Nerves and Their Maladies*. In the introduction he joined the chorus of his British colleagues: "Nervous diseases have multiplied while others are decreasing." Nervous ailments, especially in urban communities, he said, were the most common illnesses of the time.

These Scottish doctors of the Eighteenth and early Nineteenth centuries provide a preview of what today we present as a major new achievement of our time—mental hygiene and social psychiatry.

Chapter 9

THE ORIGIN AND EARLY HISTORY
OF ELECTROSHOCK THERAPY

A MERICAN psychiatric literature is surprisingly lacking in any discussion or mention of electrotherapy, a widely discussed topic in every major European textbook since 1850. Not before 1940 is electroshock mentioned, and its invention is ascribed to the Italian Ugo Cerletti. A check of the original manuscript shows that it is a two-page report from the clinic of which Cerletti is the director. The experiment was done by Dr. L. Bini, who is introduced as an expert electrotechnician. The experiment concerns the success of a high voltage shock administered to an epileptic male, who was considerably improved after receiving this treatment. This experiment was one of the many conducted by this clinic, which was mainly devoted to epilepsy, a popular field for study in middle European neurology. Studies such as "Experimental Convulsions" and "Convulsions Resulting from Electric Treatment" were common as far back as 1880.

It is possible to trace electrotherapy back to 1740, when shortly after electricity had been experimentally isolated, its application for medical purposes started. This was long before the idea matured that it would be such an important technical tool. Beginning in 1744, the *Histoire de L'Acadamie Royal des Sciences* of France brought out a report on "Electricity and Medicine" every second year. There were *guerisons* (cures) reported from all over Europe—from the Italian "miracle" priest Abbe Nollet, from the Swiss Louis J. Jallabert, from the Dutchman Leyde and from a number of others.

Among the cures reported, a majority were neurological and mental cases of paralysis and epilepsy. In the report of 1755, pages nine to eleven, a Frenchman, Dr. J. B. LeRoy, describes in detail his cure of what today may be called a case of hysterical blindness. After the patient received his first *commotion* (shock), he reacted with convulsions of the eyes and saw rays of light for the first time.

67

When he received three shocks, the third somewhat stronger than others, he screamed and fainted. As a result of this treatment he began to regain his eyesight. There is no doubt that we are presented here with an actual electroshock treatment, and probably the first one.

In 1801, the German electrotherapist Friedrich L. Augustin reported an almost identical case. With the beginning of the Nineteenth Century, however, electrotherapy fell into disuse. The reason seems to be that the scientific mind was not satisfied with the inexact application of an unmeasured amount of electricity, for we know that the first three decades of the Nineteenth Century was the period when the mechanical and technical knowledge of physics and chemistry of electricity was developed.

During that same period, the problem of shock as a therapeutic means was a concern of the first psychiatrists, who desired to find a purely psychological therapeutic technique to aid mental ailments. S. Kornfeld mentions a number of such men in his short *History of Psychiatry*. Among the literature mentioned is the amazing book of Scheidemantel, which we have described in an earlier chapter.

During the 1830's electrotherapy came into use again as a therapeutic agent with nervous and mental diseases. However, in contrast to the form it had in the previous century, there was a differentiation between galvanic and faradic electricity, the various strengths, long- and short-term application, etc. After three decades the development of this new scientific electrotherapy had matured to the point that an Austrian-Hungarian neurologist, Moriz Benedikt, had enough material to write two larger works giving specific prescriptions for all known and somatically fixed neuro- and psychopathology. The Bavarian medical writer Johan B. Ullersperger received an academic prize for a synoptic description of electrotherapy. The Frenchman G. B. C. Duchenne, who is sometimes called the father of modern electrotherapy and who wrote an entire set of works on the various phases of this subject, demanded that no sincere neurologist could practice without using electrotherapy.

The most important contributor to this entire development,

however, is Rudolf Arndt, whom we have already mentioned in this connection. His 130-page study did the most to unveil the psychological and organic background of the role and influence of electricity with regard to neuro- and psychopathology. The most advanced of our present electroshock therapists must confess that they know only about the effects of their methods and nothing about the cause and the other determining factors regarding the influence of electricity upon our body and its nervous system in general, and upon mental abnormalities in particular.

Even if the theoretical aspect and organic knowledge of Rudolf Arndt is outmoded, his approach to the study of electricity in its relationship to psychiatry seems to contain the method the present shock therapists should use to gain a sound understanding of what makes electricity a good (or bad) therapeutic agent for psychiatric disorders.

Chapter 10

SIMON ANDREE TISSOT:
A FREUDIAN BEFORE FREUD

THE battle between those who maintain that Freud's theories are a completely new, unique scientific phenomenon and those who call his formulations fantastic and feel they will soon disappear like comets may be somewhat assuaged by recalling the work of the French-Swiss physician Tissot from the undeserved obscurity into which it has fallen. As a medical writer of repute in his own time, Tissot presented almost 150 years ago what we would today call basic Freudian concepts.

Of Simon Andree Tissot history has left behind one of the strangest and most distorted imprints it has ever handed so distinguished a figure. If we consult those willing to give him at least some acknowledgement, we learn that he was the most popular writer on health and hygiene of his time. His great success in this respect owed much to the brilliant French he was able to write. However, more is to be discovered of Tissot beyond these little health books written for the general public, the socialites, the learned and the young. Those who have probed further have pointed to his major scientific work, the *Traite sur les Nerves et leurs Maladies*, but they have complained, not without a certain justification, that it was only an accumulation of the neurological knowledge of that time with little added that is new. Thus far have the books of history gone with regard to Tissot, and they have looked no further.

A more careful inquiry, however, will give us a quite different picture of Tissot. He was born in the French-speaking part of Switzerland into a well-to-do family. He started to study in Geneva and completed his medical training in Montpelier. For most of his life he practiced and taught in Lausanne, where he applied new and successful methods of dealing with smallpox which he had learned in Montpelier. This brought him rapid fame in French Switzerland, which was haunted by epidemics of this disease in the middle of the Eighteenth Century. His fame became international in the following quarter of the century, partly because of his successful methods of treatment and partly through his popular writing. As a result, the royalty of this time consulted him, they wanted him at their courts and offered him professorships.

For two years he accepted such a mission at the University of Pavia, but then he returned to Lausanne, where he was made head of a newly founded medical college. He remained there until his death at the age of sixty-nine.

His was an active and respected medical and academic career, and it certainly does not fit the historical illusion that he was merely a medical journalist. His major scientific works (including the *Traite sur les Nerves et leurs Maladies,* which is his masterpiece) are *L'Onanisme* (1760), *L'Avis du Peuple sur la Santé* (1761) and *Eassai sur les Maladies des Gens du Monde* (1770). They were translated into German and English and ran to as many as ten editions.

If we become more intimately familiar with the life of Tissot, the traits of an unusually impressive personality come to the fore. Tissot had been a lifelong pupil of Albert von Haller, some of whose works he translated into French. Whoever turns to these first decades of the Eighteenth Century faces the period in which academic medicine stepped out of the dogmatic school atmosphere to replace folk medicine and the practice of barbers and to check the flood of epidemics which had decimated the population of Europe during the previous centuries. It was the period of medical enlightenment, and this was the spirit in which Tissot's popular books, such as *Avis au peuple sur la santé (Advice to the People Concerning Health),* were written. Within a decade this work appeared in fifteen French editions and was translated into seventeen foreign languages.

We are quite unjust to measure this really fantastic success by the current standards—or lack of standards—of popular medical writing. There was a spirit of prophecy and hygienic enlightenment in Tissot's acting and writing hardly comparable with any other personal deed in medical history. He published fourteen volumes during his lifetime, half of which were popularization books.

Not until recently, however, has it become known that the library of the University of Lausanne has about one hundred volumes of thick manuscripts, two to three hundred pages each, by Tissot. About sixty of these are actual unpublished medical works. They include large manuscripts on pediatrics and gynecology, obstetrics, and elaborated works on eye and ear diseases, on diseases of the digestive tract, on cardiac and on pulmonary diseases and one on cancer. Why this or that of his manuscripts was published and others were not is a question it is nearly impossible to answer.

Although, as we have said, his negative critics were not totally wrong in saying that his major work adds nothing much that is new which might give it a place among the major neurological texts of the age, one of its aspects, which has actually angered some of the same critics, leads, in our view, to the unique and rather unacknowledged importance of Tissot. This very special quality, which goes beyond the dry presentations of Eighteenth Century neurology, is his application of a genuinely psychological or psychiatric point of view. This is particularly evident in the two chapters which, in a kind of phenomenological way, describe the physical and moral causes of nervous diseases.

The fine psychological observer of human ways of life produces here a new perspective on medical matters. His method may be called the first psychological neuropathology and neurotherapy. It not only challenges the materialistic neurophysiology, but takes concrete steps adequate for overcoming it. We can probably best see this if we compare Tissot with G. E. Stahl, who has rightly been designated the greatest psychist of the previous century. Stahl's *animismus* had been a deductive concept derived from the conceptionalism of Paracelsus; Tissot's conceptionalism was of another kind. It was a perception of psychological reactions within the physiology of human nature. It was natural science in the very modern sense. This brought Tissot into nearly the same position that Freud had to take when he, at the end of the last century, held a similar view regarding the physiological geneticism of the middle of the Nineteenth Century. Indeed, we find astonishing similarities between the concepts of Tissot and Freud which seem to me to justify calling him one of Freud's predecessors.

This similarity displays itself most impressively in a field in which both men's interests overlap—the field of sexology. For example, *L'Onanisme,* which was one of the first compact publications on sexology (1760), contains a chapter on nocturnal emissions. Tissot attributes them to dreams in a way almost identical with Freud's later wish-fulfillment theory. Tissot explains that when our senses are chained by sleep, the thoughts *(idées)* of our mind *(l'âme)* may continue the preoccupations of the day. If there was an intensive preoccupation with sexual contents *(plaisir d'amour),* it may be transferred to the will, which in turn produces an activity in the sexual organs, causing the emission *(movements dans les organs de la génération).*

Tissot also had a far-reaching insight into the relationship between sex and hysteria, which, as we know, was the basis of Freud's concepts. Tissot reports in his writings a number of cases in which women, deprived of natural sexual releases, lost their minds and became subject to severe hysterical attacks. In such cases Tissot recommended an astonishing kind of release therapy—rubbing with a towel or similar material which would create a coital excitement. Tissot reports the success of such procedures, including the case of a nun with hysterical spells.

One of his most extraordinary views has to do with sexual abstention for those who were not suited to it by "temperament." He saw in this the true source of hysteria as well as various other psychopathologies. At this point one feels how far he advanced beyond the commonly acceptable concepts. He referred to previous authors with similar ideas, such as Galen and the Swiss doctor, Nicholas Zindel, who wrote a tractate on this subject as early as 1745.

In his *Traite sur les Nerves et leurs Maladies,* Tissot discussed in great detail the problem of the relationship between complete sexual continence and psychopathology. Here he also presented a rudimentary concept of the unconscious or subconscious. The worst consequences of abstinence, he explains, are the most secret, and hysteria is one of these most secret experiences. It is very frequent among single and widowed women.

In connection with this presentation, Tissot touches an area that brings to mind Freud's theory of suppression. The term itself appears in relation to menstrual irregularities. However, Tissot uses it in a wider range than Freud allows: Tissot uses it for a physical as well as a mental process. When menstruation becomes irregular, it is suppressed, according to Tissot, and this is very often the cause of severe mental imbalance and disease. On the other hand, "suppression" can be an active process in the "psychosomatic sense," occurring in mental illness resulting in menstrual irregularities.

Tissot describes this form of suppression extremely well phenomenologically. However, he has not yet proper insight into its underlying subconscious dynamics. He was aware that there had to be something like the subconscious at the bottom of suppression and hysteria, but he was unable, due to the general attitude of his time, to get behind these facts. It was left to Freud to reveal these elements of psychopathology a hundred years later. However, there is nobody as early as Tissot who anticipated these phenomena. Tissot is certainly one of the most notable predecessors of Freud.

The historical view which is geared to try to reveal causes of usual as well as unusual phenomena insofar as they are factually or dynamically significant for the growth of human civilization is apt to want to know the reason why these concepts developed in this Eighteenth Century Swiss doctor's mind. We have partially found an explanation to this in the fact that Tissot belonged to the period of medical enlightenment. There is another factor which contributes to our understanding of Tissot's intellectual penetration: namely that he was raised in the sphere of West Swiss Protestantism, to which he belonged practically all his life. It was a protestantism strongly opposed to chastity and sex-moral concepts as they are customary in the wide sphere of Roman Catholicism. Tissot has never openly expressed this, but his entire social hygienic thinking shows itself to be in the line of this Calvinistic philosophy.

Regardless of how far one is willing to go in acknowledging Tissot as an important source of current psychiatric thinking, there can be no doubt that he deserves the historian's attempt to lift him from neglect and obscurity into the sphere of known history.

Chapter 11

VINCENZO CHIARUGI:
THE FIRST GREAT SYSTEMATIC PSYCHIATRY

D URING the period when France had its Pinel and Germany its Reil, Italy had a psychiatrist of considerable importance who is today almost completely forgotten—Vincenzo Chiarugi.

Chiarugi was born in a village near Florence in February, 1759. He studied in Pisa and spent most of his later life in Florence, where he rose from ward doctor of a hospital to professor of the newly established medical college of the capital of Tuscany.

In 1793, Chiarugi published a three-volume work entitled *Della Pazzia in Genere e in Specie (On Insanity in General and in Its Special Forms)*. In the following year it appeared in a German translation. In 1802, it had a second Italian edition, but after this it became quietly and completely forgotten. The reason for this is not difficult to establish: It stems from the judgments written by those who were regarded as the psychiatric authorities at the time, shaping and controlling academic opinion in the field. If one opens Philippe Pinel's *Traite Medico-Philosophique sur L'Alienation Mental*, probably the most distributed book of its kind at that time, one reads right on the introductory pages, "It was Chiarugi's lot to follow the beaten track by speaking of madness in general in a dogmatic tone, then to consider madness in particular and to return again to the old scholastic order of causes, diagnosis, prognosis and symptoms to be followed. The spirit of research hardly shows in his work. It is more evident in the one hundred observations which he published, although even these offer little material for conclusive implications."

This stern criticism killed not only sincere acknowledgement of Chiarugi in the scientific world of his time, but for all future times as well.

Leading English psychiatric writers like Haslam accepted Pinel's judgment. Even in Germany, the careful Griesinger assimilated Pinel's stand on Chiarugi in his textbook, which reigned unchallenged during the midcentury decades. As one of this century's greatest admirers of Pinel, Gregory Zilboorg accepts Pinel's mis-statements regarding Chiarugi in his *History of Medical Psychology*. In this book he reprinted word for word Pinel's devaluation of Chiarugi. Only the kind and wise Heinroth stepped into the flood of this misjudgment. He wrote, "As an Italian [Chiarugi] was historically minded and has mainly written about the past of his field. However, his work is indispensible for anyone who wishes to study the previous systematics and who wants to make use of the wealth which has been assembled in all previous times."

Knowing that he would receive rejection for this view, Heinroth, with his classical and tolerant mind, tried to mitigate Pinel's injustice by what he wrote on this occasion. He formulated a differentiation according to national character in his typically brilliant way. On the page before he defended Chiarugi, Heinroth said, "The Italian loves the ancient, the Frenchman the new, the Englishman the solid ground and bottom, and the German everything."

A psychological historian who cannot but acknowledge the importance of Pinel and his work must ask why he so passionately hated and denounced his Italian colleague. As we hope to prove, the latter was quite capable of holding his own in the scale of value against this sometimes quite scientifically objectionable Gallic blowhard. Heinroth offered as the reason a difference of national temperament. We today, with a wider conceptional and historical view, may also add Pinel's tendency to jealousy and his desire to overshadow all his contemporaries. A murderous dagger stab in the back of the scholarly and restrained Chiarugi was something quite natural for such a temperament. It may be interesting to add that in consequence of Heinroth's statement of admiration, Friedreich, who, as I have shown, copied Heinroth's history as the basis for his own, accepted this acknowledgement of Chiarugi, designating him as "the best Italy has contributed to the psychiatric discipline." He also devoted twenty-six pages to a reprint of Chiarugi's nosological system to which we shall devote the major portion of the present chapter. It is the greatest nosological and systematic study undertaken in the field of the abnormalities of the mind.

In recent years an Italo-American writer has published several papers* with the purpose of bring Chiarugi from among the forgotten of history back into the light of modern psychiatric interests. This attempt was not too successful, because it mainly tries to view Chiarugi in terms of modern psychiatry. This does not do justice to the real values of this ingenious mind that lived at the dawn of Europe's classical age. On the other hand, if one reads Dr. Mora's major paper on Chiarugi's contribution to psychiatry while keeping in mind his contemporary, Pinel, one must feel how very much alike they were in regard to the theoretical aspects and clinical results. Pinel, however, with his brilliant presentation, expressed many things better and had the advantage of eloquence.

In contrast, the Italian must appear to some rather coarse in his manner of expression. Careful research would probably uncover material to show that Pinel had taken a considerable amount of information from Chiarugi. He doubtlessly had studied him intensively and had borrowed quite seriously from him, as his mention of Chiarugi in the introduction of his masterwork evidences. It is certainly untrue that Chiarugi was only a book and paper psychiatrist and little active and creative in practical work and research, as Pinel wants to make us believe. Schuele and Kraepelin, as well as Kirchhoff later on, have accredited Chiarugi with primary neurological discoveries and as the first who had demanded postmortem examination of the brain tissues.

However, Chiarugi's actual importance lies in his attempt "to bring order into the scientific house of psychiatry" by presenting in "a simple way" a systematization of most of what had been established since ancient times about human insanity. Chiarugi's great merit is this amazing attempt of systematization and classification of previously established abnormal forms of the human mind. To do this was his extraordinary gift. It is expressed in the final systematization of the forms of insanity as well as in the entire lay-

---

* MORA, GEORGE: Respect the insane individual as a person: Chiarugi's regulations of the Hospital Bonifacio, 1789. *Mental Hospital, 10*:9, 1959.
MORA, GEORGE: Vincenzo Chiarugi and his psychiatric reform in Florence. *J Hist Med, 14*:4, 1959.
MORA, GEORGE: Vincenzo Chiarugi: His Contribution to Psychiatry. *Bull Isaac Ray Med Library*, 2:1, 1954.

out of his three-volume work, *Treatise on Insanity in General and in Its Special Forms.* The book considers the major aspects regarding insanity. This is developed through an enumeration of the variety of its forms. His nosology follows, with summarizing synoptic tables at the end. Finally, one hundred collected case histories from practical experience are listed to illustrate the theoretical presentation. Certainly this is a carefully planned, all-out coverage of the task.

Already the first part shows this unusually clear and systematic approach. *Pazzia* (in German, Wahnsinn)—which we may best translate *Insanity*—is not simply defined in the usual way. Chiarugi attempts a characterization of a set of general symptoms which are deduced from normal mental behavior. This represents a basic difference from the typical style of describing mental abnormality used at that time. It is a way which only became the more common form fifty or sixty years later. In modern scientific language we would designate this method a differential generic analysis. Accordingly, Chiarugi starts out, "Where insanity occurs, one or several of the following three symptoms are to be found: Continuous false judgment, continuous confusion of thoughts and inconsequential and irregular general behavior, expressing a weakening of applied psychic functions, especially of the will."

Comparing such a purely psychological conception with that of his time and especially with that of his condemner, Pinel, one cannot but feel that Chiarugi was almost half a century ahead of the latter.

Based upon this analytical and descriptive postulation, Chiarugi established three major forms of insanity, designating them as *melancholia, mania* and *amensia.* The German translator designated the last one as *Bloedsinn,* which we may best translate "imbecility." At first glance such postulations may appear to be rather superficial and traditional, but as we shall learn later on, these terms were chosen and defined in such a way that they could become the basis of an entire system comprising all the previously formulated forms of mental disease.

In the next chapter Chiarugi treats what in the widest sense must be called the causes of insanity. What he actually intended was a detailed study of what causality really means in the wider scope of mental disease. Again, a thorough realism of an almost phenomenological character is combined with his astonishing sense for the systematic. For earliest symptoms of insanity we must look for a certain unevenness in fantasy or in the sense perceptions. They can be of either too strong or too weak a character. They can consist of excitement or collapse. The actual causes for this are either inward, a certain state of the brain and the nerves, or external, certain circumstances on the surface of the earth or the atmosphere.

After the prescientific micro-macro-cosmic concepts of Paracelsus, we must say that Chiarugi was the first who presented a social psychiatric approach based upon the growing natural scientific point of view. He attempts to establish causes of insanity from the atmospheric conditions, from temperature, the influence of the air, the changes of the seasons, as well as the variety of conditionings due to various locations on the earth. Added is a somatopsychological aspect of chemical character, unusual for this period, which enumerates substances which, from inside the human body, could be the potential cause of insanity. The end of this part is a detailed enumeration of all passions which might create actual mental pathology, and finally, a survey of all the different social experiences, such as education, that may become instrumental in the development of insanity.

Further chapters of this general type deal with the process and course of development in insanity, an aspect which for the most part only became the object of psychiatric interests at the start of this century. A most challenging chapter discusses the basic aspects of treatment. Chiarugi presents himself as an early representative of a dualistic aspect. Treatment should apply either a calming or an exciting method. He demands the application of a careful symptomatic and inclusion of organic insight into the effect of therapy. A last chapter is an attempt of prognosis for cure.

In the second main part of the book, which is devoted according to its title to the special forms of insanity (together with the third part containing a nosology), Chiarugi offers a very elaborate summation of previously established information on various forms of insanity. As we pointed out above, Chiarugi distinguished three basic forms already known by their frequently applied designations: *melancholia, mania* and *amensia.* He now sets forth the use of these terms and, above all, he differentiates the variety of their uses.

At the start Chiarugi gives his motivation for what he calls the generic use of his concepts. *Melancholia,* for instance, is for him any mental state in which the psyche loses the conviction and experience of the truth of reality. This can lead to an unhappy and fearful state of mind. This state Chiarugi designates as the True Melancholia. As we know the term in the form it has come down to us over the centuries in, it indicates a pathological state of a severely depressed character.

For Chiarugi, however, this is not the sole meaning of melancholia. He has also established a concept of melancholia which is not of so emotionally negative a character, but is simply a disorientation with a peaceful and cheerful emotional undertone. These two forms—according to Chiarugi—do not yet cover all that he wishes to include in his concept of melancholia. A third form he designates as "raging melancholia." It covers cases with symptoms of madness and fury.

In the description of these three forms of melancholia Chiarugi goes into the greatest detail, allowing himself almost eighty pages. Not only are symptoms described but also their causes, predisposition and cure. The three basic types are described, as well as a great number of varieties covering all the major forms which had been formulated during the previous history.

To give an impression of this remarkable achievement, I wish to reprint here the classification and coordination Chiarugi has set forth in order to cover the multitude of forms which fall under the category of true melancholia. For his systematization Chiarugi applies three principles: First he puts together those forms which he believes are identical or synonymous; a second group arises out of the variation of contents or symptoms; a third group is based on the variation of strength or degree.

For a concrete impression of this amazing system, I am reprinting here the part on true melancholia from Chiarugi's nosological table. The names in parentheses are the authors from which the individual concepts are taken. The reprint is from the German edition of the work.

Erfte Gattung.

Melancholie.

Ein partieller und immer auf einen oder nur wenige Gegenftände eingefchränkter Wahnfinn.

Melancholia, Cullen Nofol. Gen. LXVI.
Bellini de morb. capit.
Boerhave aphor. §. 1089.
Savonarola Pract. Maior. Tr.
VI. cap. I. Rub. XI.
Melancholia nervea, Lorry Ueber die Melancholie I. Th.
Mania, Haller Elem. Phyfiol. Lib. XVII. Sect. I. §. 17.

Erfte Art. Die wahre Melancholie.
Die mit Furcht und Traurigkeit verbundene Melancholie.

Synonimieen.

Melancholia, Hipp. Aph. 23. Sect. VI. Fernel. de part. morb. L.V.
Aurelian. de morbis chron. L. I. Willis de morbis, qui ad
animum etc. cap. 11. Sauvages Nofol. Gen. 234 Linnée Gen.
morb. Gen. 71. Vogel Mm 2
Gen. 332. Sagar Gen. 347. Makbride Introd. ad praxin Lib.
VIII. cap. 1.
Delirium melancholicum, Ettmüller Coll. Pract. L. II, Sect. VI.
Art. 2. Hoffmann Med. Ration. Tom. IV. P. 4. cap. 8.
Infania lupina, Mercati de intern. morb. curat. L. I. cap. 17.
Infania triftis, Celfus de Medic Lib. III. cap. 18.
Athymia, Vogel Gen. 329.
Daemonium Avicenna.

Varietäten des Gegenftandes.

1. Noftalgia, (Heimweh) Ilifci der Araber. Savonarola, Pract. Mai.
   Tract. VI, p. 69. Scheuz. Com. Inft. Bonon. T. i, pag. 307.
   Noftomania, Harderi Diff.

2. Melancholia vulgaris, Sauv. Sp. 1.
   Religiofa, Sauv. Spec. 3.
   Superftitiofa feu Defperatio aeternae falutis; Willis de
   morbis, qui ad animum etc. Cap. 11.
   Argantis, Sauv. Spec. 4.
   Aegritudo imaginaria, Chicon Diff.
3. Erotomania, Sauv. Path. Meth. Willis Cap. 11.
   Furor eroticus, Belleni de morb. cap.
   Melancholia erotica, Iohnfton Idea medic. L. IV. c. 5.
   Hereos, Savonarola Pract. Mai. p. 69.
4. Hypochondriafis, Sauv. Gen. 46. Spec. 1. 3. 4. 5. Path. Med.
   Vogel Gen. 76.
   Melancholia hypochondriaca
       Schenkii, Willis, Mercati, Iohnfton, Holleri, Montuc, Sen-
       nerti etc.
   Mania a ventriculo, Galeni de loc. aff. L. III. Trincavelli
       Tom. I. Confil. Lib. I.
5. Daemonomania, Sauv. Gen. 236.
   Daemonia, Linnée Gen. 69.
6. Melancholia metamorphofis, Willis de morb. etc. cap. 11.
   Melanch. zoantropica, Sauv. Spec. 12.
   — Scytarum, Sauv. Spec. 10.
   Hipp. de aere, aquis etc.
   Infania lupina, Aetius Tetrabl. II.
   —canina—Serm. 2. cap. 10.

Varietäten des Grades.

1. Melancholia vulgaris, Sauv. Spec. 1.
   — myfantropica, ⎫ Sauv. Path.
   —Heraclitica,   ⎭ Meth.
2. Melancholia errabunda, Bellini de morb. cap. Iohnfton Idea
   med. L. IV. Art. 5. Sauv. Spec. 7. Hipp. de morb. popul. L. II.
   Melanch, fylveftris, Mercati de intern morb. cur. Mm 3
   Hydroleros ⎫ der Griechen. Sauv.
   Leocomoria ⎭ Nof. meth.
3. Melancholia attonita, Bellini de morb. cap. Sauv. Spec. 6.
   Exftafis, Tertullian, de anima
   Cap. 45.

Mania, Chiarugi's second major psychopathology, is designated as mainly a raging insanity, for which he also uses descriptive symptoms we must translate as delirium and frenzy. Basically Chiarugi considers his mania a derangement of the will. With great care he works out a specific characterization of the finer pathological traits among the variety of forms in which he sees mania occur. What we today call *paranoid* is for him a predominant factor. Methodologically significant is the way in which he tries to differentiate mania from the previously described melancholia and from what he later on presents as imbecility. The great quality of Chiarugi's descriptive art comes especially forward in the contrast between the ways in which he describes these manias and the ways in which he has previously characterized his melancholic forms of insanity. Since he considers mania specifically a will pathology, the cause-effect aspect is made a basic one for the differentiation in various types. Of these he distinguishes five:

1. *Mania mentalis:* Caused immediately by psychic incidents.
2. *Mania reactiva:* Due to the exhaustion of the nerves.
3. *Mania plethorica:* Caused by high blood pressure.
4. *Mania immediata:* Due to poisoning of the brain.
5. *Mania consensualis:* Due to an actual injury of the nervous system.

Among these five major types, sixty different historical occurrences of mania are inserted and organized, reaching from Hippocrates to Cullen. The method by which differentiations are achieved is not only an external and intellectual one, but is based upon a rather sensitively detailed description as well. More than in the part on melancholia, these descriptions of exemplifications taken from earlier authors predominate. Again, with considerable care, various basic aspects are worked out: the aspect of the causes of individual forms of disease, the early stage of development, the course of disease, the predictability and finally the means of cure. Especially in his strict discipline of presentation, one cannot but feel that Chiarugi easily matches his enemy, Pinel.

Concerning the third form of insanity which Chiarugi enumerates, *amensia,* we must again admire the sensitive way of characterization of the aspects and symptoms he has in mind. The basic factor of imbecility, he emphasizes, is a high degree of insensibility,

not only in regard to the intellectual functions, but also in regard
to the emotions and the will. The imbecile is the most animal-like
human being, but he is without the natural adjustment to nature
the real animal has through his senses. There exist different grades
of imbecility, reaching from bare silliness to a complete insensi-
tivity and unresponsiveness. This leads Chiarugi to a basic differentiation of two types of imbecility. He designates these as an
active and a defective kind. The main cause of imbecility Chiarugi
sees in actual abnormality of the brain, which either is too soft
or too hard. This determines the limitation of the effectiveness of
functioning of the brain and this in turn determines the kind of
imbecility.

There are many other sections in the work which could be
quoted to show the character and the unusual quality of Chiarugi's
thought. However, I wish to present here a few lines from his description of imbecility, since it appears to me to make a good ending for this chapter to offer a sample of the actual text of his book.

> Imbecility is the kind of insanity, which, along with a lack of judg-
> ment, combines a certain insensitivity with an inability to pay atten-
> tion to impressions made upon it by reality. Because of this, the dis-
> eased only slightly or not at all participates in the events he meets, and
> is not moved to emotions by circumstances which would arouse normal
> people.
>
> A man who has no emotions is very much like an unreasonable
> animal. He is guided by the appetite of his instincts and not by rea-
> soning. Being without the utterances of the power of judgment, he
> can be considered brainless, and can therefore be called *amens*.
>
> One of the most characteristic traits of this kind of insanity is an
> apathy which causes great disturbances of phantasy. The deteriorations
> of the phantasy in imbecility is considerable, and the roads on which
> the insight into ideas occur are impaired or obstructed. Because of
> this, reflection about ideas and their connections, which are the basis
> of our emotional life, cannot take place. This explains the unfortu-
> nate indifference and apathy with regard to a proper conduct of
> human life.
>
> In *mania* the power of imagination is distorted by the intensive
> trend to activity, and the memory does not function adequately. Think-
> ing is completely confused, because the mind does not give itself time
> to compare individual judgments. Therefore the imagination is car-

ried away, fed by intensive emotions which do not touch reality. In *imbecility* the individual thought contents are impaired so that they cannot connect properly one with the other. Therefore emotional life has no real basis either. This makes the impulse to phantasy die out and sound emotions can never develop.

These sentences certainly show astonishing insight into the dynamics of the normal as well as the abnormal psyche, an insight that can hardly be found anywhere before the dawn of the Nineteenth Century. Its originator deserves a foremost place in psychological history as its first organizer and thorough surveyor.

Chapter 12

THE GENERAL IMPORTANCE OF
JOHANN CHRISTIAN REIL

IN Kirchhoff's *Deutsche Irrenaerzte,* Johann Christian Reil is called "the conscious discoverer and founder of rational psychotherapy." Outside his native Germany hardly more than his name is known. Reil lived from 1759 to 1813. During the mature decades of his life he was professor of psychiatry at the middle German University of Halle. Three years before his death he was called to the University of Berlin. His *Rhapsodien ueber die Anwendung der psychischen Curmethoden auf Geistes-Zerrüttungen (Rhapsodies on the Application of Psychotherapy to Mental Diseases),* the first major work of its kind issued in middle Europe, appeared in 1803. No psychiatrist before 1900 presented more of the basic ideas of this century's psychotherapy than the author of this book.

There are also a number of shorter and now completely unknown works of Reil published during the last five years of his life. Together with his colleague, Hoffbauer, he produced, in 1808 and 1812, two volumes of essays originally intended as a journal. It was entitled *Beträge zur Beförderung einer Kurmethode auf psychischen Wege (Contributions to the Advancement of Psychotherapy),* and included nine major contributions by Reil. The longest one, *"Ueber die Centricität der Organismen"* ("On the Centricity of Organisms"), presents the most magnificent psychological-biological philosophy I have ever encountered. In another paper included in the 1808 volume, *"Das Zerfallen der Einheit des Koerpers im Selbstbewusstsein"* ("The Disintegration of the Unity Experience of the Body in the Self-Consciousness"), Reil presented a somatological concept of schizophrenia which appears clearer and more convincing than anything presented since.

Reil is a psychological phenomenologist for whom the modern concepts of *Ganzheit,* totality, unity, centricity are basic elements of scientific interpretation. Psychologically, human experience is

86

a unit experience of body and mind, which are inseparably bound to one another in the self-consciousness. If, by the process of abstraction, one boils down all bodily and psychic experiences, one arrives at a final self-recognition which Reil calls the *Gemein-Gefuehl*—the basic feeling of being and existence. He describes it as a "completely empty" feeling in which the body is sensed vaguely, but the experience is nevertheless that of unity. There is no notion of space or weight, but only of time. For those born blind and deaf, the *Gemein-Gefuehl* is the major sense. For all human individuals it is the most elementary experience.

It is the *Gemein-Gefuehl* as psychic function that holds our mental life together and mediates among its multitude of constituent elements. It is the carrier of our ego as well as the frame of our self-consciousnes. It is therefore practically involved in all our perceptions and activities.

A disintegration of the *Gemein-Gefuehl* is the cause of a large number of mental ailments. Its disfunctioning means loss of the ability to bind together and control the complex psychic dynamics. Reil distinguishes two forms of such disfunctioning. The first, the minor form, is a *Lockerung* (loosening) of control. The major form, its complete destruction, renders the *Gemein-Gefuehl* unfit to coordinate the various mental functions. In Reil's examples we see the most evident cases of what Kraepelin and Bleuler called *dementia praecox,* what Morton Prince called the split personality, and what we today commonly call schizophrenia.

Reil first discusses at length what were at that time considered two other major forms of mental disease. He designates them as *fixer Wahnsinn* (which may be translated as *paranoia*) and *Tobsucht* (accumulation of the various forms of restless insanity). He then describes this third type, which he calls *Narrheit.* The meaning of this word, however, is not the common translation *foolishness* (in the sense used in the phrase "April Fool's Day"); rather it should be translated as *madness,* or better yet, *oddness,* since the author's discussion is concerned with an actual serious mental disturbance.

In the section of Reil's description which is presented here, I have tried to keep as nearly as possible to the German form, selecting oddness as the translation of the word used by Reil.

Oddness is a general disorientation and weakness of the psychic forces without any raging and delirium or imbecility. However, it is more related to the latter than to the former. For the presentation of definite symptoms I am at a considerable loss, since I feel unable to give a clearly delineated picture of this disease. As for specific characteristics, it can only be said that this disease does not fall into any of the other major groups of mental illness. In addition, it must be pointed out that even the term "oddness" is in itself less definable than any other term in regard to mental ailment. Perhaps it is not actually a specific soma, but represents a somewhat chaotic mixture of several specific different abnormal states of the mind. I therefore feel I cannot do better than present the character of this disease in a descriptive way as I have observed it in many cases.

The insane who represent cases of oddness pursue no straight line of thinking or acting, but are permanently in a state of change. They are apt in all situations of life to do just the wrong or unexpected thing. Besides a general disorientation, there is a considerable weakness of all psychic functions, especially that of judgment. There is also a constant change going on in their imagination. Fantastic conceptions are sometimes slowly built up; on other occasions they appear suddenly, like lightning, only to disappear as fast as they had come. These fanciful ideas appear isolated from the main stream of thoughts because they are not associated with any continuity of thinking. Such patients have a considerable urge to talk and to communicate their chaotic ideas which have no meaning or relation to anything in reality. They speak in one breath, for example, of swords and toothpicks, children and hats, of broken china and capsized ships. Therefore unrelatedness, flightiness, habitual absent-mindedness, lack of thoughtfulness, forgetfulness, and weakness or incapability of judgment are frequent. Joy, scorn and sadness are interchangeable, without any cause or reason, and come and go without leaving any imprint on the patients' general attitudes. They have general temperamental outbreaks which appear and disappear from one moment to the other. These, their spells, are like those of children which one is able to control or banish with a frown. Similar symptoms can be found in the patients' activity. They are always on the go, but without intensity, purpose, or aim. They enjoy themselves in this childish manner with foolish activity and silliness. Their actions appear to be severed from their thinking. There occur automatic muscle mechanisms which appear in various groupings, neither interrelated among themselves nor with any imagination. These mechanisms are executed without any purpose, nor do they ever have any concrete connection with reality. Therefore those who are insane in this fashion are little concerned about the success of their actions or how badly they may be performed. Usually such patients are contented, good-humored, and happy. They are good-natured and tend to do harm neither to themselves nor to others. In case something does occur to upset them, they can easily be calmed.

Various degrees and modifications of this disease occur. The ability to reason may be greater or smaller, and in some individuals decrease to the point of imbecility. Some patients have more contact with reality than others, so that they do not forget what has once been promised to them. They observe clearly how their odd behavior and peculiar actions are reacted to by their environment. They understand how to avoid punishment when they are disobedient and can ward off neglect by pretending sickness. Some are even able to assume a measure of responsibility for their actions and can be guided by an appeal to their honor.

This disease generally has the character of continuity; it appears rarely in the periodic form we can observe in paranoiac and deliric ailments. However, some traits of the last-named diseases may appear mixed with oddness, as if they developed out of them. It seems that oddness can result from any cause which manifests itself in weakening of the brain. An intellectually superior individual is less apt to develop oddness directly; usually it appears only after he has gone through an episode of paranoiac or deliric illness. Oddness only affects a mentally inferior individual directly because he has not enough energy for development of the other types of mental ailment. Therefore we find more cases of oddness among people who do not belong to the more cultured class.

The cure of oddness is rather difficult. Because the existence of weakness and the dissociation of all psychic faculties is based upon an innate disposition, or is the result of severely disturbing experiences, it proves to be a deep-rooted condition developing slowly over a long period. The sickness of the intellect makes the patients insensitive to outside stimulants and they are unable to concentrate on anything because of their flighty ideas.

Reil saw clearly the general symptomatology and the differential typology, even if he was wrong in believing that the majority of these types of schizophrenia are the result of other earlier mental illnesses. However, points of this kind raise stumbling blocks that have not yet been completely surmounted by even the most advanced and sensitive schizophrenia researchers.

Reil was far from believing that all mental illnesses are entirely psychic. He recognized the actual neurological diseases and the importance of somatopsychological elements, but with his concept of the *Gemein-Gefuehl,* he maintained that they were "diseases of the psyche," that is, of the basic unity of our mental or psychic disposition. At one point he designated the phenomena as illnesses of the centricity power of the organization of the psyche, which has primarily a dynamic function.

In the cases described, says Reil, there exists a relationship between the psyche and the nervous system as well as the rest of the physical organism, which may or may not have become involved or affected. Basically, however, the disintegration that he describes is a psychic pathology. Although the theory that schizophrenia is entirely or primarily a psychic disease has been seriously challenged in recent years, it has yet to be determined whether the psychiatrist who was the first to describe it as such was right or wrong. Nevertheless, the amazingly clear presentation by Reil in 1808 deserves to be known, and it should survive the struggle of opinions about it.

Reil's *Rhapsodies on the Application of Psychotherapy to Mental Diseases,* published in 1803, is written in an unusual way and introduces us to a unique temperament, mixing unrestrained radicalism with ingenuous qualities, heartwarming wisdom and even humor. The *Rhapsodies* is neither a program book nor a text with systematic presentation, but rather a work in which the author ten years before his death summed up his life experiences, though he died at the early age of fifty-three.

At the time of its appearance the book received great attention from his friends and followers as well as from his opponents. Heinroth, who criticized him severely, could not avoid mentioning him regularly. Even the controversial school of somatic psychiatry could not fail to acknowledge him as one of the most important early psychiatrists.

In the following pages I wish to quote a set of passages from the *Rhapsodies,* which, one will agree, could have been taken from books published yesterday and express viewpoints which have a vision even far beyond our present achievements and aims. In order for you to appreciate the essential character of Reil's sen-

tences, I will reproduce here the opening paragraph of his Introduction. One will easily realize the difference from the ethical and
religious approach to the task of helping the insane with which
Benjamin Rush opened his *Inquiries,* speaking of the "consecrated
ground" upon which one steps in entering a mental institution.
Reil's thinking is realistic and modern.

> One is overcome by a strange sensation if out of the throng of a
> large city one suddenly enters the institution for its insane. One is
> presented here with the appearance of a stage show of all of what one
> has encountered outside. There are the scoundrels, the swindlers,
> tyrants, slaves, criminals and defenseless sufferers, the fools who laugh
> without reason and the fools who torture themselves without reason.
> False pride, egotism, vanity and avarice and all the other idols of
> human weakness hold on this small pond the rudder of life just as
> they do on the ocean of the big world. However, these odd people of
> Bicêtre and Bedlam are more open and harmless than those in the
> big foolhouses of the world. The vindictive demands that fire shall
> fall from the sky, and the imaginary conqueror who believes in his
> paranoid mind that he could destroy half the earth with his own
> sword. . . . However, nowhere do we find smoking ruins of destroyed
> villages and no people whimper because of afflicted wounds. . . .

Let us start with what Reil has to say about diagnostic and experimental endeavors in psychotherapy. We must remember that
experimentation in psychology did not start before 1840, and
that application of perceptive and sense-psychology in the abnormal field did not occur until about twenty-five years later.

> The foremost senses are touch, sight and sound, smell and taste,
> and provide us less with clear impressions but more with mere sensa-
> tions. They belong to another group of psychotherapeutic means.
> However, I believe that at least with the organ of smell, with the aid
> of a well-arranged set of perfumes, one could conduct certain worth-
> while experiments and, by exercising the psyche in learning, distinguish
> smells and further develop its range and sensitivity of perception.
> Touch is an important element in psychotherapy. We may have to
> develop and train the experience of smooth and rough, cold and warm,
> light and heavy in their various forms. At times when one wants to
> exercise this sense, one has to exclude all other activities so that con-
> centration is possible. For instance, one could bring the patient into
> a dark, soundproof room, filled with various objects, fixed or moving,
> dead or alive. With some patients one could call for scary sensations.

Other patients who are sensitive, should have objects selected so that fear could be avoided. . . .

We have various boxes for each of the senses containing a number of objects of various sizes and kind, natural as well as artificial things. From this collection a set can be selected for an exercise, according to the abilities and needs of the individual patient. The patient is induced to name each object and point out its major or specific characteristics which he has to combine into a description of the object, which we induce him to put into writing. We give him building blocks which he has to arrange according to given instructions. Or we give him a picture of a landscape cut up into a jigsaw puzzle which he has to put together. In the beginning he is supervised in this activity. Later he is induced to perform these exercises alone and finally he has to memorize these activities. In this way we are able to reeducate the imagination of the patient and his relationships to reality. During the time a patient is knitted to reality by such activity, his sick phantasy is put out of action.

The Swiss-French neurologist, Tissot, was the first to formulate the applicability and psychotherapeutic value of music. However, no one before or long after Reil has expressed such a mature insight into the use and validity of music psychotherapy.

The ear is the sense organ which we are least able to close to outside impressions. It is therapeutically of such great importance because of the amount of pleasantness and unpleasantness it can mediate from the total world. It is also the receptor of the spoken word, the major communication system of our mental relations. Pure tonal experience in its pleasant as well as in its unpleasant form can have therapeutic value. Loud and piercing noises may shake a paranoid patient. Water drops dripping from a water faucet have been found to induce a peaceful attention in a patient, leading to peaceful sleep. Music has its therapeutic effect through its rhythm as well as its melody. This effect is much more intense since it is not perceived like speech and poetry by an application of the mind, but directly affects feelings and emotions. Therefore it enters more easily into the depth of the psyche where other means do not reach. Music can calm the storms in our soul. It can chase away depressions and melancholic tendencies. It has a calming effect even upon cases of greatest restlessness. It has proven especially helpful in all cases of depressive states. In paranoid and manic states it may help to divert the strive towards unreality. It is exceptionally helpful during convalescence and as a form of occupational therapy, also to distract, to entertain and strengthen the mind of the mentally ill.

Reil was convinced that for innumerable psychopathological states music therapy should be specially adapted and he called for research to determine what instrument and what scores should be applied to different mental ailments. This problem has not yet been satisfactorily solved in our days.

One of Reil's most amazing foresights of specific modern psychotherapeutic techniques is his vision of what we call today psychodramatics.

Each mental institution ought to have a specially arranged theatre with the necessary machinery to present various settings. The employees of the institutions should be trained to play various roles— that of a judge, an executor, physician or an angel who comes from heaven, or a dead man risen from his grave—all personifications which might play a serious role in the mental status of this or that patient and that might impress his imagination therapeutically. Such a theatre should be able to present scenes from a prison, the lion's den, a place of execution, and an operating room. There would be Don Quixote knighted, imaginary pregnant women freed from their load, fools skinned, repenting sinners absolved in a ceremonial play. In short, such a therapeutic theatre could aid individual cases in a variety of diseases, awaken the phantasy and the speculation, call for the most contradictory emotions, such as fear, fright, astonishment, anxiety or mental calm, according to what may help the patient to eliminate his fixed ideas or his misdirected emotions.

Why could there not be written real plays for the purpose of the work with mental patients, to be performed by the patients themselves. Some may be acting and some watching. The roles would be distributed according to the individual therapeutic needs. The fool, for instance, could be given a role making him aware of the foolishness of his way of behaving, and so on.

Hardly anything has been considered as important in modern psychotherapy as the field of occupational therapy. It is regarded as one of our most modern achievements. Let us hear what Reil wrote about it.

In all mental institutions the inmates should be induced to work, even if this has to be done with slight pressure. Such activity will help improve physical health, assist in the development of a good institutional spirit and will sustain rule and order in the institution. More important work is an excellent therapeutic means to cure mental ills. Such work should be done as much as possible in the open air. It

should be combined with physical activity and should not be mo-
notonous. This last is especially important if one deals with paranoid
patients. All such activity should be adjusted to the strength, ability
and also to the preference of the inmate. It should be sufficiently attractive to get him away from his fixed ideas. Therefore, in or near
any mental institution should be shops of various kind which could
occupy the patients according to their abilities and interests. It is
doubtlessly possible to develop a system of activities by which all
types of mentally ill could be given an activity according to their
therapeutic needs. However, we must not let ourselves be pressured
by the narrowminded budgetist who, with a tear in his eye, points to
any skein of wool which the insane might spoil or who may even
hope for an income from such work. Mental institutions, like theatres,
are not fit to earn money. For both, the community must be willing
to sacrifice. Finally we must point out that this therapeutic occupation
should be changed according to the course and progress of the cure.
In the beginning one might consider primarily to occupy the body.
This might later advance to forms which occupy more the psyche
by proceeding from mere handicraft to the arts, and finally one could
add mental activities.

Gymnastics and calisthenics which have been specially adjusted for
the use of the insane, should do them a lot of good. We also suggest
instructing the inmates in drawing and painting, in singing and in
music and any other artistic activity which could be made available
to them. Concerts seem to me an excellent means of training them
in maintaining attention.

Those who still believe that Freud's basic concepts are abso-
lutely new and that in certain ways his ideas in nuclear form had
not been envisioned by earlier workers, could learn otherwise from
Reil.

If we concede that passions can be the cause of mental disorder,
which indeed unfortunately is rather frequently the case, it is the
task of the psychiatrist to discover and unveil them, especially if they
are the kind which the patient would want to conceal. Without the
knowledge of the cause, there can be no cure. Even demented patients
are able to conceal certain of their conditions by hiding them behind
fabrications and lies. It must be the professional ability of the psychiatrist to have enough understanding of human nature, cleverness
and psychological skill, besides knowledge of the various expressions
of the different mental diseases and a keen capacity for observation of
all the patient's utterances.

How can one protect people against the disadvantageous influences of passions, especially in view of the danger that these

may lead to mental disorders? First of all, one should not suppress them but let them be acted out fully.

> They are like a rapacious torrent which gets more forceful the more one tries to confine it. Vengeance when it is satisfied and love when it has found response, are less dangerous. Sadness finds release in tears; wrath when it gets a chance to cool. The impact of passions is the more intense the less they come to the fore. It is most important that one should give aid as soon as possible. Insanity caused by mishaps or death can usually be prevented if one is able to interfere early, before a fixed idea has taken root. Here distraction is one of the best medicines. Loneliness feeds depression; occupation eliminates it. One should satisfy passions but eliminate their cause and offer the patient substitutes which can attract their interest. Finally, one should apply the light of reason, to make the patient understand his error, to see things as they are in nature and give him real value. The understanding of real value is the key to that final satisfaction which cannot be separated from the existence of man.

Finally, I would like to quote a passage turning the view into quite a different direction of modern psychiatric achievement, actually not relating to psychotherapy but to a diagnostic insight of his highest importance for present day psychiatry. It refers to the question of differential topology. In this field, Ernest Kretschmer's physiopsychological types still hold the ground solidly. Here is what Reil envisioned in the direction of Kretschmer's types.

> There are general differences in the human organization which one must bear in mind. There are people, most of whom have blond hair, large blue eyes, soft skin, who are so delicately organized that they get bruises if one grabs their arm. Others have mostly a rather hard skin, firm flesh and dark hair, a contrasting type. Between them are such analogous differences as exist between the flesh of a peach and an apple. The second type has a stubborn nature, the first is smooth, sensitive to the sufferings of mankind and shows a tendency to dream phantasy. Both types have their own tendency to different kinds of mental disorders.
>
> In classifying such mental disorders it is more important to look for basic motivations than for a set of symptoms. However, one basic difference appears in such a tendency to mental disorder, depending on whether the patient is of sthenic or asthenic nature. This sthenic and asthenic character has a direct relationship to mental disorders. If there are physical characteristics, they can develop into physical illnesses which require physical treatment. In their relationship to

mental abnormality, they can have an inverse character. Often a psyche can be rather hyperactive in an individual with a rather weak physique, or psychic activity is stifled when the brain is flooded by blood in a supernormal energetic activity.

All these modern psychotherapeutic thoughts were published in 1803. Much similar data is available from Reil and other authors of the same period. In making an inventory of all this early knowledge, one question forces itself on one's mind. How much is actually new in the modern psychotherapy of this century?

Chapter 13

THE FORGOTTEN SYSTEMATIC PSYCHIATRY OF JOHANN CHRISTIAN REIL

IN his own time Reil had received wide (although somewhat divided) acknowledgment. Heinroth called him "the originator of real psychological medicine," but on the other hand, also wrote about Reil that he was "incomplete and unable to overcome previous mistakes," and he denounced his "ideological and impractical therapeutic proposals." Similar criticisms and condemnations of Reil were heard throughout the past century and were topped off by the undignified caricature drawn of him by Zilboorg in his historical text.

Most of the condemnations are based solely on a reading of his first major book, the *Rapsodies*. In 1805, however, Reil published a second volume on the same subject. It not only supplemented the *Rapsodies,* but was a fully rounded text embracing the entire field of neuropsychiatry. It proved to be superior to any psychiatric publication that had appeared to that time.

The 670-page book bears the simple title *Die Nervenkrankheiten.* The volume is completely unknown today, although it was once noted and briefly discussed by Albert Gregor, who wrote the chapter on Reil for Kirchhoff's *Deutsche Irrenärzte.* The reason this book fell into oblivion seems to be primarily that it appeared as the fourth volume of Reil's large work on fever. Speculation as to why Reil published this work as a part of his *Fieber-Lehre* will hardly yield a satisfying explanation.

It is true that Reil gave fever a wide role in almost all human ailments. He also placed great emphasis on the factor of temperature changes, which he believed were connected with all mental diseases. The basic pathological role that Reil assigned to fever cannot, however, alone be considered a satisfactory reason, especially since *Die Nervenkrankheiten,* in neither frame of reference nor arrangement, fits into the *Fieber-Lehre.* The work reaches out in every direction, and outside the scope of *Fieber-Lehre,* is an almost exhaustive treatment of all phases of nervous and mental diseases in the scope of the early Nineteenth Century. Throughout the book Reil complains about the limitations and still insufficient status of insight into the field of nervous and mental diseases, and the most fascinating parts of the volume are those in which he reveals his intuitive insight and vision concerning aspects of the field still unrevealed today.

An impressive illustration of the reason why Reil's *Nervenkrankheiten* has not received the attention it deserves, is the recent otherwise excellent attempt by Ingeborg Petzold to gain contemporary acknowledgment for Reil. Her paper was entitled "Reil, The Founder of Modern Psychiatry." Dr. Petzold apparently read only the first volume of *Fieber-Lehre,* from which she quotes one sentence. Her bibliographical reference gives the date of publication as 1801, the date of issue of the first volume. As has been pointed out, the fourth volume, which contains *Die Nervenkrankheiten,* did not appear until 1805.

Our attempt to give some deserved acknowledgment to this most important document of psychiatric history must be limited to a briefer presentation than we feel is needed to adequately describe it. For this we shall have to console ourselves in the manner of Reil himself, who emphasized in the book that he had everywhere to limit himself to what he felt was of the utmost importance if he was to present the entire field. Nevertheless, it is hoped that the present attempt will give a good impression of the contents of the volume.

Die Nervenkrankheiten is divided into two parts. The first is devoted to what we today call nervous diseases, and the second to what we designate as mental diseases. The first part opens with a careful description of the nervous system. Although Reil generally remained on the level of the status of the neurophysiology at that time, one cannot but be astonished to find in his presentation considerable deviation from the conventional views. Nervous experience, he claims, has two basic elements, stimulability *(Reizbarkeit)* and temperature. The importance attributed to nerve temperature apparently served as justification for including the work as part of the five volumes of *Fieber-Lehre.*

The intensity of the vitality of the nervous system does not have a stable *niveau* but is subjected to a swaying of temperature. It appears likely that this peculiarity of the nerves is transmitted to the other organs of the body. The temperature depends on the specific character of certain parts of the animal body. In a squirrel the nerves connected with muscular movement have the highest stimulability. In a dog the stimulability of the sense of smell is most intensive. Orientals have a more stimulable nervous system than Occidentals. During sleep the stimulability of the animal part of the nervous system [e.g. the autonomic system] is almost entirely eliminated. In the fetus and among the aged this stimulability is greatly reduced.

The nervous system has to be considered an independent organic reality which is somehow inserted between the other organs but whose forces possess autonomic functioning independent of all other organs.

It is the nervous system that unites the various organs, which otherwise function only mechanically, into a total unit.

In addition to being the carrier of nervous stimulation, the nervous system is the organ of the psyche *(Seelen-Organ)*. The functions of the *Seelen-Organ* are perception *(Vorstellungen)* and feeling. The most elementary and basic perception, that which makes us aware of ourself and our body, Reil calls, as we have told *das Gemein-Gefuehl*. He considers it a special psychic sense organ in its own right and also a constituent of the *Seelen-Organ*. Beyond the *Gemein-Gefuehl* is the variety of psychic experiences that are drawn together by the brain, which is also the dispatcher of all the directing impulses of the psyche. The brain is the locale of the major faculty of the psyche—thought. Thought is the image-forming process of the brain evoked by the stimulations and experiences of the psyche. With this Reil rounds out his basic neurological and psychological concepts which, although they are in considerable contradiction to our major modern concepts, are astonishingly realistic and not easy to challenge.

The second part of *Die Nervenkrankheiten* comprises mainly a description of the general pathology of nervous diseases, which is first viewed from the neuropathological and then from the applied psychopathological angle. The first pages of this part are of especially great importance not only from the historical point of view but from the point of view of present-day speculation concerning these problems. Reil's brilliant mind, geared by a radical empiricism, struggled with the problems of neurological symptomatology and diagnosis. He speculates. Since only the visible effect of the pathogenic factors of neurological diseases can be established, how can a proper pathology be developed out of these symptoms? How can we learn something about their causes? Only if we can determine these causes can we develop a logical therapy and means of cure. Of course, besides these physical outer symptoms there are also inner, psychological symptoms, which Reil, following the psychiatric practice of his time, calls the *moral*. These inner symptoms, however, give us little help. We must therefore consider it as established that nervous diseases are actually hidden diseases. In a remarkably radical way, Reil exclaims, "In regard to a nervous ailment of the eye, how can we know which is the causal factor, a disease of the retina, of the ocular-motor nerve, or of the brain?"

Battling his way through the various known and unknown aspects of neurology, many of which have hardly changed up to the present, Reil divided pathogenesis into two parts: First, the organically and hereditarily caused nervous diseases; second, those he referred to as occasionally conditioned. This second category he describes in great detail. He says this group of nervous diseases arises from outside the body and is influenced by such factors as climate, the seasons, location, faulty nutrition, improper medication, the wrong use of electricity and magnetism, etc. The list of causes arising from inside the body begins with indigestion, stones, worms, gases, chronic illness and fever, poor secretion, menstruation and last but not least, too much or too little sleep. In the list of psychic, or as we would call them today, psychosomatic causes, Reil includes, among others, overwork, pain and a variety of emotional upsets. Finally, he does not omit social pathological causes: social status, luxury, education and occupation.

Reil, more than any other author up to the beginning of this century, struggled with the problem of systematizing nervous diseases. First he does so according to what he calls a dynamic approach analogous to certain physical conditions. He distinguishes cataleptic-like (for which he uses the old designation *synocha*), typhoid-like, and paralysis-like nervous ailments. He differentiates also according to what we would call function. He separates nervous conditions of the outer and of the inner senses. The latter he subdivides into those of the *Gemein-Gefuehl* and the coordination of the physiological functions of the nerves themselves. There follows a differentiation of nervous diseases according to whether or not they have outer causes. Those with outer causes are divided, according to the terminology of the time, into endemic, epidemic, sporadic, sympathic, ideopathic, symptomatic and protopathic.

There are further distinctions: local and general, acute and chronic, simple and complicated and active and passive. Nervous diseases differ also according to whether they are actual fevers or only connected with fever or febrility. The first section closes with a number of short chapters, one of which deals with nervous disease as a process. Here again Reil's farsightedness is impressive. Unable to do more than touch on the deeper aspects of this problem—which did not receive proper attention until the beginning of this century—he nevertheless realizes the importance of it in the study of nervous ailments. The last part of the first section is a rather pessimistic chapter on prognosis.

In the section that follows, Reil offers his therapy. As always, his theoretical speculations are challenging. He emphasizes here the need for differentiating symptomatology on the one hand for purely diagnostic purposes and on the other as the basis for therapy. Therapy, he says, must always aim at the removal of the underlying cause of a symptom, whether it be a toxic condition in the patient's physiology, weakness, too rapid growth, faulty nutrition or incorrect medication.

In his actual practical therapy and medication, Reil remains within the frame of the therapeutic knowledge of his time, as he had described it a few years earlier in his *Rapsodies*. However, he here clearly narrows his direction by separating nervous and mental diseases, although the difference is not great as compared to the modern distinction between neurological and psychiatric treatment. Of special interest here again is Reil's broad outlook: treatment of nervous ailments should never be on the overall basis. There should always be concentration on the specific condition. He emphasizes the importance of study of the diseased nerve, which should be viewed separately from the bodily environment in which it occurs. Treatment of nervous diseases, he sums up, calls especially for a directing of the activity of organic forces to aid the diseased part. Treatment must produce a therapeutic equivalent that cures. Treatment of the environment in which the nervous disease occurs will contribute much to the cure of a specific nervous ailment. There must be awareness, however, that it is the environment that is being treated and not the nerve itself. Great emphasis is given to psychotherapy as applied in treatment of nervous diseases and to specific regulations of living to be prescribed for such pathologies. The importance that Reil attaches to this may be seen in the fact that he devotes twenty pages to a *Dietetik* of nervous diseases, which he elaborates in the style of the Swiss psychiatrist Tissot, whom he frequently quotes.

The second part of the book is devoted to the *Geisteszerrütungen* (mental diseases). In the *Rapsodies* Reil had discussed mainly the therapeutic side of mental diseases with, in the back of his mind, a strong opposition to the therapeutic views of his time. Here he offers a description of a systematic treatment of these mental illnesses. Unlike later writers of textbooks on pathology, Reil starts out by presenting his system of normal psychology, which for conciseness, clarity and precision cannot be considered less than a gem of psychological literature.

Before beginning the presentation of his systematic psychopathology, however, Reil inserts a chapter which leads from the nervous to the mental diseases, and in which he discusses the interrelations between them. The problem rests on whether only parts of the nervous system or parts of the brain itself have been affected. If parts of the nervous system are diseased, we will receive false information about the sphere of experience that these parts concern. If the brain is diseased, we may receive false information about even the normal functioning of the rest of the body.

There are two basic tenets in Reil's actual psychiatry: First, that pathologies must be viewed as deviations from normal functioning of the psyche; and second, that pathologies can be properly understood only if their causes can be clearly determined.

Reil begins with the pathology of the *Gemein-Gefuehl,* the general feeling which is the basis of consciousness. Such pathologies manifest themselves in imaginary illnesses, "losing of the head," loss of intellectual control and delusions. Reil points to what was then called hypochondriac melancholia as a specific somatic picture of this *Gemein-Gefuehl* pathology. In such a form of illness, he emphasizes, the nervous system may be in good health, but the *Gemein-Gefuehl* is seriously disturbed.

Next he discusses mental diseases resulting from a pathology of the senses. These conditions lead to false perceptions from the outer world but not to actual insanity. In a more serious form they lead to unrealistic daydreaming and imaginings approaching what we would call the paranoid.

In succession, Reil studies pathologies of memory. If the memory is pathologically weakened, the condition results in various stages of forgetting. The causes of this pathology are overtiredness, head injuries and excesses of living. Next are the pathologies of attention, which are mainly the result of overtiredness of exhaustion. The symptoms are lack of precise perception and giddiness. If the power of reason is involved, this is shown by dissipation.

Reil then comes to pathologies of feeling. These may arise from two directions, overstrain or dulling. In an extended elaboration of this subject, Reil reviews the major types of feelings and emotions, ending with pathological forms of passion.

The largest part of this chapter is devoted to a presentation of pathologies of intellectual functions. Reil here proves himself to be a predecessor of the intelligence pathology of this century. However, another aspect of Reil's totalistic conception comes to the fore here. While the pathologies of the previously enumerated psychic functions apparently have merely—to use the modern terms—the character of neuroses, with the pathology of the intellect we enter the field of the psychoses. To the latter Reil applied the German word *Verruektheit*. He emphasizes that insanity is always an individualized disease which may be involved in different ways. Because of his desire to organize facts and materials, Reil classifies the forms of psychotic disease. First he goes back to the differentiation of the bodylike diseases that he had already presented: cataleptic-, typhoid- and paralysis-like ailments.

Reil's concept of paralysis was much wider and more psychological than the one held today. Basically, Reil believed, paralysis is a weakness which tends to appear in various forms from foolishness or silliness to idiocy, fixed ideas and lunacy. There follow other differentiations, such as intensity and extensity, acute and chronic, sthenic and asthenic and the ones corresponding to those presented in the part on nervous diseases.

In a section devoted to general aspects of pathology, Reil emphasizes that mental disease should be viewed as a process and not as a status. He considers it most important to distinguish between slowly developing *(vorbereitende)* and occasional causes. He is still a firm believer in the extended role of heredity in mental disease, and believes that stature, facial expressions and temperament should be accepted as major hereditary symptoms. It is clear to him that pregnancy and birth can be factors causing mental disease. However, he considers the major cause of all mental diseases to be the lack of or faultiness of the *Seelenkultur* of his time. In Reil's time the concept of *Dietetik* had replaced the earlier concept of religious care of man's inner life.

In the ensuing enumeration and description of the various causes of mental disease, Reil follows the scheme he had set up in the part on nervous diseases. He again proves himself not a one-sided Psychist, but a man of broad views and insights. The possible causes coming from outside the body, from the world we live in, and those arising within the body and the nervous system are enumerated. Finally there is a careful description of the neurological causes of mental diseases.

Here we face again one of those strange concepts of Reil's which we are today at a loss to properly understand. However, a man of Reil's scientific stature must have had something meaningful in mind when he maintained that "mental diseases are caused by an intemperature of the vitality of the brain and not mainly by irritation." In other words, mental disturbance is more a caloric problem than a problem of stimulation. The importance that Reil attributes to the caloric conditioning of the nervous system is our main indication as to why he included the text of *Die Nervenkrankheiten* in the *Fieber-Lehre* volume. There is lacking any detailed explanation, aside from the quotation given above and Reil's remark at this point that "intemperature changes the normal association and sympathy of the nervous system. That is, it disturbs the rules according to which its parts relate themselves to each other." Today, while we may give attention to actual fever in mental patients, and while we are familiar with the not too rare conditions of nerve fever, we have no symptomatological standard according to which temperature changes would be considered a significant factor in all neurotic or psychotic states.

The section of this second part of the book which is devoted to therapy in mental diseases is shorter and more concentrated than the therapy section of *Rapsodies,* but it reveals a number of unusual and important insights. These concern especially Reil's general directions and plan of cure, which he sets forth under eight headings: Cause, Character of the patient, Physical constitution of the patient, Influence of various parts of the body on the brain. The interrelationship of which may influence the case, General soma and special features, Physical and dietetic care, Preventive and protective measures.

Reil emphasizes how frequently physical circumstances may be implicated, and how much one must be aware that there may be invisible causal elements at work.

One of Reil's most extraordinary ideas should be mentioned: In severe mental illness one should consider that cure may be achieved by retransforming the mental pathology into a physical one that might be more easily cured. A fantastic thought, which in itself contains an almost demonic incentive to speculate about it and to test its possibilities.

At the close of the entire volume are two short chapters on nightmares and convulsive diseases, two problems that Reil apparently felt he had not done justice to in the main body of the work.

Chapter 14

J. C. A. HEINROTH'S ATTEMPT TO FORMULATE A SYSTEM OF PSYCHOTHERAPY

S INCE ancient times and all through the history of medical development medical writers have been offering advice for the improvement and cure of mental disease, but it was not until 1818 when Johann Christian A. Heinroth of Germany undertook to write the first systematic textbook of psychiatry that an attempt was made to establish an actual clinical system of psychotherapy. This was done in Heinroth's *Disturbances of the Mind (Lehrbuch der Störungen des Seelenlebens)*.

Heinroth's book was a precisely executed presentation of what psychotherapy meant and what it could achieve. Of course, Heinroth wrote in the light of the psychiatric knowledge of the first quarter of the Nineteenth Century.

Insights into methods of treatment of insanity indeed were in the air at the start of the Nineteenth Century. Many a psychiatric author not only touched upon these problems but even presented them rather fully in accordance with a specific orientation. Thus the Philadelphian, Benjamin Rush, applying his "Quaker pathos" with his call for humane treatment of the insane, had shaken the entire English-speaking world. Shortly after, in 1803, Reil had issued his *Rhapsodies*. Reil, a psychological empiricist and an inductive experimenter, was sharply criticized by Heinroth as a man working without method and without clear objectives as a practical alienist. We see between these two equally important and exceptional men the typical contradiction of the inductive and deductive approach. In their grasp of their subject, both reached far beyond their time, offering insight into some of the problems still unsolved today and some results from which we still could learn.

In the same year in which Heinroth's book appeared, another Berlin alienist published a detailed, illustrated report on the prevailing status of institutional mental care. For over a decade A. L.

Horn had been a psychiatrist at the Charité Hospital. In his "Public Report on My Twelve Years of Service as Associate Physician at the Royal Charité Hospital in Berlin," Dr. Horn gives an impressive description of the treatment of the insane in public institutions as it was practiced at the beginning of the Nineteenth Century. It is a tragic and horrifying report. At that time, the institutionalized insane were handled with extreme crudeness and in a most primitive fashion. The report gives a clear picture of these existing conditions and serves as background for a vision of really effective and humanized therapy as conceived by men like Reil and Heinroth.

In his theoretical concepts Horn seems to be widely dependent on Reil, who became his senior at the hospital a few years before he died. Horn also seems to have shared some of Reil's novel ideas on social adjustment, occupational therapy and reeducation. In practice both men did not get very far. In fact, one might assume that Reil's struggle to get his progressive ideas accepted may have been one of the reasons for his early death. He died still a young man with a vision of humanizing the treatment of the insane, a vision which modern institutions could point to as encompassing widely advanced therapeutic measures. It was left to Heinroth to present it in a way which in many respects has not even today been surpassed.

The larger portion of the second volume of *Disturbances of the Mind* contains Heinroth's psychotherapy. His systematic presentation is divided into three sections: (1) A Technical Methodology (Heuristic); (2) A Survey of Medical Treatment *(Heilmittel Lehre)*; (3) A Practical Psychotherapy *(Kur-Lehre)*.

In the beginning of the heuristic section Heinroth discusses the basic attitudes he deems essential for work in the psychiatric field. He emphasizes accuracy of perception and tactful approach as the two major tools. The first is the theoretical, the second the practical key for good therapy.

As a first task for the heuristic consideration, Heinroth considers it necessary to determine how far any pathological state needs therapeutic help. Life itself, he points out, contains a healing force which is better than what any human therapy can offer. This healing force should be given every possible chance to be effective in cases where there is hope that it may restore the patient's sanity. Therefore, the therapist's first consideration ought to be to determine at what point he should step into the life of the patient.

The next step is evolving a specific therapy plan. The physician should determine what available therapeutic implements fit best the particular patient and the specific ailment. There are many somatic conditions which appear correlated with psychic illness. This relationship must be carefully investigated. There are also the elements of sex, age, social and professional standing, type of personality and psychological characteristics which must be considered in a heuristic preparation of any case. Last but not least, the possible deviations and even anomalies of the individual case must be taken into consideration.

All these are, according to Heinroth, necessary preliminaries if the psychiatrist is to help the patient and ease his life as well as the fate of those who live with him, especially if he is a custodial case. But even Heinroth's heuristic approach cannot be treated as a set of dogmatic prescriptions. It must be applied by the psychotherapist as a sensitive art and find expression in highly individual directions used at the proper moment.

There are basically two methods which the heuristic approach uses. Heinroth designates them as the indirect and the direct psychic method. He presents six forms of the indirect method. The first he calls the negative treatment.

The psychiatrist here takes a standby position, letting nature itself cure the patient. Heinroth discusses this in great detail. Nature's help is relative because it is dependent on favorable conditions. Thus, the idea of "getting better by oneself" needs most careful supervision.

No healthy person can live without contact with and help from the surrounding social world. Still less can a mentally diseased individual do so. By the aid of nature, a physically sick individual may be able to develop the right instinct which would induce him to recover. A psychically sick individual can hardly do so, since it is precisely his instinct and his consciousness which are disturbed. Therefore, one may ask whether a negative method is of use at all if it means leaving the diseased person to himself and to nature. There are definite circumstances in which the psychiatrist should exercise restraint. We know, for instance, how important it is to give periods of rest to a disturbed mind. Time itself is a healing factor. Heinroth formulates the aphorism that "one ought to give time its own time" *(Der Zeit ihre Zeit lassen)*.

However, there are other conditioning factors which we may call negative: (1) Giving the patient a chance to help himself as much as possible by holding back the aid of the psychiatrist when it is not needed; (2) Guarding against any negative influence the therapy may exert upon the physical condition of the patient so that no new physical ailment is created; (3) Keeping in mind that mental diseases are of chronic character, and refraining from applying any quick methods which fit only acute diseases. Chronic diseases which may endure for decades call for a more inactive treatment that gives the nature of the patient the first chance to be the healer; (4) Ascertaining whether a method applied is really helpful and refraining from the use of any other until certain that it will help the patient to recover; (5) Finally, the environment of a patient may be of a kind that it would be disturbed by the intervention of the psychiatrist. It might make the task of the latter easier but not advance the health of his patient.

The psychological principles of the negative method do not mean that the psychiatrist is not watching and observing attentively. On the contrary he must be like the Roman, Fabius Cunctator, waiting to do the right thing at the right moment.

The second form of treatment Heinroth calls the gradual treatment. Today we may prefer to call it *differential treatment*. It is the application of various means for various abnormal states.

There are, Heinroth explains, two basic abnormal states of mind which occur in one form or another in almost all mentally ill persons: The patients are either excited or depressed. These pathological moods *(Stimmungen)* have to be balanced to the "right psychic temperature."

Certain types of mental diseases fall predominantly into the class of abnormal excitement. They differ in degree. We find them combined with mania and restlessness as well as with almost all other forms of insanity. On the other hand, we also find depression connected with various mental states such as melancholia, imbecility and various forms of listlessness or lack of will power.

This differentiation between various forms of mental disease is of major importance for therapy, and therapy will be sound if it affects the thinking, fantasy and will of the patient. For example, the patient's will power may have to be encouraged or it may have to be limited—if necessary, by force, but this force may be "soft" and we may express it by a loving attitude. In some instances the capacity for fantasy of the patient may have to be revived; in others it may have to be calmed. The most difficult task, the one which calls for the most refined psychiatric art, according to Heinroth, is to inculcate will into those lacking it, to give back the power of joy to the melancholic and the power of thinking to the imbecile.

A third type of treatment Heinroth emphasizes is the formal treatment. Formal treatment actually means *differential therapy*. Heinroth points out three major tools it employs: In the emotional sphere, it is change and stabilization; in the sphere of the intellect and reason, it is correction; in the sphere of volition, it is direction. For practical application Heinroth gives his advice in a highly concentrated form which I should like to quote here.

> One ought to calm the emotions by which the fantasy was ignited; in melancholia, in which all fantasy is dead, one ought to try to vitalize the emotions. In paranoia one ought to try to correct the wrong concepts, to bring flighty thoughts into relationship with reality, and to give understanding to the foolish about right ways of thinking. Insight is the magical word to overcome all delusions, falsehood and error in the pathologic as well as in the normal states of the mind. As regards imbecility, with its lack of will power, psychological medicine is at a loss. But so far as the state of restless insanity is concerned, the master in psychiatry can try with his art to bridle the uncontrollable will.

Each mental case, Heinroth says, should be considered individually. There is an aspect in the treatment where the personal status, the characteristics of the man or woman must be taken into account. This individual element is comprised of the patient's sex, the age, the constitution and the basic elements of his character. Heinroth means here more than the descriptive inventory that is shown on our hospital charts. The elements of differentiation which play an essential role in the woman's personality pattern or those of a man with specific mental abnormalities are included. In Heinroth's time great emphasis was laid, for instance, on the differentation of age and the fact that it creates a specific pattern in certain mental diseases.

The constitutional elements also play a part in determining the choice of the physical treatment. "Weak" or "strong" constitutions should be taken into consideration if one wants to achieve success or avoid harm. Heinroth still believed in the old concept of the four temperaments in man and recommended that they be noted in various forms of mental disease.

In this chapter we also find the first indications of what we now call social psychiatry. Heinroth wishes those factors of the natural as well as social environment of the patient considered which can cause a mental abnormality. In addition he describes the role such factors may play in treatment. Thus climate, natural environmental conditions, national differences, residence in a foreign country and the homesickness it may cause, and finally, home and family relationships belong in the circle of Heinroth's observations. He has thought them through in their particularly therapeutic and pathological aspects and formed definite ideas about them. One of his most astonishing conclusions is that because of the variations in national character, individuals belonging to different nations ought to be treated differently.

Heinroth then presents what he calls the somatic supporting treatment. The term *somatic* at that time was used in a much broader sense than it is today. According to Heinroth, there are certain physiological factors involved with most mental illness which must be taken care of by physical medicine. He sums them up as sleeplessness, constipation, dryness of the skin, various congestive disorders, convulsions and different forms of paralysis. These conditions appear in various forms with different mental ailments, and therefore need a different therapeutic approach in each case. One symptom which today is less frequently emphasized than in Heinroth's time is the condition of the skin which in certain forms of mental illness seems to be an important objective of therapy for him.

Phlebotomy is also still an important therapeutic tool in relieving high blood pressure and certain other "congestive conditions." Heinroth emphasizes that good physical health of the inmates of an institution is the basis for their mental cure.

The last aspect of the indirect psychotherapeutic method that he discusses is what he calls the *palliative treatment*. Today we would name it *custodial care*. The following guiding principles are emphasized: (1) Acknowledgment of the individuality of the patients, not only regarding the kind of ailment from which they suffer but also regarding their psychological individuality, their character and sensitivity; (2) care of their physical existence and prevention of physical illness; (3) making their life endurable or even pleasurable.

Heinroth points out that constructive, thoughtful institutional arrangements can lead to much easier handling, even of difficult custodial cases. He pleads for a family type of organization for those who must endure lifelong internment and commitment.

In addition to what we have reported, Heinroth recommends another procedure which he calls the direct method. He does not present it dogmatically, with definite directions. He calls this seventeen-page chapter "Ideas on a Direct Psychic Method." We could also call it a "Philosophy and Psychology of Treatment." Some earlier readers of this chapter passed too quick a judgment in condemning Heinroth's point of view as that of a veiled theologian. We know that he studied theology before he turned to medicine, but he also was a member of the medical faculty, and at the height of his career, its dean. He was also a member of the philosophy and law departments of his university.

Actually Heinroth was one of the most universal scholars of his time. It is true he was a religious man. So was Thomas Kirkbride and Benjamin Rush, and in modern times, Robert Sommer, but he clearly separated theology and psychiatry. To maintain that Heinroth's psychotherapy was but a poor theology is to badly misinterpret his ideas.

For the universalist more than for the theologian Heinroth

there had to be a place for religion in the total human experience and existence. In him we find a philosopher of the Fichte and Hegel type rather than a theologian or metaphysician. Religion as Heinroth envisions it is an integral part of psychotherapy. The activity of the mental physician is a religious thinking within a philosophical and epistemological framework. A few short sentences will illustrate Heinroth's thinking in this respect.

"To be in unity with the truth, this is belief; the will is the mental force and the original creative power; will is the power of healing and belief is the self-ability of this will. True freedom is not possible without insight into truth and is not possible without acknowledgement of sin, wrong-doing and awareness of God."

Thus Heinroth believed that direct psychotherapy is mainly a redirecting of the will into "truth." Guiding it to acts which correspond with ethics, the psychotherapist can motivate his patient's will into leading the good life. For this reason, he must not only be a man of knowledge but an individual of high ethical standing, who can inculcate his own standards to his patients. If he acts in this fashion he is in accord with the highest principles of religion.

Thus we see that there is nothing theological in this psychotherapy. On the contrary, one may say that this is a therapy to which something has been added, something that modern routine therapies are badly lacking, namely a sound metaphysical basis. For psychotherapy is not only a science of therapeutic techniques, it must also be a science of living, a way of life for those to whom it is to be of assistance.

The second part of Heinroth's psychotherapy is a survey of the various remedies that were available in his time. After a short general introduction in which he emphasizes that all means of cure should be selected according to the specific purpose and the effect one desires to achieve, Heinroth again warns against dogmatism. All cures are relative, he points out, and the surest medications may sometimes fail. This is what makes psychiatry an art. The good psychiatrist uses the right medication at the right moment.

In the detailed presentation of his "Survey of Mental Treatment" Heinroth proceeds once more in his amazingly systematic way. He outlines procedures in the same manner as in the heuristic part.

First are the remedies that reduce or increase the patient's excitement: (1) physiotherapy: cold applications, hydrotherapy, fresh air, dimmed or darkened rooms and silence; (2) pharmacotherapy: Here Heinroth enumerates in great detail what in his own time were considered sedatives. Among them he mentions camphor, belladonna, quinine and digitalis; (3) physical restraint: strait jacket, the famous Cox Rocking Chair and the isolation room; (4) diet: It may be fat or lean or even a starvation diet. With these dietary measures Heinroth combines his therapeutic efforts in relation to sleep; (5) psychotherapy: This is the most interesting part for us. One of his basic theories is that of removal or increase of irritation. This, he says, can be done by external means, such as diet, physiotherapy and even by methods we would hardly use today. Among the latter are deprivation of sleep and what at that time was rather frequently used: chemicals causing nausea and vomiting, phlebotomy, purgation and even physical punishment. However, Heinroth points out that these crude physical means should be used only where the psychological means have failed. He enumerates the latter as calm therapeutic environment, work and all kinds of productive activity, including reading aloud, music, artistic activity, social intercourse and finally, direct influence by therapeutic treatment of the patient's will.

A wide range of treatments for the depressive states is presented next. First he recommends physical stimulation such as hydrotherapy, electricity, etc., and then pharmaceutical means. Instead of physical restraint he suggests strong physical stimulation. Of the types he mentions, probably only massage would be still acceptable today. Dietetic prescriptions seem very important to him, as does forced feeding, but he is against bad sleeping habits, daydreaming and "doing nothing." In regard to psychotherapy, Heinroth recommends stimulation of the psychic and mental capacities of the patients, coupled with constructive and enjoyable activities.

In the final group of gradual treatments Heinroth discusses what he calls the vitalizing measures. He underlines the need of great caution in the choice of treatment. Many of the previously mentioned measures belong here. But, he says, there is a different aspect of therapy which may have to be applied in this group. He enumerates oxygen, sunlight and warmth, and as special therapies, electricity and magnetism. He assembles a long list of drugs and vitalizing pharmaceuticals. In some serious cases he even suggests transfusion of animal and human blood. Our knowledge of the blood groups may make us shudder at the possible results of such transfusions. Heinroth does not report on the success of such treatment. Of course, a healthy diet is most important, and here he gives a long list of recommended foods, which appear to be selected with insight. Most seem to be still valid today. Great emphasis is also placed on good psychological treatment as a means of arousing the patient to enjoyment of life and renewed vitality. He closes this chapter with the maxim, "Joy is the life-blood of man."

The next section covers the therapeutic means of formal treatment. Here, too, Heinroth has two therapeutic patterns: sedation and vitalization. Regarding disturbances of intellect and reason—mental disturbances—his therapy is one of correction. He divides it into problem solving and coordinating. He enumerates various intellectual exercises, games, collecting, art and music. For both types he emphasizes that patients should be educated "like children," and that they should be given merits and demerits.

In the sphere of volitional disturbances, Heinroth designates his therapy as a directing one, ranging from restraint to encouragement. He goes rather far in regard to restraint and deprivation, which he tries to achieve by exhausting work and even confinement. On the other hand he feels that physical exercise, the development of self-confidence and training in self-determination fall under the classification of encouragement. He talks at length about practical applications as, for instance, how simple threats might have the same effect as actual punishment. He further points out that kindness and warmth on the part of the therapist are a major factor in succeeding with the depressed patient whose will power is defective.

The next section contains most of the purely psychological and psychotherapeutic aspects of Heinroth's views. At first, he presents in great detail the differences of treatment in male and female patients. According to him the specific sex characteristics in the psychopathology of men are pride, ambition, avarice and intemperance of various kinds. In the psychopathology of women they are love, jealousy and vanity. Accordingly, stimulation therapy should be varied between the strong and the weak. Pride and ambition, for instance, have to be treated with weaker stimuli than other characteristics he regards as paramount. The best way of dealing with pride is to counter it with still bigger pride. This does not upset, does not enrage the patient, but has a calming effect.

As the best means of handling women Heinroth suggests empathy and ignoring. He does not, however, wholly repudiate the use of strong-arm methods such as deprivation, work, force or punishment; but he wants them applied according to the individual case and after most serious consideration of all other possibilities.

Next comes the differentiation of treatment according to age. He emphasizes the period of puberty as one of great potential danger for the individual and one in which mental ailments may originate. He again points out the need of careful choice between strong and weak means of therapy, especially in dealing with youth or with older people.

Youth is a period of fantasy and enjoyment of senses. Age strives for security in life and the establishment of solid social circumstances. This basic difference directs the therapeutic approach. Another factor to be considered is the patient's physical constitution. A patient with a delicate constitution and slender body should be treated differently from one with a robust and vigorous physical structure.

Temperaments are discussed here as well as their influence on therapy. Heinroth pairs two of the temperaments together: Sanguine and choleric patients need cold, dimmed light, sedatives, purgatives and phlebotomy, light diet and much sleep. Psychologically, they will be helped by restraint, calm and temperance. The phlegmatic and melancholic patients need warmth, electricity, stimulating medications, vitalizing foods, a limited amount of sleep and encouragement to engage in physical activity. This type needs enjoyable and stimulating social relationships.

Heinroth distinguishes personality from temperament. He defines personality as "the individual's most intimate and interior existence." Today we would probably call this the ego or the self. There are certain stimulants which may influence the ego directly. Again, calming and animating means are mentioned, and special reeducational and suggestive directions are offered as means of helping the patient in this or that direction.

A short chapter deals with the "entire external relationship of the patient: his business, social position, family, home, as well as his economic and social conditions." A list of practical suggestions corresponding to modern social work activity concludes this really amazing survey.

Following this we are offered a long presentation of physiotherapy with mental patients. Here we see for the first time a detailed discussion of the treatment of insomnia. According to Heinroth, sleeplessness is always caused by some kind of irritation. He distinguishes between irritation in the blood, the nerves, the skin and the intestines. He feels that sleeplessness can also be caused by localized pain, lack of physical activity and consumption of energy as well as by mental and emotional upsets. Heinroth carefully studies each type of irritation and has for each a definite set of therapeutic prescriptions.

The next chapter deals with the various kinds of constipation in mental patients and the need of vitalizing the skin condition which he found in many cases. Another important factor for Heinroth concerns the various "congestions" found in the blood and the digestive organs. These call for serious attention. Strangely enough, considering his great sensitivity and knowledge, Heinroth shows no deep understanding of epilepsy. He hardly touches it, devoting a single page in a long chapter that also contains various unsatisfactory suggestions about the treatment of convulsions and spasms.

At the end of this long section on general treatment there is a short one devoted to what in the first part of the book was called *palliative treatment,* or custodial care of the patient. Here Heinroth presents in detail ways of taking care of these patients. He points out the need for manifesting devotion to them as well as sympathetic understanding and feeling, especially for those who never would be able to leave the mental institution. He discusses separately the physical care, activity, rest, as well as the occupational and recreational therapy they require.

The following part, devoted to the *Kur-Lehre,* presents phases of individualized treatment. The beginning of the last century was the period in which speculation about mental therapy began to assume real importance. Heinroth was the most philosophically inclined of all his fellow psychiatrists. What he presents as a kind of speculative introduction, under the title *Organon,* belongs without doubt to the most animated writing on psychotherapy.

According to Heinroth there are three types of mental conditions which represent the limits of therapy. They are the congenital, the chronic and those forms of mental disease which occur in old age. However, Heinroth denies any justification for withholding help from these types. Chances may still exist in this or that individual case or the borderlines of incurability may still be pushed back.

Here, too, Heinroth warns against routine and mass treatment. This or that remedy may work in a hopeless case if properly applied. There follows here a kind of ethical code for the psychiatrist, requiring him to be certain that he really knows the patient and all the aspects of his case: "Don't act until you are sure you really know, and if you act, be sure that everything is under control." He finally warns that it is important to be a good physician as well as a good psychologist, because frequently organic and psychic conditions overlap. There cannot be any stereotyped treatment. All mental cases are individual cases and perfect cures can be achieved only when all facets have been accounted for.

To give one example of Heinroth's method, I should like to quote here his approach to melancholia.

"Melancholia is composed of two elements: One is depression, the lack of ability to control oneself, which is an important element in the disintegration of the capacity for positive feeling and emotion; it is replaced by gnawing pain. The other is a fixed idea which may concern the sickness or death of a relative or a friend or a loss of property. It is this fixed idea that keeps the patient in the depressed state. If one wants to cure melancholia one must separate the two components and pay special attention to the notions and imaginings which stimulate and change feelings and emotions."

Heinroth himself applied this technique of treatment. He points out that melancholia may be discovered in its early stages by the symptoms of withdrawal. The most important aim in its treatment is tracing the sources and the reasons for the withdrawal, which may be fear or a severe loss or even only the fear of such a loss. One should display persistence in tracing the sources of depressions. If one cannot help the patient by replacement of the loss, or influence the depression by reasonable imaginative methods, one has to lift the patient out of his condition by force or by invigorating his emotions, by inducing new interests or by transplanting him into a new, more stimulating environment. The best forms of treatment are change of scene, activity or even exposure to trouble and hardship. Traveling may be called a universal medicine for such states. It will also help to restore in the patient his appetite and ability to sleep. The changing environment and company, with the need for constantly new approaches, will leave the patient no time for his old thoughts and feelings. Where traveling is not possible, all kind of distractions and activity, even if they have to be applied by force, should be attempted.

There is, however, another type of melancholy patient who immediately develops dullness and stupor. In a case of this kind it is necessary to start with physiotherapy. One may have to use strong methods to shake the patient out of his stupor. In addition, attractive food, music and other forms of pleasure, besides a rigorous work schedule and occupational therapy could be tried. Simultaneously, one should attempt to remove the imaginary causes of the illness. If all these means prove futile, one must assume that melancholia has entered its third stage. This means that the sickness has taken root in the physical structure of the patient. Here the doctor has to fall back on "physical medicine of the strongest kind." Heinroth also recommends physiotherapy, sleep therapy, special care in feeding and keeping the digestion functioning. However, one must assume that the illness is in this stage chronic, and all the social considerations enumerated above for such states should be employed.

These paragraphs on melancholia show an astonishing insight and clarity in the systematic presentation. Heinroth's psychotherapy proves valuable not only as an historical document. From his way of systematic thinking and his thoroughness of approach to the details of each problem, many workers, especially the younger ones, could profit. While reading Heinroth's complicated language in the original is not easy and much of his terminology and pharmacology is outdated, there is something refreshing and inspiring in the sincerity and deep humanity of this great psychiatric practitioner of the past century.

Chapter 15

J. C. A. HEINROTH'S CONCEPT OF THE PSYCHIATRIST'S TASK

IN a period when the need to map the basic areas of psychiatry and their adjacent and overlapping territories can no longer be avoided, it is worthwhile to turn to the early years of the past century, for it was then that the scientific psychiatry we know today had its beginnings.

Benjamin Rush wrote the first American textbook of psychiatry in 1789. In its first paragraph he speaks of "treading on consecrated ground in wanting to attempt to lessen a portion of the greatest evils of human life." Although not many today will agree with the formulations of the doctor of Philadelphia, his words carry the ethical strength of a psychiatric Hippocratic Oath.

Rush's *Medical Inquires and Observations on the Diseases of the Mind* lacked a systematic scholarly quality. Two decades after his book appeared, however, Heinroth published his *Disturbances of the Mind*.

Heinroth was an amazing universalist of the Wilhelm von Humboldt type—of whom only a very few have ever lived. He was born in January, 1773, the son of a Leipzig physician. As a young boy he showed prodigious abilities in the arts and languages, but after graduating at the head of his class, he decided to follow his father's profession. Then, after he had completed his medical studies with the highest honors, he suddenly turned to a study of theology. This choice was not unanticipated since as a secondary school student he had published several papers dealing with theology which had received considerable attention. Nevertheless, three years later he turned to medicine again, with a distinct interest in psychiatry. From an assistant professorship in medicine he rose in ten years to head his school's department of psychiatry. In another decade he became dean of the medical school of the University of Leipzig. He was also a member of the theological and law schools of the university, and from time to time, taught courses in them.

Heinroth's fame as an academic lecturer, though great, was surpassed by his ability in writing scientific textbooks. There were few fields within reach of his interests in which he did not contribute basic books which remained in use for decades. There were such works on general physiology, anthropology, general pathology, psychopathology, psychotherapy and criminal psychopathology. He wrote a book against homeopathy and another on psychological mistakes in education. There was also a book on criminology entitled *The Lie,* and a psychology book with the title *Psychologie als Selbsterkenntnis-Lehre (Psychology as the Search for Self-Knowledge).* Besides this he published several novels and a great deal of poetry under a pseudonym.

Heinroth was the most prominent representative of the school of "psychological psychiatry" which included Reil and Neumann. His basic thesis was that abnormal psychological facts should not be defined from hypothetical constructs but should be observed and diagnosed as psychological phenomena. He rejected the *Nervensaft* and the other physiological theories of the Eighteenth Century. As his years of theological study show, Heinroth was a highly religious man, and his religious faith had its effect on his attempts to make a strictly scientific approach to psychological facts. From his combination of interests grew his belief that participation in a sound religious life is important in preventing mental abnormality and in helping the mentally diseased. However, as will become clear in the next chapter, he separated medical psychology altogether from clerical counsel. This position has not been understood, but has been the major target of his critics.

Heinroth became the chief object of attack by the school of somatic psychiatry. Its followers maintained that there was nothing in the psyche or mind of a healthy or mentally diseased individual which did not result from physical pathology of the brain or the nervous system. Friedreich, whose brilliant pen was the mainstay of the somatists, made Heinroth the butt of his sarcastic polemic. As has already been pointed out, his history of psychopathology was a turncoat version of Heinroth's own history. He denounced

Heinroth to such a degree that hardly more than his name appears in the history of psychiatry. This has been due to the great influence of Friedreich's book.

Nevertheless, Heinroth is one of the most important forerunners of modern psychiatry. In many respects it is therefore worth our while to rediscover his work—not out of sentimental regard for the past, but because he expressed thoughts and presented points of view worth reconsideration, provided one takes the fact into account that he lived before either the exact science of physiology of the nervous system or the science of modern psychology was formulated.

There is scarcely a psychiatrist prior to 1900 who measures up to his importance. In his *Disturbances of the Mind* there is an introductory chapter on basic concepts *(Vorbegriffe)* which contains several paragraphs dealing with the task of the psychiatrist. The clarity of his thought makes valuable reading material for any modern psychiatric thinker. For this reason the writer has attempted its translation. In doing so he has had to interpret and modernize Heinroth's language, which most readers accustomed to today's scientific terminology would not find easy to understand. For instance, the term *psychische Doktor* has been translated as "psychiatrist." At one point, a line in which Heinroth identified himself with the Protestant theology of his time is omitted. It was felt that this was necessary to avoid a misconception which has become traditional because of a succeeding general attack upon Heinroth's views.

His opponents claimed that he believed all mental illness to be the result of sin committed by the diseased person. The passage translated here will thoroughly dispel this accusation. Heinroth's comments here can easily be applied in their original form to pluralistic religious thinking or to agnosticism in our own time. In many places in the translation Heinroth's long sentences have been broken up in order to present his thoughts in readable English. Heinroth wrote as follows.

> Assuming that it is possible to cure mental disturbances completely or at least in part, the following question arises: Since it is a human state of health which must be reinstated, and since abnormal psychic

life has to be turned back to normality, is this a task for the physician, clergyman, philosopher or educator? Each of these professions seems justified in considering itself qualified to exercise some kind of corrective care over abnormal human mental states. It is necessary, therefore, to examine and decide which should be permitted to assume such a task by right of tradition or law, and which should be considered a branch of medical science and art.

Since we are dealing here with medical science and art, we should believe that no one other than a physician could assume the right to study and treat such disturbances of the mind. Indeed, physicians have exercised this right in their compendia as well as in monopolized practice. (Nonphysicians, however, have also written on abnormal mental states. It is well known how much nonphysicians have distinguished themselves, especially in England, by their excellent treatment of such conditions.)

In the way we have described abnormal states of mind in contradistinction to normal ones, based on exact observations of human nature, we have proved that we are dealing with phenomena which cannot be judged in the way physicians have become accustomed to evaluating all diseases. The physicians who are at home only with physical nature are not familiar with these phenomena. This observation concerns their understanding as well as their treatment of this sphere of the mental (or psychic) life. Medical writings in general prove to be completely uninformed about this field. In addition, the point of view and the techniques our medical schools instruct and prescribe for the sickbed are completely different and are separate from those which are methodologically demanded and presented in this textbook. Those doctors, therefore, who as students being initiated into medical science have made this disturbance of physical existence their only concern are not fit for the psychological task.

The clergyman, whom we must acknowledge as an influencer of the human soul, is equally unfit for the work considered here because of his point of view, education and the scope of his work. His field of activity is the moral nature of man—so long as it exists. This does not hold in cases where it has perished or disappeared for a time. The clergy's concern is therefore in a completely different direction than that of the psychiatrists. The philosophers (or more specifically, the psychologists) have indeed ventured, even if primarily theoretically, into the field of the disturbed psychic life. They should become what up to now they have not been—students or faithful observers of nature—if they wish to achieve something worthwhile concerning the theory of psychic disturbances. In actual fact, this has not yet happened, as we shall point out later. So far as the practical aspects are concerned, one can expect nothing, since they are accustomed only to working at their desks. Such practical action is the purpose of the science of medical psychology, which should teach the art of restoring the disturbed psychic life to normality.

Far more related is this science and art with that of the educator. Even physicians are of the opinion that the cure of psychic disturbances require something like a reeducation. However, the educators have not as yet invented this science and art of reeducation, even if it can be found elsewhere. The eductor, like the clergyman, can only educate and train the self-directing powers in man, and not re-create them when they can no longer function or when they have gone out of existence. In addition, the scope of the educator's activity is like that of the clergyman, of such size and demanding so much strength that it would not be just to heap a new burden upon the educators even if they felt they had the ability to carry it.

The abilities that are necessary have a character—at least in part—that neither the educator nor the psychologist nor the clergyman could possess. In the first place, the psychiatrist must be a physician in the real sense of the word. He must be educated in a medical school and trained as a practising physician, since psychic disturbances are very frequently tied to physical sickness. The former are frequently caused, supported and modified by the latter, and in many cases, psychic disturbances cannot be influenced except through physical medicine. This makes it imperative that psychiatrists come from the ranks of physicians. We say specifically that they must come out of these ranks because psychiatrists should not remain in ranks occupied quite enough by their own physical tasks. The field of psychological medicine is so wide that it absorbs all the strength of a very active man. Furthermore, the psychiatrist needs his own education and outlook, which differentiate him considerably from any physician's work.

Anyone who wants to become a psychiatrist must in the very real sense go into the schools of the psychologist, the clergyman and the educator. He must develop the talent of psychological observation. He must learn to take into account the religious point of view. He must try to live the life of a priest or of a person guided in his living by religious inspiration. That is, it must be a life lived by reason, as laid down in the religious documents, which means a life in the light of the spirit of truth in which all is united. Finally, he must train himself in the technique of the educator and assimilate it into his own field. In the last analysis, however, he must receive training in the use of reason in the special form corresponding to the task of the psychiatrist, since—equally—neither real psychology nor the real art of education is thinkable when it is not guided by the eye of reason. Only fully developed reason can understand psychological disturbances in all their forms, and only reason can cure them if they are to be cured at all.

Chapter 16

HOW HEINROTH DIVIDED THE TASKS OF THE CLERGYMAN AND THE PSYCHIATRIST

A S a young scholar, Heinroth was requested by the publisher of Danz's *Medical Symptomatology (Allgemeine Medizinische Zeichenlehre)* to prepare a new edition, which came out in 1812. The original book contained very little relating to psychiatry, so Heinroth decided to include at the end a 110-page section on psychopathology *(Psychische Semiotik)*. This completely unknown study, unnoticed even by his biographers, proves to be the first dynamic psychiatry ever attempted.

His concern for clarifying in his mind the mutual roles of psychiatry and theology, first manifested in his theological studies, here finds full expression. He begins his treatise by an attempt to establish a clear and definite boundary between the two fields, a boundary which today is not only still unclear, but whose lack of clarity is the underlying cause for a disagreeable and seemingly unending struggle.

To Heinroth's way of thinking this problem was not too difficult to solve, and if we today are able to follow his concept of psychology and appropriate it for ourselves, the task ahead of us will be made easy. Unfortunately, however, Heinroth's thought is strongly influenced by German objective idealism and will appeal to only a few of the present-day workers in the field. Yet his technique for solving the problem is so amazing that even an opponent of his basic psychological point of view should enjoy the brilliancy of his presentation. The reasoned development of his argument may induce reflection and offer seeds for constructive thinking for many who seek to unravel this question. For others, his presentation may seem repetitious, but as one becomes familiar with the precision of his mind it will be realized that he has thought this problem through from all directions. To follow his candid treatment of such a basic problem we offer here the first chapter of his treatise in a translation which tries to keep as close as possible to the original manner of expression.

We do not need any excuse for the purpose of the diagnosis of psychic diseases to start with a consideration of psychic health, because it seems to be generally understood that one must be familiar with the very nature of an object if one wants to determine its special reactions and the conditions which could disrupt or even destroy it. Only if one knows the character of health can one determine the nature of sickness. When the medical doctor tries to determine what psychic health is he is apt to have a collision which he can avoid only if he strictly observes the boundaries of his field of science. Since that which we must consider the basis of all psychic life, *Freedom,* is an object of metaphysical and moral philosophy, the searching medical doctor could easily be misguided and in his activity trespass into these foreign regions in order to explore and determine completely the very nature of psychic health. However, this should not be permitted to the medical doctor, whose field is that of the phenomena of nature, lest the scientific order and the division of practical activity be badly disturbed.

But how can the medical doctor avoid becoming entangled and losing himself in the field attributed to the metaphysician or the moral philosopher or even the clergyman? He must strictly separate the two sides of psychic life. He must leave its moral sphere to those workers who deal with the soul insofar as its health is a degree of ethical quality and for whom only moral failures are psychic illnesses. He must also strictly adhere to the natural aspect of the psychic nature of man, the integrity of which means psychic health, since integrity of the organic nature is identical with the concept of health. As a moral entity the psyche is outside, as a natural entity it is within the medical doctor's sphere of work. This, however, does not mean that we deny to the psyche, if it is viewed as a natural entity, the ability of reason and freedom. Both belong to the very disposition of man's nature. But the *application* of this freedom in the function of reason, this special aptitude of man, is where we separate the moral capacity from the natural being of man, and it is in this alone that we see the task of the medical doctor. The medical doctor in no way oversteps his task if he tries to regain for a person *who has lost* the ability for proper reasoning and for freedom, these basic conditions of human existence. Only a man reequipped with reason and freedom by the medical doctor's assistance can be made an object for training in the realm of reason. Where such training starts is the boundary for the scientific and practical activity of the medical doctor. With this I have pointed out for the medical doctor and the moral educator the realm for their activity, and I hope I have eliminated some of the border clashes between them.

However, let us pursue in more detail the definition of the concept of psychic health. I hope many may understand by now that this concept means something quite different to the natural philosopher than to the theologian. But up to now we have only defined the meaning of the medical concept. Integrity of the natural psychic disposition, we said, constitutes psychic health, which is the objective of the medical doctor. What this natural disposition consists of is generally known. Who does not know that every human being who does not deviate from the normal disposition has a desiring heart, a cognitive mind which—if completely developed—documents itself as reason, and finally a will, the basis of which is freedom, which means self-determination. These are our psychic capabilities collected in one consciousness or in the personality with an "I" *(Ich)* as the focal point. It is equally not difficult to show of what this integrity of the natural disposition of man consists since our self-observation, the feeling and the consciousness of ourselves, offers us ample material for doing so.

We are all born with a susceptibility for joy and pain, with a heart capable of love and pain. In anyone for whom this susceptibility is vitally real there abides a natural integrity of the soul. We are, from our present viewpoint, not concerned with the actual culture of the soul. This is the domain of the educator of the psyche, for whom the soul is only healthy if it is pure, refined from low desires and free from egotism. The medical doctor's problem is only whether the psychic energy is there and not whether it is educated. Only if it should be strained by disease or exhausted by overtension or heavy pressure is it apt to be placed under medical care, and it may be released from this again as soon as it has regained its natural strength. When the demented has rediscovered himself and the melancholic has found the world again through medical aid, both are sane again from the point of view of the medical doctor, because they have recovered the natural capabilities of man. Meanwhile, in the eyes of the moral educator, because of the lack of moral culture, they still have to be considered neglected and sick beings in need of long education and purification until they can also be considered psychologically recovered from his viewpoint. In this way, the doctor of medicine always works into the hands of the moral educator, and his task is completed where the task of the other starts.

As it is with the emotions, so it is with the other psychic capacities of man. The human mind possesses natural integrity or it is psychologically sane from the point of view of the medical doctor if it is able to perceive and judge. Whether it is, in addition to this, subjected to illusions and errors due to overhaste in judgment or the lack of training is not the business of the medical doctor who should only be concerned with the satisfactory condition of the amount of psychic energy. However, if a person's abilities of perception and judgment have dangerously diminished or are completely disintegrated, it will be the doctor's task to take care of him until his natural energy of thinking is restored. But the medical task goes only to this point. The same is valid for the will. A man who can direct himself, who can make decisions and execute them, independent of the fact that it is in complete accord with reason or not, must from the point of view of the medical doctor be considered healthy. (Nevertheless, such a person may be considered sick from the other point of view.) As emphasized above, will is nothing more than the capacity for self-determination. But if a person has lost this capacity, if he is either swept away by uncontrollable instincts or is driven by outside provocations, unable to resist blind actions, then his will is no longer to be considered healthy from the aspect of the medical doctor. His business is now to restrain such uncontrolled actions—which because of this character can no longer be considered directed by the will—or to awaken new energy or to strengthen the weakened energy unable to resist. The first is the case of the restless insane, the second of the introvert or the imbecile. But the task of the medical doctor does not go further than this revitalization of the source of independence of the will.

Meanwhile the training of the will to the supervision of reason is the task of the moral educator. With emotions, mind and will knitted together into one consciousness and one "I," the psychic nature is complete. And the sensitivity of the emotions, a vivid mind and an energetic will, these are the three components of psychic health which the medical doctor can bestow on them. The character of this psychic health is the free relationship of these psychic forces among themselves in a lively consciousness or, in other words, freedom of the entire psychic life with its inner independence, which means its capacity for self-determination.

However, the moral educator is not yet satisfied with this. He wishes the natural, free psychic life refined to a morally free condition, he wants the emotions religiously tuned, the mind devoted to truth, free from illusions, confusion and error, and the will directed only toward the good and venerable, rejecting all bad and evil impulses. Only after man achieves such a state is he psychically sane for the moral educator. In all other states he is not sane, because any uncultivated state is sickness to him. If our energies do not have the right direction, they will cause repercussions which must unbalance the true psychic life, the life guided by spiritual impulses, and such disturbance must lead to destruction.

This entire moral point of view with all its unique qualities must be strange to the medical doctor. And if the moral educator says only a person whose emotions, thoughts and actions correspond completely with the laws of reason is psychically sound, in other words only the completely moral and godly man, then the medical man replies that for him psychic health exists in everyone in whom the needed psychic forces are properly developed and in whom free and self-determined use is not disturbed for a long duration. Disturbances for longer durations caused by passing states of sickness like typhoid fever, drunkenness and intoxication do not belong to this kind because they are only temporary interruptions of man's freedom.

Chapter 17

BENJAMIN RUSH:
AMERICAN PSYCHIATRIC AMBASSADOR
TO EUROPE

IN the whole history of medical psychology only Paracelsus and Sigmund Freud have been as overwhelmed by controversial judgment as has the Philadelphia psychiatrist Benjamin Rush. In the public opinion Rush is the great humanitarian representing, in the care of the mentally ill, the spirit of Quakerism, freeing the imprisoned insane from the chains and the cruelty of his time. Rush, however, was not a Quaker at all. He belonged during his life to a Presbyterian and then to a Unitarian church. And he apparently had little sympathy with what he himself might have called Quaker sentimentalism.

There is a wide range of judgments on Benjamin Rush in the literature. There are unjustified praises and equally unjustified condemnations. We find him called the "Father of American Psychiatry," and we find him compared with Hippocrates, Sydenham and Fothergill. Some have accused him of plagiarism, and there are violent condemnations especially from his immediate medical and professional environment. What astonishes the historian is how much his writings were read and discussed by the leading medical and psychiatric writers of the Old World during the entire century at the beginning of which Rush lived. And here again we find the same controversial opinions of overestimation and ridiculing condemnation. On the whole we must admit that the negative far surpasses the positive evaluation.

There have been two things in particular for which Rush gained attention on the other side of the Atlantic and for which he was quoted and discussed. There was first his application of blood-letting, which was only twenty-five years later very seriously condemned even in the United States as a complete misconception and an actually dangerous procedure. His conception was that nervous energy was ferried through the body by the blood, and therefore, upset and raging forms of insanity should be cured by bleeding patients to the stage of weakness and even exhaustion.

His second major contribution, which one may say actually reaped for him a certain negative fame, was the Rush Restraining Chair. Many contemporary and later authors drew and reproduced pictures of this chair following Rush's verbal description. In a publication of the Pennsylvania Hospital of Philadelphia which apparently had been planned to become a periodical but was issued only once, we unearthed the original drawing by Rush of his "gyrator" or "tranquilizer," which appears to us today as painful a restrainer as a chair can possibly be. The body was strapped back into this chair very similar to an armchair and the hands were strapped to the arms of the chair. The feet were in a wooden log such as we know from Seventeenth Century logging punishment. The head was enclosed in a wooden helmetlike box with a small aperture in front allowing vision only straight ahead. This instrument was certainly not used to appease a person, especially not a person ridden by fear. Although it seems to have been used under Rush's authority at Philadelphia's Pennsylvania Hospital, it has usually been reported as a paradox, being an even more severe restrainer than the so-called Cox chair, but it actually took thirty years before it was officially condemned and discarded by a meeting of hospital superintendents of the Eastern American states. We know that similar tools used in the European institutions had begun to be ruled out already in the second decade of the century.

Nathan G. Goodman has written the most worthwhile book on Benjamin Rush. He subtitled the volume "Physician and Citizen." This seems to be more appropriate than to make of Rush the first great American psychiatrist and savior of the insane. Indeed, in this book Rush appears more as what seems to have been himself, namely a politically and socially active physician of unusual personal intensity. His work extended from an active part in the political formation of these United States and welfare organizations in his hometown to formation of a medical school and the proper installation of hospital care. He was equally active in fighting virus epidemics and keeping the lunatics protected from cold and providing them with proper bathing facilities.

There was nothing special in the latter. As Rush fought for the Declaration of Independence he fought for what he felt was the decent and right kind of care for the mentally deranged in the framework of a general hospital. If one compared Rush's reformatory demands with those of the great European vanguards, especially Pinel and Reil, one could not say that the American had added anything to what they demanded at the same time. If one reads the history right, one can see more clearly, in a quotation of Rush, a note not openly expressed: "See, even in America a doctor demands these improvements."

It had been Benjamin Franklin's appearances in France that had set the New World in a better light than it had before. This charming and outgoing publicist had made Europe view with respect what these runaways and expulsees had created as a new society. There was now even a medical man who started to write substantial books and to make somewhat original proposals.

Otto Beyerholm, the Dane, wrote one of the most thoughtful books on the history of psychiatry (*Psykiatriens Historie,* Copenhagen, 1937). He tried to answer the question of why we find Rush so frequently quoted in European psychiatry by pointing out that it was Rush's youthful and practical realism which appealed to the Old World. Even where Rush was falling in step with the general humanitarians of those days, he tried to remain a practical physician. This made him especially sympathetic to the generation which, under the trademark of somatism, tried to inaugurate a practical institutionalism. Rush, writes Dr. Beyerholm, was most typical for this pattern of the theoretical transition from sentimenal Psychism of the type of Heinroth and Reil to the somatic physiologist of the Friedreich school. It was this that made the Europeans of those days take note of this "New Worlder." Daniel Hack Tuke, the literary man among Nineteenth Century psychiatrists, singled Rush out as the psychiatrist of facts and common sense. This is indeed a more valid and valuable evaluation than those who put him into the shadow of a Hippocrates. We must learn to see that in certain fields of science progress is not only a matter of a big buildup of ideas. It is also a matter of the balancing and solidifying influence of practical realizations. This is what has engraved Benjamin Rush's name into the history of the science of the mentally ill.

Chapter 18

A PRE-FREUDIAN COMPLEX THEORY

NOT only devoted believers in Freud but also some who have been critical of him consider that one of his major contributions to psychiatry has been his complex theory. C. G. Jung, writing in 1934, said, "Without the existence of the complexes the unconscious would be nothing but the residue of obscure representations. Through his investigations of these dark areas Freud became the discoverer of the psychological unconscious."

Was Freud really the first to formulate the complex theory? The historian of the human mind will be rewarded again and again by astonishing revelations in regard to important theoretical concepts and so-called major discoveries.

There is to be found an actual statement of a theory of suppression, which cannot but be considered a nuclear form of Freud's theory, as early as 1824. I refer to the book of F. E. Beneke which we have considered in another chapter, *Contribution to a Purely Psychological Study of Mental Disease*. I present here an excerpt from Beneke's book. I have translated it from a difficult Hegelian German into the modern form of expression of psychological facts. The quotation is from a long chapter dealing with what we might call the psychopathology of memory in which Beneke used case histories from the *Moritz Magazine* as illustrations.

> These puzzling observations can easily be understood with the aid of our own theory of the origin [dynamic] of psychic activity. For easy application we have formulated the theory as follows: An individual psychic activity [experience] is always caused or induced by another one. This law, of course, also has validity in regard to the facts of inability to remember discussed here. However, such a relationship also occurs in more complicated connections [circumstances]. One psychic activity has not only formed a relationship with another single activity; each has formed a relationship to a multitude of other psychic factors. Therefore one activity can awaken into consciousness the entire psyche, or at least a larger complex of factors to which it has formed an affinity in the past. However, one such activity or fact can have

different kinds of relationships to other different facts. Meanwhile it may have formed a positive relationship to one, and can therefore easily call it back into consciousness; it may have formed a negative [contradictory] relationship to another fact which it opposes in becoming easily conscious. All depends on the character of the relationship.

This explains why a certain activity may have quite different results in the way it becomes conscious, depending on the kind of relationship it has formed, and may lead us to an understanding of why there are difficulties in awakening certain earlier experiences into consciousness. We also must always count on the fact that there are experiences which are little conscious, and that these play a withholding role. One of these little-conscious factors alone may be ineffective. But there may be a number of such negative little-conscious factors which together may develop a great power over the psyche. For purposes of comparison, we might bear in mind how greatly physical illness can incapacitate our mental faculties. It might also happen that two little-conscious factors have a contradictory negative effect upon one another, making one or both incapable of becoming conscious.

There can be no doubt that we are dealing here with an early detailed concept of the subconscious and suppression. It is doubtful that Sigmund Freud ever read or knew of Beneke's book, since Beneke has been up to now completely forgotten.

Chapter 19

F. E. BENEKE'S FIRST PHENOMENOLOGICAL PSYCHIATRY

IN 1820, the year in which Schopenhauer made his unsuccessful attempt to lecture at the University of Berlin, another twenty-two-year-old youth established himself as *Privat-Dozent* in philosophy and psychology at the same university. The young man was Friedrich Eduard Beneke. He was born the son of a Prussian subaltern administrator. His mother was the sister of the famous popular educational writer and magazine editor, Wilmsen. Young Beneke had been a prodigy at school. At the age of eighteen he started his studies in theology, which he completed in 1820 under Schleiermacher in Berlin. During his years of training as a clergyman he had called attention to himself through several brilliant essays and papers on philosophical problems which awakened in him the desire to become a teacher in this field.

In contrast to Schopenhauer, Beneke's success was amazing. At his lectures the auditorium was filled, while across the hall G. W. Hegel, the head of the department and considered the greatest philosopher of his time, attracted only a handful of students. We are told that it was the *Herr Geheimrat's* justifiable jealousy that induced the Prussian government to cancel Beneke's lecture permit after two years. It was said that Beneke's book, *Fundamentals of a Physical Concept of Morals (Grundlegung der Physik der Sitten)*, published in 1822, was too far outside the accepted concepts, which of course were those of Hegel. Beneke was unable to obtain another academic assignment at any Prussian institution or in any of the neighboring German states under Prussian influence. He finally gained admission again as a *Privat-Dozent* at the Thuringian University of Göttingen.

In 1832, five months after Hegel's death, he was recalled to Berlin, where he was reinstalled, this time as an associate professor. Although rejected and laughed at by the representatives of the Hegelian school, who continued to hold the limelight at the academic center of Berlin, he developed a solid academic career. In spite of a considerable student following, he lived a withdrawn and lonely life. He had written twenty-five major books in the fields of philosophy, normal and abnormal psychology, ethics and education before he died in 1854 by drowning in a Berlin canal. It is still not clear which of the various opinions as to the cause of Beneke's death is correct—whether the embittered and lonely man had committed suicide, been murdered or had drowned by accident as the result of a fainting spell caused by the chronic liver ailment from which he suffered.

Beneke took a most singular position in the mental sciences of his time, presenting a point of view which appears to us extremely modern. He intensely opposed the deductive idealism of the Kantian, and even more, the Hegelian type. Against Kant's theory of ethics expounded in the famous *Fundamentals for a Metaphysic of Morals (Grundlegung zur Metaphysik der Sitten)*, he wrote his *Fundamentals for a Physical Concept of Morals (Grundlegung zur Physik der Sitten)*. He rejected the *a priori* as well as any metaphysical source of human ethics. To him, man was a part of nature, and ethics was therefore a compound of natural physical laws. In this he was close to the scientific view of Goethe, who similarly saw man as a being inside nature and acting according to the laws of nature. But Beneke would have rejected Goethe's idealistic concept of entelechy, which was almost identical with Hegel's basic concept of "idea." It is therefore not surprising that he was rejected by the philosophical school of the University of Berlin, which considered itself the center of Hegelianism.

On the other hand, Beneke did not subscribe to the physical materialism of the somatic school led by Friedreich. Friedreich maintained that psychic or mental experiences had no autonomous reality and were nothing but utterances of the bodily functioning of the nerves. Beneke's empiricism claimed reality for the psychic phenomena, which he believed should be studied independently as pure psychic factors by a kind of objective introspection. Several of his titles reveal this remarkable mode of thought.

In 1820 he wrote *Empiricism as the Basis of All Knowledge,* in which it is clear that empiricism meant for him *phenomenological perception.* In 1826 he published *Relationship Between Body and Psyche.* This was followed in 1832 by *Textbook of Psychology as a Natural Science.* Later he used the term "psychological pragmatism," but in a quite different sense from the concept of historical pragmatism as we use it. Beneke's psychological pragmatism was based strictly on experience and was, in our sense, a phenomenological method.

It was actually at the start of his career and during the most trying years of his struggle for academic acknowledgment that Beneke wrote one of his most important works, the one which primarily interests us here—*Contributions to a Purely Psychological Study of Mental Illness (Beitraege zu einer rein seelenwissenschaftlichen Bearbeitung der Seelenkrankheiten).* This work appeared in 1824; it attempts to present a "phenomenology of psychopathology." Little as we know about Beneke's private life and how he earned his living during his long years of unpaid academic teaching, we know even less about how and where he collected the medical and psychiatric knowledge upon which his book is based. He emphasized in the introduction his lack of knowledge of physical medicine, but the contents of the 530-page volume bear witness to the fact that he must have studied medicine and psychiatry extensively and must have had practical experience in the diagnosis and treatment of the insane. Also, his quotations from the pertinent literature show that he had read all the major psychiatric writers of his time. He quotes from Boerhaave, Stahl, Haslam, Herz, Horn, Hoffbauer, Neumann, Pinel and Heinroth.

However, it was neither out of the medical nor the psychiatric tradition nor from contemporary speculations that Beneke's concept grew. It grew from his psychological background. Because he had to fight for an opening in a field solidly held by concepts deriving from the Kantian and Hegelian idealistic philosophy, he had to begin his book with an argument. This argument he enunciated in a letter addressed to the philosopher-psychologist J. Fr. Herbart, which serves as the introduction to the book. Herbart, who was holding Kant's chair at the University of Königsberg, had become the exponent of metaphysical *"a priorism,"* and had attempted to widen Kantian categories into a more specific system of scientific principles.

Herbart was more of a psychological empiricist than even Kant had been. It was on precisely this point that Beneke focused his attack. From Beneke's psychological point of view, metaphysical principles were nothing more or less than simple elementary psychological experiences. So-called metaphysical principles, and even our thinking about them, are secondary to phenomenological psychological experience. They are not outside but inside its frame; they are abstractions of it. Whatever one may call them, metaphysical principles are nothing else than perceptions, and as such, psychological phenomena. Proper science, therefore, cannot be based upon the separation of metaphysical principles and other factors of experience, but must consist in the establishment and clear description of phenomenological differences and organization of the manifold empirical facts. As regards psychology, for example, a basic scientific task would be a descriptive establishment of the human psyche as reasonable, compared with the animal psyche as unreasonable.

In this discussion of Herbart's concepts, Beneke maintained that the quantitative mathematical concepts which Herbart wanted applied as basic psychological measurements were unsatisfactory as a means of establishing a specific science of psychological reality. The principles of a real psychological science must be taken from psychology itself in a manner we would today call autonomous. Beneke called his concept "radical empiricism" and maintained correctly that it had not previously been formulated by anyone.

In applying this phenomenological empiricism to the field of abnormalities of the psychic life, that is to the various forms of insanity, Beneke was greatly limited by the fact that mental illness had in his time been neither properly accounted for nor clearly described. Beneke was aware of these limitations and because of them felt himself restrained in developing a more detailed psychopathology.

Although Beneke worked during a period in the history of psychiatry which was under the sign of psychologism (the period of Reil, Heinroth, and Neumann, whose aim was the study of abnormal states of the mind independent of the body) he did not blindly follow this path. Body as such and bodily involvement in mental ailments were very real to him. He denied neither somatopsychological nor psychosomatic realities, but he felt it important for obvious reasons to attempt to develop a solid foundation for a purely psychological psychopathology, something that none of the representatives of psychological schools had attempted.

Because of the status of psychiatry at the time, Beneke felt it best not to start his task by describing individual somatic pictures, but rather to take the normal psyche as his basis and to describe pathologies as deviations from it. In our century, this scientific point of view, modified of course by changes in general scientific concepts and medical thinking, has been revived by C. G. Jung.

It was to be expected that Beneke would start his book by presenting his basic concepts of the normal and a justification of his concept of the phenomenological aspect. The source—so he begins —of all our experience is our perceptions. A differentiation is usually made between perceptions from the outer world and those from the inner world. We know that our perceptions from the outer world do not give us a full and complete insight into the reality of the outer world. This is true even of our own bodies, but if we look at our inner experience, we find that our perceptions about previous inner experiences and our thinking about them or about other previous thoughts are the same. It is here that we touch reality. It is here that we have the self-assertion of reality.

This area of self-experience we call consciousness. In this area there is no material difference between perceptions from the outer world and perceptions from the inner world. In the common experience, we identify our perceptions of the reality with reality itself. This becomes a matter of major importance in relationship to our experience of our own bodies. We believe the hunger we experience is real and not merely perceived. However, we know that we experience the real truth and security only when we bring the outer perception into accordance with those inner perceptions which we call our thoughts. This we designate as recognition, and the organization of recognized facts we designate as knowledge. Although there is no difference, basically, between our perceptions and our faculty of thinking as factors of our consciousness, there are degrees of weakness and strength in the quality they have as such factors. We may say that our thinking has greater power of consciousness than does the perception of a bird that passes quickly in flight outside our window. On the role that a normal or deviant experience has as an individual element of our consciousness, Beneke bases his psychological pathology.

One aspect discussed in the introductory pages that Beneke considers of the utmost importance for his phenomenological psychopathology must be mentioned here. This is the question of how the mind of a normal observer can experience, judge and understand "abnormal" experiences without actually experiencing such states of mind. It would appear that we would ourselves have to be hysterics or imbeciles in order to learn something real, from a phenomenological approach, of such a state of mind. Otherwise, it seems, we would be unable to gain the proper experience. Beneke sees an acceptable approach to what he calls intermediary forms of experience. We are all familiar with and able to reconstruct states of inner indisposition which are not actual mental abnormalities but are preliminary forms of them. Mental illnesses are more developed forms of such indispositions. Through our experience of these indispositions we can gain understanding of the experiences of the insane. The use of experiences of indisposition as a basis for understanding mental illness has importance also in the understanding of therapeutic processes and provides an approach to "dietetic," the prevention of the growth of mental illness.

As the first element of psychopathology Beneke points out abnormal forms of sense perception *(Sinneswahrnehmung)* which appear to occur in all mental illness. For instance, imbeciles and psychologically depressed individuals seem not to be able to see, though their eyes are open, remain unimpressed by the loudest noises, and lack the ability of attention. Different senses have different grades of perceptivity. Many animals—dogs, for instance —have a more developed sense of smell than of sight, while in man the visual sense is best developed.

Beneke attributes the lack of proper sense perception (when not due to physical disability) to lack of mental power *(Mangel an geistiger Kraft)*. Imbeciles are not only deficient in perceptivity

(Empfängnisfähigkeit), but also in apprehension, in the ability to reproduce their perceptions and even more in the ability to remember. In addition, a full-fledged imbecile is unable to comprehend what he may, to a limited degree, perceive. In this respect he resembles an animal; but a normal animal has by nature a well-functioning sense perception.

To compare imbecility *(Blödsinn)* with stupidity *(Dummheit)*, which others had done only in terms of degrees of difference, Beneke introduces a new aspect of the basic theory of this phenomenological psychopathology. As proof of the validity of his theory, he points to the nearsighted and the hard of hearing, who are not at all stupid or imbecilic. He attributes imbecility to a lack of mental power and stupidity to a lack of vitality *(Mangel an Lebendigkeit)*. The stupid suffer from a lack of alertness of perception and comprehension.

Imbecility in humans is to be found in varying degrees. In its lowest form it is not even up to the ability of the higher animals. Its occurrence is almost always congenital, and it must be considered incurable. There are certain forms of imbecility, however, which are neither hereditary nor constitutional, but seem to have functional causes. Certain deeply affective and prolonged circumstances may cause a kind of laming or disfunctioning of the major part of a person's capabilities and result in a form of imbecility. In all such cases there is to be noted a considerable slowing down of mental functions.

Another phenomenological element to be considered is *experience in time*. The mental life of humans occurs in a process in time which has a dual aspect. Function can be too slow or it can be too rapid. As the latter functions, we know not only of a "flight of ideas" as it appears in the world of thinking, but also of a too-rapid perceptivity. Such a deviation in regard to the will appears in the furor or even delirium of rage that we find among those insane we call restless. In addition to these basic patterns, pathological rapidity in psychic life may manifest itself in other abnormal forms. It may weaken or incapacitate certain psychic experiences and place others in a wrong light. It may lead to overlooking perceptions in favor of imaginings *(Vorstellungen)*, so that the latter are taken as real and as actual perceptions from the outer world. This can lead to exhaustion and the unhealthy expenditure of strength, which leads in turn to more serious weakness. In many cases this psychic rapidity may appear combined with what Beneke designates as *psychic overheating (Erhitzung*—a term to be understood in a symbolic way, as we speak of a heated discussion). In following up these various forms of time pathology, Beneke comes to one which was a focus of study for Sigmund Freud, the phenomenon of certain real and important psychic experiences being suppressed by others. To restore apprehension of the truth and normal psychic life, these suppressed experiences must by therapeutic measures be reestablished in their appropriate role.

The next element of our psychic experience to be studied, because it is a basic factor in pathology, is what Beneke calls *psychic space (psychische Raum)*. As Beneke used the term, space has a substantive character aside from its quantitative one. For this reason it might be more realistic to translate the word *Raum* as *volume*. The basis of our psychic volume is memory, upon which all our experiences are imprinted. Although the same experience may be imprinted on a memory many times, it remains an element of the same volume in our consciousness. Memory grows in two ways: by the addition of new experiences to existing ones, and by the recollection of earlier experiences, the memory of which has faded from lack of interest in them. On these two elements is based what might be called the strength of consciousness. An important question here is where the psychic energy *(Bewusstsinns-Stärke)* comes from that enables us to recall these elements of memory. Beneke sees this energy stored in the affinity which one element of our consciousness has for any other. If two elements struggle for place in our consciousness, that one will win which has the greater volume. This part of the experience of our consciousness is increased by our being consciously exposed to new experiences which, because of our power of perception, we have a great desire to assimilate. This desire may become so strong that it involves the major part of the volume of the psyche. In most individuals, however, the intercourse with memory takes up the major part of the volume. Perception and memory together comprise the total of man's inner life.

There is a second element which Beneke considers basic to his psychopathology. He calls it overstimulation *(Überreizung)* or overheating of the psyche. We must, however, separate the disposition of the psyche which is to be stimulated and the factor of stimulation itself. Here Beneke considers it necessary to separate (1) a too-weak stimulation, (2) stimulation just right for the disposition of the psyche to produce the appropriate effect and (3) stimulation which is too strong (overstimulation). In regard to the latter, we must again apply the separation used before: between the factor of mental power *(geistige Kraft)* and vitality *(Lebenskraft)*. Overstimulation of mental power creates tension, and overstimulation of vitality creates overheating, or what we would today call excitement. Considered as a process, that is, as an occurrence in time, tension is slow, while excitement is rapid. Tension and excitement in our perspective experience are not necessarily of pathological character, but they provide the dynamics out of which much of the psychopathology arises. To simple stimulation there must be added the factor of specific disposition. The kind of disposition which most frequently leads to psychopathology is weakness. Finally, overstimulation tending to pathology is not always and only due to negative and unfortunate experiences. An excess of excitement caused by an excess of happy events may also lead to pathology.

Lack of psychic volume and inadequate stimulation can equally become sources of mental illness. The result of a serious lack of volume is, as we have seen above, imbecility. The most serious lack of ability to respond to stimulation we know as melancholia. From the combination of strength and weakness of mental power and vitality on the one hand and volume and stimulation on the other result four basic types of mental illness. The first three are imbecility, melancholia and mania (which had been known to earlier medical psychology as basic types). To these three, Beneke adds a fourth type: a combination of mania and melancholia. A description of these four psychopathological somatic types comprises the main content of Beneke's book.

The first type results from an excessive psychic volume. In this case some psychic factor takes in too much of the psyche, disturbing or destroying what in a normal psyche represents the natural status. Such a disturbed psyche Beneke calls off-balance. As a characteristic example, he points to individuals whom we think of as possessed by a fixed idea. Here we see the definite preponderance of an imaginary element over the perceptions. The prepathological form in which the tendency to this type of pathology occurs, says Beneke, is the habit of riding hobbyhorses and the slight manias which are only too often present in all of us. Beneke sees the characteristic symptoms as slackening of perceptivity and of judgment, comprehension and motility. The really sick individual will be in a net of unrealities. In some, motility by itself may be functioning normally, but if one views motility when it is directed by a pathological imagination, one will find it also has pathological trends. The same is true of comprehension. Observing in this type those sidetracked psychic functions—which, because most of the psychic volume is occupied otherwise, are unable to function normally—we cannot but call them repressed or suppressed.

Such suppressions have repercussions throughout the general course of life. Because of them, some individuals lose even the ability to sleep. Such a factor overpowering the rest of the psyche need not always be composed of one and the same emotional element or of a single thought. It may also be what we might call a mental state, one of brooding induced by a boiling up and running over of an indefinite number of imaginings. This overpowering element can also be an entire paranoid system. It always, however, means the concentration of the mind on some specific contents. As regards the cause of such an unbalanced state, Beneke finds that it can result from negative experiences like fright and fear as well as from a succession of too-pleasant experiences.

Referring to his earlier differentiation between the strong and the weak mentality, Beneke believes that it is the weak mentality rather than the strong one that is apt to be dominated by a fixed idea. The extent to which such fixed ideas may take over the entire inner world of an individual is unlimited. Any kind of factor may become the motive. Beneke offers examples from the famous case collection known as the *Moritz Magazine*. Among his examples is the story of a young man who hysterically adopted an arm ailment of his mother, imposing it upon both his perfectly healthy arms. The cure effected by a doctor was what Janet later applied as hypnosis, namely to make the patient believe by an imaginary process that he had been cured.

In the section of his book dealing with this type of cure, Beneke comes near to what we know today as Freudian psychoanalysis. Basically, cure consists in weakening and limiting the major pathological portion of the fixed idea and replacing it with positive and healthy psychic volume. Occupational therapy, that is, getting the patient away from his fixed idea, is emphasized as one of the most helpful techniques.

Beneke emphasized a direct and indirect therapeutic approach. The direct approach, if it can be applied at all, is faster, though in most cases, Beneke believes, only a temporary cure can be effected, since such a paranoid condition tends to regress from time to time. Newness and attractiveness of therapeutic methods are most essential for success in drawing the patient away from his pathological tendencies.

The second mental abnormality Beneke describes is due to a too-small psychic space or volume. Lack of psychic volume is most common, in its pre-pathological form, among uneducated, primitive, or undeveloped individuals. In most cases, lack of psychic volume is due to low vitality. Lack of psychic or mental volume becomes pathological when it is due to lack of mental strength. In its most serious form it is what has previously been called imbecility. However, although lack of vitality may border on psychopathology, Beneke designated it earlier as stupidity.

In the course of the chapter under discussion here Beneke elaborates on the characteristics of imbecility, which had not been discussed before. In the most serious form of imbecility there occurs an impairment of the sense perceptions. The capacity for comprehension is of course also greatly impaired. The stupid individual is generally able to perceive normally, but comprehends only in limited and routinized patterns. Imbeciles have no judgment at all. Because of his lack of understanding, the imbecile is very distrustful, while the stupid person may even enjoy being teased, because he seeks social contacts and likes to laugh with others even if he does not understand what it is all about. Because of his lack of memory, the imbecile is restless and jumps from one thought and occupation to another, unable to hold on to anything or get mental satisfaction from it.

There are various degrees of strength and extent in imbecility. In some cases weakness may extend to the total existence; in others there may be good physical development but mental weakness. In some cases physical overdevelopment brings about mental weakness. In congenital imbecility we are dealing with a static condition which can hardly be improved. In noncongenital cases it is necessary to establish the cause of the condition, which in many cases may be false overstimulation. Prolonged false excitement and joy as well as fear and grief may be the cause. Another cause may be weakening due to an excess of physical activity or serious disease. If there is a complete lack of stimulation, the imbecility is called cretinism. Aging may also lead to forms of imbecility, which we call senility. Imbecility may be interconnected with other mental diseases such as melancholia and mania.

No mental ailment is more difficult to cure than imbecility. The primary treatment should be stimulation. It is most difficult to determine the proper dose of stimulation, which must be of a most individualized character, since overstimulation might weaken instead of strengthen. This is true not only for sense stimulation, such as of the eye or ear, but also for stimulation of physical development; for example, by gymnastic exercises or occupational therapy. It is true also in regard to feeding and medication. Limited doses may help; overdoses harm.

Beneke gives special consideration to pathological impairment of memory, which he considers a form of imbecility. Here he offers the most extraordinary preliminary presentation of what later came to be called the complex theory and was expounded by the Freudian school in connection with its repression and suppression concepts. Beneke's presentation is of course limited to a somewhat abstract sphere: certain contents of the mind can, momentarily, so greatly overshadow consciousness that they do not permit other material to appear which may be weaker or which has a negative or controversial relationship to those holding the consciousness under their domination. Since Beneke, as a phenomenologist, denies existence to anything in the sense of the present concept of the unconscious or subconscious, he designates such suppressed factors as of little or minimal consciousness *(Gering-bewusst)*. But he uses the term "becoming again conscious" *(Wieder-bewusstwerden)*. To this we shall return in the next chapter and offer Beneke's own formulation.

Because of this consequential thinking, Beneke includes in imbecility forms of mental weakness and abnormality which we today would hardly put in the same category, such as forgetting and sleep and dream pathology. Here we meet again the mental mechanism that permits certain elements to take up more volume than is justified. This causes other contents to lose out and forces upon us disturbances of the natural experience of nightly rest. Indeed, Beneke's concept of imbecility is most extraordinary when compared to present thinking in the field of psychopathology.

The longest chapter in Beneke's book is devoted to what he calls *abnormalities due to overstimulation*. On the whole Beneke attempts to deal here with what previous psychopathology called mania. Beginning again with a discussion of prepathological forms, he refers to what he had earlier described as deviant behavior in this sphere—excitement *(Erhitzung)*. The basis for the necessary differentiation between disease patterns is again the separation of mental powers and vitality and the different stimulants connected with them. Differentiation seems necessary to Beneke because the basic dynamics of stimulation, the tension resulting from an increase in activities, has a quite different effect on mental power than it has on vitality. Excitement and the resulting increase in vitality interfere with thinking and the formation of concepts. In states of high excitement even simple sense perception becomes impaired or totally extinguished, while on the other hand, increasing self-created fantasies and imaginings. Ethical feelings do not have sufficient time to be properly formed and mental development is driven to unhealthily rapid growth. A slight amount of overstimulation may have a good effect by increasing mental activity and stimulating correlation of thought, which can become the impulse to poetic fantasy and creativeness in every field including religious ecstasy.

However, where overstimulation is the cause of crossing the border into psychopathology, the result will be a flight of ideas and chaos of all psychic functions to the point of mad rage. Beneke analyzes most carefully the psychological process of crime due to states of rage. Most homicides, he maintains, result from rapid flight of imaginings which lead to nonconsciousness and end in mere muscle reaction. The satisfaction in such action is due more to release of tension that was present than to the actual shedding of blood. Frequently a major part of the motive seems to be the desire to overcome painful feelings.

This leads Beneke to the study of impulses, which are the driving forces behind man's will. Again he tries to get at the roots of the whole problem. He emphasizes the necessity of distinguishing between stimulants which are motivated perceptions, and drives which induce pleasure. Basically, he believes all human activity is spurred by drives, but activity becomes pathological when it is motivated only by perceptive impulses, so that we act without will, or more accurately, in the absence of conscious functioning of the will. Such actions also represent states of extreme weakness of mental power.

However carefully one observes the process of excitement, one can never establish that it reproduces itself. It always works in the direction of a specific stimulation *(Reiz)*. Increased excitement will create dizziness which, if more excitement is added, may lead to fainting. This is the specific development on the mental side. The influence of excitement upon our physical nature is quite different. Here the reaction to increase is slower and hardly ever leads to a fainting spell. Beneke affirms that all states of excitement start with an influence upon our physical nature in the form of sensation. For instance, even states of dizziness, delirium or rage start out with a feeling of being ill or a feeling of nervousness in the stomach. The physical symptoms may be worsened by weak physical conditioning, hard labor or undernourishment.

Beneke's acknowledgment of the impact of physical weakness goes much farther than one might expect from a phenomenologist. He stresses the important role of fever as a cause of deliric disease. Any fever, he points out, has some effect in the direction of overstimulation. There is also an acknowledgment of physical involvement in his discussion of seizures and cramps, which are muscular overstimulation in which both mental power and vitality are under the influence of the stimulation. Epilepsy also belongs in the general category of muscular overstimulation. Beneke on various occasions touches on problems of alcoholism, and in this section of his book we find an extensive discussion of *delirium tremens.*

A few concluding paragraphs deal with the problem of cure in cases of overstimulation and mania. Beneke especially emphasizes the pattern of repetition in this psychopathological condition as well as the great role that outside influences, like change of weather, the seasons and so forth, appear to play. In more serious cases there is a considerable tendency to develop melancholia and imbecility.

As regards therapy, Beneke joins with those who believe that these ailments are the most easily influenced by treatment. After enumerating physio- and chemotherapy (as these were customarily used in his day), he formulates his psychotherapy upon the basic thesis that pathological overstimulation is connected with a weakened constitution and momentary adverse conditions. The therapeutic approach is a double one. First, the stimulation must be reduced, while at the same time the weakened constitution must be strengthened. Beneke suggests that in certain cases it may actually be good to destroy the overstimulation completely and create a general state of disinterestedness. There are even proposals for inducing fright and fear to reduce the stimulation, but by means which today would never be considered therapeutic. The famous technique advanced by Beneke's contemporary, Heinroth, of leaving the mental patient mainly to his own inner powers of health restoration with the "psychological doctor" acting only as a supervising bystander, is to a limited degree also advanced by Beneke. Beneke, however, gives the therapist a considerably enlarged role. With greater emphasis than any of his predecessors or contemporaries, Beneke advances the concept of relaxation and describes various forms to be applied for various conditions. As a final suggestion he points to the need for wide differentiation so that for the individual case and for the specific type of overstimulation pathology the most appropriate psychotherapy will be found.

The fourth and last major type of mental disease Beneke describes is the lack of stimulation, or actual nonstimulation. In its prepathological form this condition appears in all the so-called low-spirited and depressed mental states which are known to everyone. In its pathological form, Beneke maintains, the condition does not occur as frequently as does overstimulation. However, it can be found to affect practically all forms of expression of psychic life. To see this condition in its proper aspect, Beneke advises that it not be viewed merely as an outside symptom. For instance, in the case of a serene person who rarely laughs, this is not due to lack of stimulation. Real pathological lack of stimulation is actually a lack of capability. Lack of capability centers in the emotions and the will and is commonly known as *melancholia*. Beneke points to homesickness as one of the most characteristic examples of this pathology. The psyche, in these cases, is not naturally stimulable by the environment and fills its volume with dreams of the faraway homeland which have been stored in the psyche as rudimentary memory. A characteristic of this condition of lack of stimulation is that it rarely restricts itself to the psychic sphere, but in almost every case has strong impact upon the physical nature.

This lack of stimulation occurs pathologically in three forms: (1) the lack is really experienced; (2) the lack takes on a kind of secondary function creating a hypochondriac note in the psychic life—a form most common in individuals who have a routine job or pattern of life which, for instance, forces them to sit all day in the same position, a circumstance that always has physical repercussions; (3) a general emotional feeling of indifference marks the background of the mental existence. Individuals suffering from this form of pathology may have a tendency to change suddenly from a low- to a high-pitched state of stimulation and drop back just as rapidly. There is no continuity in their mental status and there is apparently no element through which they can control their changes of mood or various waves of excitement. Every psychopathologist recognizes these symptoms as momentary fits of excitement or irritability which occur in most cases of severe melancholia. If such waves of change of stimulation increase in strength, they may lead to restless insanity. Cure of such cases of lack of stimulability should follow the course of attempting to remove the grip of the pathology as a continuous pattern and slowly redevelop the natural ways of response to stimulation.

A final chapter of the book bears the title *The Development of Other Kinds of Psychopathology.* At the outset there is a survey of the earlier description of the four basic types of psychopathology. Beneke raises the question whether, in addition to his basic pathogenic sources of volume and stimulation, one might also include the element of capability *(Vermögen)* in establishing a somatic picture of mental illness. This question leads him to a reconsideration of his two previous concepts. We find him now on the path of his contemporary, Heinroth, that is, on the borderline of ethics and religion on the one hand, and abnormal mental behavior on the other. But while Heinroth wished strictly to separate the function of the psychic doctor from that of the theologian and the educator, Beneke sees the task as a widening of the general concept of psychopathology.

Here the phenomenologist wants to widen the concept of abnormal behavior to include not only all of what we call mental disorders but all immoral behavior as well. Ethics thus becomes a kind of prophylactic for mental health, and psychopathology becomes the psychological side of criminology. Immorality goes back to desire *(Begehren),* which results from a stimulus. If a desire overreaches the capacity of the psychological controls and takes over the major volume of the psyche, it becomes immoral. While a desire may thus take over a large volume of the psyche, it actually indicates weakness. Beneke disagrees with the moral philosophy of his time, which has a tendency to stamp all experiences resulting from pleasure *(Lust)* and enjoyment *(Genuss)* as sources of immorality. His belief was that only a too-great desire can lead to immorality.

Beneke discusses in great detail the relationship between action and will on the one hand and thought and imagination on the other with regard to tendencies toward desire, and he tries to establish a new borderline between the normal and the abnormal. The point at which both meet he calls the "irresistible desire," which is the result of an incapacity of control. Seen from the other side, it is a paralysis of the psychic functions. By way of deepening this concept, Beneke sees himself forced to reject the idea of responsibility as the measure of what is mentally sane or sick in the performance of a criminal act. In its place, he advances the concept of the victorious free will as the final judge. There can be no free will, he explains, when blind desire takes over the major volume of the psyche. It is at this point that Beneke also establishes the difference between immorality and other psychopathologies, since the latter do not result from an overreaching of desire. As to the cure of immorality, Beneke steps outside the views of his time regarding criminology, with their rigid punishment patterns. He believes that this mental abnormality should be dealt with in the frame of psychotherapy.

At the end of this chapter Beneke attempts an intensive discussion of preventive and prophylactic aspects. There is a detailed presentation of the interrelationship of pleasure and displeasure drives. Combining this discussion with the concepts of psychic volume, mental power and vitality, and adding as a new concept that of evaluation (Wertgebung), Beneke closes his amazing book, which goes so far beyond the thinking of his time. Indeed, reading this concluding portion of his book and many of the individual passages, the reader feels that he is confronted with modern speculation on philosophy and pathology. Beneke's idea of a purely psychological psychiatry, a phenomenology of psychic life, is as modern as any contemporary concept.

Chapter 20

KARL KAHLBAUM, TERMINOLOGIST

IN the history of mankind there are certain individuals whose success and fame have been secured through wealth and social status and who leave nothing behind except a tombstone and a meager shadow. There are others who lacked all the apparent necessities that make for success. They were born poor and in adverse circumstances, all the political, social and educational powers that usually carry an individual to the forum of success are beyond their reach and every step forward seems a great struggle. They go unsung to their graves, but sooner or later their name and work are rediscovered and they rise to the stature of greatness in their field and even stand among the heroes of mankind.

Karl Ludwig Kahlbaum belongs among the latter. He was born the son of a truckman in eastern Germany. He managed to get through high school, and with the help of scholarships went to the university. After an initial inclination toward the natural sciences he turned to medicine and got a secondary position in one of the minor mental hospitals of eastern Prussia. His scientific urge, however, induced him to seek admission as academic teacher at the University of Königsberg. His most important contributions to his field are contained in the major short studies he wrote during these years of work as an unpaid instructor. It appears, however, that the administrators of the university, fearing the ideas and academic ambitions of this progressive thinker, stifled his career by giving the chair Kahlbaum was aiming at (and now vacated by the previous professor's death) to another man. Realizing there was little hope for him in the academic field, Kahlbaum resigned his post as a "wild reader" and accepted tenure as assistant to the director of a private mental institution at Goerlitz. His practical work was as exceptional as his academic work. Thus, after a short period Dr. Reimer made him executive director of his institution. Kahlbaum's ingenuity increased. He enlarged Reimer's *Nervenheilanstalt* greatly during the following period;

as a result it became famous all over Europe. Many young doctors came there to learn and to intern. Among them were several who later rose to fame themselves, such as Johannes Bresler and Theodor Ziehen. Along with his technical improvements Kahlbaum created a special section for juveniles—his *Pedagogium.*

Hidden away in the small print of the fortieth volume (1883) of the *Allgemeine Zeitschrift für Psychiatrie* is a reprint of a lecture given by Kahlbaum before the forty-seventh meeting of the Berlin Psychiatric Association on June 15, 1883. The eleven-page reprint is entitled "About Nervously and Mentally Diseased Juveniles and Their Pedagogical Treatment in Institutions." In this lecture Kahlbaum pleaded for specific handling—what he called "pedagogical treatment"—of institutionalized juveniles.

Kahlbaum has never received the acknowledgment he merits in the history of psychiatry. Those who reject him consider him "the fellow from a small east German private institution who made up so many strange and unnecessary words and titles." Those who esteem him consider him the originator of the concepts of catatonia and hebephrenia. Kahlbaum's concept of hebephrenia was similar to the concept of pubertal neurosis held by British workers of the same period. His refined description of the condition must be designated the first realistically established concept of child psychiatry.

The point of view presented in this lecture shows a unique understanding of what we today call child psychiatry. It represented a significant forward step in the history of the treatment of the mentally abnormal child. The lecture begins with an observation on the increase in the number of fourteen- to twenty-five-year-olds afflicted with nervous and mental diseases of both the acute and chronic kind, including practically every known form of insanity. Kahlbaum, however, observed a specific juvenile deviation which took the form of "ethical peculiarity and perversity," and of "a more or less pronounced intellectual limitation and weakness." Because in a number of these cases one or the other of these symptoms was so dominant, it appeared justifiable to consider them two autonomic forms of mental disease. Although Kahlbaum was not able to provide proofs of the validity of his concept, he nevertheless presented—in 1883—a definite formulation of specific forms of juvenile mental disease.

In the lecture Kahlbaum described in great detail what he called "ethical and intellectual pathology in youth." Ethical pathology, which can be of both negative and positive character, is seen in the form of laxity in responsibility and social and familial feelings up to the point of crude egotism, and also in the form of ethical pathological purism. In either form it disturbs the development of a life concept beneficial to the individual and others. In the case of intellectual weakness, the concern is not only with the inability to learn, but also with the weak tendency toward fantasy and lying, the latter condition also appearing in two forms —the *floride* and the *torpide*.

Viewing these forms of juvenile psychopathology from the etiological aspect, Kahlbaum notes that one must first consider hereditary factors; in a preponderant number of cases the parents of such children are nervous people. Another element to be taken into account is physical disease and physical "pauperization," or undernourishment. Orphancy is also named as a frequent and serious etiological factor in childhood psychopathology. Still another element is a false, too-strict or overprotective and lenient attitude on the part of the parents. Poor marital relations between parents and other negative circumstances of the family situation must also be seriously considered as important factors in the illness of the child. Kahlbaum was evidently well aware of the pathological social elements in child psychiatry, which we today maintain were first recognized in our century.

Kahlbaum emphasized individual treatment as a basic factor in the treatment of institutionalized mentally ill young persons. First, physical impairment must be treated. Occupation and opportunities for study for those patients for whom study is possible are important elements in treatment. This broadened treatment of juvenile patients Kahlbaum calls "medical pedagogy," and this type of institutionalization he calls "medical pedagogium."

Kahlbaum developed a specific system for the medical pedagogium: First, patients should be physically well and well rested; they should not be overburdened with learning; free choice should be a major therapeutic element; physical and mental activity should be combined harmoniously. It is interesting that Kahlbaum emphasizes as another element in these cases—one that is today so frequently attacked first—the habitual and manic pattern of bad behavior. Kahlbaum describes in some detail the practical functioning of the pedagogium in his own institution: he had three resident teachers who were with the juvenile patients all day and who applied group and individual care according to the needs of the individual child: handicrafts, art education, gymnastics, gardening and games.

The Kahlbaum pedagogium was famous for a time in middle Europe, but it was soon entirely forgotten. It represents the first fully developed system of institutional care for mentally ill children, some of the treatment procedures of which are found today only in the most modern and progressive child care programs. Its initiator, a courageous pioneer, should therefore not be forgotten or left out of the history of child psychiatry.

Besides his inexhaustible devotion to institutional work, Kahlbaum devoted himself intensively to the scientific development of psychiatry. He never published a large book and apparently had considerable difficulty getting his few small pamphlets published. It appears very likely that the most important of these he had to have printed himself. It is still open to question whether this was due to a lack of academic backing or to the extraordinary character of the material he presented. All we know is that in Königsberg he had the opposition of Karl Rosenkranz, the editor of Hegel's works. In the chapter on Kahlbaum in Kirchhoff's *Deutsche Irrenärzte* there is an episodic report that makes this fact very evident.

Kahlbaum's first and probably most important treatise, published in 1863, shows his opposition to all that could result from an Hegelian or even a Kantian theory of science. This pamphlet is entitled "The Grouping of Psychic Diseases and the Division of Psyche Disturbances." The subtitle—"Outline of a Historicocritical Presentation of the Previous Classification and the Attempt at an Empirical Scientific Basis for Psychiatry as a Clinical Field" —indicates an empirical phenomenology in clear opposition to deductive idealistic concepts. This approach is clearly expressed in the introduction. Here Kahlbaum asks for the rejection of preconceived schemes *(Vorgefasten Schematen)* and demands that the real appearances in the sick person *(Die wirklichen Erscheinungen am kranken Menschen)* be the principle for scientific work. This was written after he had been forced to give up his academic career, yet it reflects his opposition to the point of view represented by the Hegelian Karl Rosenkranz who closed the university door on him.

To describe the major origins of Kahlbaum's psychiatry one must dwell on the fundamentals of his contributions. These are the most important part of the concepts of the man whom the future will probably single out as one of the greatest speculative minds the field of psychiatry has had up to now. It is remarkable that most of those who have seriously written on the history of the science of the mentally ill have only acknowledged Kahlbaum with a few generalizations. Furthermore, thousands of practitioners in the care of the insane who daily use terms like catatonia and hebephrenia do not know of the man who created these concepts. The recent study by Wolfgang de Boor* is the first to recognize the great importance of Kahlbaum in developing psychiatry as a science, placing him beside Kraepelin and Kretschmer.

Kahlbaum himself was very much aware of the importance of his fundamental theoretical concepts for all his contributions to his field. In order to make them known to the representatives of his field he again and again presented philosophical treatises. He once offered an "Outline for a Theory of Science Based Upon Natural Science Methodology." On another occasion he lectured on "The Unity of the Sciences and Their Classification and Organization."

This latter title clearly indicates his manner of approach. He was a scientific thinker whose mind was geared to a systematic presentation of the entire field to which he had devoted himself. His purpose was to clarify the whole field of psychiatry—the sciences of the various abnormalities of the human mind. He was not content to deal with pathology only practically or individually.

---

* DE BOOR, WOLFGANG: Psychiatrische Systematik. Berlin, Springer, 1954.

He had to have in his mind a clear picture of the entire field, showing how the various forms were related. Only a few psychiatric thinkers have ever accepted the challenge of this task of systematization. There have been many who wanted to confer their successful practical experiences or their observations and somatic descriptions. There was always the score of others who attempted to state what they believed to be their experiential knowledge of the entire field. There were a few who desired to survey the field historically. Most rare, however, are those who really had the ability to view the totality of the field and the systematic interconnection of its contents.

In his major treatise Kahlbaum correctly pointed to Felix Plater as the first to attempt a systematization of the field of psychiatry, but strangely enough Kahlbaum never came to know about the one other beside himself who attempted an early systematization of the psychiatric field—Vincenzo Chiarugi. In comparing Chiarugi's great but relatively unsuccessful attempt to that of Kahlbaum we see more clearly the real importance of the latter's work. Chiarugi realized the confusing state of many concepts regarding the mentally ill. He tried to gather these various notions from all the authors of ancient times as well as subsequent writings. He sought to classify all utterances on the same thing or usage of the same term. It was the most prolific effort made to date. However, the vision of an organizing concept within the variety of pathological pictures was lacking. This was Kahlbaum's basic approach. Chiarugi had collected details and arranged them in a system, that is, he had proceeded inductively. Kahlbaum sought first of all an insight into the very idea of systematization and then showed how the details were related in accord with this. Thus he was led to a total vision of the entire system of psychiatry. This, however, was only the first point in Kahlbaum's contribution to his field.

In the introduction to the essay already mentioned Kahlbaum tried to set forth his principle of approach as clearly as possible. In his review of previous and contemporary systematizations he noted that so far psychiatrists had only made it their object to study and present the pathological symptoms. Accordingly, they were all only systematizations of symptoms. Kahlbaum found that previous systems had classified material only in a formal way without getting deeper into the inner specific character of the diseases. This did not satisfy him. Mental illness was for him more than a group of symptoms. Mental illnesses were various forms of processes, and their differentiation could be achieved only by clearly separating and describing these processes.

This was indeed something new in the field of psychiatry. This fact needs to be emphasized at the beginning, because it came to be the basis of modern clinical psychiatry as presented by Kraepelin and Bleuler. However, those who have recently discovered Kahlbaum have not quite been aware that he placed himself in an already existing scientific tradition, even though its application to the field of human mental abnormality was new. At the central point of his most important treatise Kahlbaum points out that *Die Formenlehre musse zu einer Metamorphosenlehre werden.*

To view process in nature as metamorphosis was nothing new. It implies the study of processes instead of merely the forms and symptoms. It had existed in ancient times and had been the basic concept of classical physiology and anthropology at the end of the Eighteenth Century. However, it was lost and understandable for the somatic type of psychiatry of the first half of the Nineteenth Century. Even as it was revived in the real scientific modern psychiatry it was something quite new and different. Indeed, Kahlbaum's own concept was not merely a revival but contained a completely new element. He introduced into the idea of metamorphosis an element we may call the differential aspect. It was the characteristic of early metamorphic thought that it was the application of only one idea. In Kahlbaum it became a variety of metamorphic processes. Thus an entirely new scientific technique, the comparative method, was inaugurated by Kahlbaum. The earlier one could be designated an identification method. Bound to the differential approach, however, is the point of view of process, which we have just characterized. These two aspects taken together became, in Kahlbaum's hands, the tool for an entirely new system of classification of mental diseases.

However, there is a third element involved which must be brought out to make Kahlbaum understood properly. It is not a dominant part of his method, but rather an undertone, an underlying concept, but it proves to be basic to Kahlbaum's thinking. It is a concept that had actually been thought out by a contemporary of Kahlbaum who is now completely forgotten—Heinrich Neumann. Neumann had developed what one might call a unilateral psychiatry. He was convinced that all previous differentiation between mental diseases was wrong. For his part, he claimed that there was only one mental disease—insanity—and all variety in symptoms were only different stages of this one disease. This kind of totalistic monism impressed Kahlbaum greatly. We therefore find it applied as a basic view: All mental diseases are abnormalities. He did not take the question of varieties so lightly as Neumann had done. The variety of processes started from the basic disease and created the variety of forms. These varieties were transformations. Kahlbaum also designates them metamorphoses from the normal. They produced the various diseases.

On this theoretical basis Kahlbaum distinguished three types of mental illness, for which he selected names which have today completely banished from the terminology: *vesania, vecordia* and *dysphrenia.*

Vesania are all psychoses which afflict the total structure of the psyche. According to Kahlbaum, they grow out of a dynamic metamorphic process that leads from one to the other pathology and ends in complete disintegration if the process is not stopped. Today, of course, we look somewhat differently upon the variety of psychotic states, but the basic idea of total affliction and total disintegration can still be helpful, not only in understanding certain forms of the *dementia praecox* type but also in their treatment. In studying Kahlbaum intensively during recent years I have been led to speculate whether a similar thought was not in Bleuler's mind when he wrote his famous book. Knowing Bleuler personally from numerous discussions, I was able to confirm in my mind that his careful empiricism would not permit him such keen speculative reaching out as Kahlbaum felt entitled to. I have previously pointed out the very cautious way in which Bleuler went about applying Semon's concept. I remember a discussion with him in which he excused himself almost apologetically for not being able to follow Semon completely in his intuitive perceptions.

Vecordia was used to designate all mental diseases which were only partial pathologies of the total psyche. Kahlbaum presents himself to us here as one of the representatives of the threefold systematization in psychology which reigned all over Europe toward the end of the past century. Here in the United States even the early John Dewey was one of its representatives. It separated psychic activity into intellect or thought, feeling and emotions and will. Kahlbaum accordingly distinguished three kinds of partial pathology—that of the intelligence *(paranoia)*; that of the emotional sphere *(dysthymia)*; and that of the will, which he calls *diastrephia*.

Here again we find the clear grouping in terms of a process of deviation from the basic concept of normality. It was not the actual symptomatology, but a complicated complex dynamically united into a somatic picture that Kahlbaum felt justified to give the name of *paranoia*, which received such a definite role as a classification item. I wish to point especially to the *vecordia* picture of paranoia since we know it later only as a partial symptom of a kind of somatic complex in relationship to other pathological traits. De Boor, in his presentation of Kahlbaum, pointed out an important element in the difference between *vesania* and *vecordia* diseases which helps in understanding Kahlbaum's concept in its basic character. He noted that *vesania* diseases are irregular and incalculable in their course of development, whereas *vecordia* diseases show a certain continuity. *Vesania* diseases are complex; *vecordia* diseases, simple or partial.

Dysphrenia is characterized by Kahlbaum as being comprised of diseases with a total character but only a partial duration. He here refers to diseases which express themselves in the form of shorter- or longer-lasting attacks. For Kahlbaum the characteristic *dysphrenia* is epilepsy in the way it was understood in his time, that is, mainly as a disease of the mind.

Today, when the diagnostic and symptomatological considerations of Kraepelin and Bleuler are established as valid, one who reads of these classifications of Kahlbaum will probably find them deductive, too abstract and highly one-sided, even superficial. However, the further one studies Kahlbaum's presentation of these types, the more one will feel the deep reality he has touched in wanting to get away from the old way of symptomatological identification and seeking to capture the actual process character of psychopathological occurrences. In the introduction to his description of his new attempt at classification Kahlbaum indicates impressively his struggle to find some way of group identification clear and complete enough to lead the way out of the "chaos of classification" which he had been confronted with in his own day.

That Kahlbaum was not merely an abstract constructor but a very realistic phenomenologist is evident in the less completely forgotten part of his psychiatric research and writing. Kahlbaum was the creator of the well-known and much-used terms *catatonia* and *hebephrenia*. Presently these terms are used as symptomatological categories in the wider field of schizophrenia. They had been developed by Kahlbaum in collaboration with E. Hecker, who was second in command in his institution and his best friend. Kahlbaum's approach to these concepts enlightens his badly understood and rejected classification system of mental diseases. We must thank W. de Boor, who was the only one of the considerable number of psychiatric historians and writers on schizophrenia to take the pain of following, at least historically, the development of Kahlbaum's catatonia concept. De Boor shows how Kahlbaum, from 1863, struggled with the idea that a set of symptoms were the picture or the expression of an actual specific kind of mental disease. Observing this set of symptoms again and again he differentiated it from the variety of *vesania* types of disease. He slowly conceived a very specific somatic picture, which he designated, after 1866, as catatonia.

There was nothing of a construction or dogmatic formulation. There was a descriptive kind of demonstration. This was new and unacceptable to the speculative psychiatry presented at Königsberg University by the Hegelian philosopher Rosenkranz, and Kahlbaum's attempts to introduce new names for pathological pictures received very serious resistance. For us today Kahlbaum's way of describing his pathological soma and presenting it as a specific pattern appears as modern as it can be. It was not until Kraepelin applied the same method and gave Kahlbaum the palm of authorship that the label of unsoundness was removed from him. However, the actual acknowledgment was still lacking.

It was not until 1874 that Kahlbaum came forward with a final presentation of the catatonia idea in the form of a monograph. This monograph must be considered as the beginning of the establishment of the schizophrenia syndrome. Nevertheless, as we have shown on previous pages, it was almost seventy-five years earlier that this syndrome as such had been observed and described. Kahlbaum describes catatonia as "a brain disease with a cyclically changing course, of which the symptoms that unfold in the diseasing process show a soma of melancholia, mania, stupidity, dementia and finally, imbecility." In this description is immediately to be observed a rather wide and detailed observation. It appears most worthwhile to follow the technique by which the entire study is presented.

First of all Kahlbaum tries to formulate his method as such. He designates it a clinical one. By this he does not mean only simple observation and description of the pathological symptoms and their inductive combination. He maintains that this method had already been used by the so-called Somatic school, whose founder was Friedreich. Clinical method for Kahlbaum is the observation not of the disease as such, but of the total existence of the sick individual in all his functions of living. This includes his physiological as well as his mental existence. He emphasizes from another point of view that mental diseases must not be viewed merely psychologically but also as *naturwissenschaftlich:* that is, according to broad aspects of the natural sciences with a special diagnostic aspect created for such a purpose, but without a specializing prejudice. Kahlbaum actually speaks of a *naturwissenschaftliche* psychology or psychophysiology. Such a psychology should not work with uniform principles but tangentially circumscribe the facts studied. The efforts of Kahlbaum to point out a new way to present diseases expresses, on the one hand, his wish to distinguish his method from that of the classical psychological and somatic schools. On the other hand it expressed his awareness of the need for an entirely new approach for presenting the new facts which he wished to communicate.

After this broad theoretical introduction, Kahlbaum presents his catatonia concept worked out in the most carefully composed way. He offers a set of chapters on symptomatology, etiology, pathological anatomy, diagnosis, prognosis and therapy that cover one hundred pages. This organized and detailed presentation shows that Kahlbaum wished to do more than to make known some newly observed facts, which he could have written up in a superficial and abstract way. He wanted to present his observations in the form of a basic scientific effort. Moreover, it seems, as the introduction expresses clearly, that this new way of presentation was as important to him as the mediation of the new facts.

He claimed a certain neutrality in the battle between the psychistic and somatic points of view that still went on at that time. Kahlbaum felt from the beginning, as evidenced in his catatonia study, that he was nearer to the somatic than to the abstract way of the psychological point of view. It was the physiological, muscular involvement with the psychic processes that fascinated him and presented him with a scientific task for which the somatic point of view seemed to be the more revealing. In this matter one could not proceed from a theoretical constructive point of view but only from one of the observer. In Kahlbaum's methodologically speculating mind this was a completely new task. One had to observe facts and narrow them down by what he called *Umgrenzung,* a concept which is difficult to translate and for which I find it best to speak of as a tangential procedure. Individual observations should be put together like parts in a picture puzzle until a *Gesamtbild,* a total picture, was achieved. However, this was not done by an inductive method, but by one which might be called symptomatological.

In following the small study carefully one soon realizes that Kahlbaum intended it as an example of methodological procedure. He starts by pointing out a well-known psychopathological form— that of *Melancholia attonita.* He singles out a certain number of cases—nine in a row—which are deviations from the common pattern in regard to a quite similar peculiarity, that of a kind of tension and suspense *(Spannungs-Zustand).* By trying to put to-gether symptomatologically various traits contained in these case histories, Kahlbaum gets the *Gesamtbild* of what he designates as catatonia. However, the *Gesamtbild* is not yet complete for him after describing only a set of static symptoms. We may remember from his study of psychopathological types how important was the point of view of seeing mental diseases as a process. This again becomes a major aspect for the catatonia study. He wants it viewed also as a process. There is a beginning, an increase and then a de-crease with a high point between them. There is also the observa-tion of what became later a major symptomatic element for all schizophrenia cases and was designated in German as *Schuebe,* the wavelike reoccurrence. Kahlbaum points out that catatonia has a cyclical character of occurrence.

After having given in this way what one may call the skeleton of the symptomatology of catatonia, Kahlbaum proceeds by point-ting out various details, always presented in a case history he has reported and discussed. Special initial traits frequently found as melancholic traits are pointed out. There are others which are occurrences of exaltation and maniacal episodes. There are certain rage states, abnormalities of speech, of thought and of the mobility process upon which he feels he must dwell in greater detail.

He similarly treats the etiological, pathological, anatomical and other aspects. Again and again he exemplifies special facts or processes he wants to present. There remains actually no ground for accusing Kahlbaum of producing his theories out of abstract constructions. We are everywhere offered a kind of phenomeno-logical descriptive presentation of individmual facts which are then combined or used to fill in a total picture.

In the chapter on diagnosis we find a review of the results of the total study. We become here reminded of the mode of presen-tation of the psychopathological types. If one were to read this paragraph out of context one could maintain that it is an ideo-logical construction; however, we now know how this result has come about. This justifies asking whether Kahlbaum had not carefully prepared in his mind his psychopathological types, but had not presented the process with equal care in his written presentation. On the other hand, we may speculate that Kahlbaum undertook this careful elaboration of the catatonia study to show those who had criticized him so harshly on his typology that his scientific thinking proceeded in a specific and careful way.

From this we may also understand why almost all his later small publications are methodological and theoretical, attempting to justify his point of view. He later brought out little in the way of new and detailed results, except his practical development of institutional techniques, which is really magnificent. His psychopathological types, as little as they are known today, are the major result of his entire scientific effort, but we may well say that aside from the concrete views on schizophrenia and the definite alignment of juvenile psychopathology, his greatest contribution was his laying the groundwork with his types for all later psychotypology.

However, considered historically, Kahlbaum's greatest contribution was his basically new approach, which, though completely forgotten, marked the beginning of modern scientific psychiatry. No one knew this better than the man to whom we like to hand the palm—Emil Kraepelin. Kraepelin, in his straight and clear mind, has given him the greatest acknowledgment to date. In his presentation of the psychiatry of the Nineteenth Century he writes, "Time has proven that the way Kahlbaum took was the right one. The careful pursuit of the course and culmination of mental diseases in individual cases, including autopsy and a refined understanding of the causes, have led to the fact that we today can distinguish a set of clearly defined somatic pictures of mental diseases, which we are able to recognize symptomatically."

This high acknowledgment alone should give Kahlbaum a foremost place in the history of psychiatry. This is even more evident when one goes into the detailed working of his mind as we have done here.

Chapter 21

AT THE CRADLE OF CHILD PSYCHIATRY

VERY few child psychiatrists have concerned themselves with the origins and history of their field. In America there have been only three, the earliest of whom, Roberta Crutcher, has presented the most comprehensive and historically far-reaching account. The second, Leo Kanner, has concentrated on the first four decades of this century. The third, Lawson G. Lowrey, has mainly traced only recent orthopsychiatric trends. None of the three has viewed child psychiatric work within the frame of the general field of psychiatry.

More searching historical investigation into the origin and growth of scientific preoccupation with the mental ailments of human youth reveals that psychiatrists of the classical period, from Pinel and Rush to Reil and Heinroth, had been concerned, if only to a limited degree, with the abnormal juvenile. We offer here a short presentation of what might be called a total view of the history of nervous and mental diseases of childhood, as we have been able to ascertain it.

A bird's-eye historical view of efforts made to deal with the mental suffering of human youth establishes three periods in the development of what we today call child psychiatry.

The first period goes back to the Sixteenth Century and the efforts of monks to provide custodial care for defective youths and to apply to them a primitive kind of remedial education. It is the remedial education approach which characterizes the early interest in the mentally impaired child. The history of the *sauvage de l'Aveyron,* about whom Jean Itard wrote his famous educational treatises, and the educational history of Kaspar Hauser are the most characteristic examples of this approach, in which there is less interest in the actual kind and degree of illness than in the means of relieving the social and moral problems created by defective children and of adjusting these children as far as possible to the educational and religious standards of their time. Interest

168

was focused mainly on the mentally retarded, the idiot, the imbecile, the mongoloid, and those subject to various kinds of seizures, rather than on what today would be considered the mildly psychotic or psychoneurotic.

We know that this approach of the first period is still applied in the form of the movement for the institutional care and education of the most severely mentally handicapped, a movement that has been active during the entire past century and today still plays a major role in that sphere in which the administrative view of mentally impaired youth is predominantly cultivated.

The second period of child psychiatry began early in the Nineteenth Century, when pediatrically inclined medical men, as well as specialists in neurology and psychiatry, became aware of the occurrence of actual specific psychopathologies in children and began to record them. One of the pioneers of this period was Benjamin Rush, who recorded in his *Inquiries* specific mental abnormalities of adolescents. In 1836, Esquirol spoke of a *folie de puberté*. Among English case histories, William Perfect's descriptions of mental afflictions of children appeared as early as 1787. In his *Observations of Insanity* (1798), John Haslam described, in a most characteristic way, three cases of insane children in addition to thirty-seven cases of adults. Haslam was one of the first to become intrigued by the frequency of occurrence of insanity in youth, and his statistics on the subject have often been cited. He based his findings on the observations of Pinel, who had begun to make such counts at his Bicêtre Hospital in 1784. Within a period of ten years Haslam had found seventy-one cases of insanity in persons aged fifteen to twenty.

Esquirol was probably the first to speak of specific mental diseases in childhood when he attempted to classify insanity by age groups. He said, "Mental abnormalities could relatively be divided by age groups; childhood would be the period of imbecility; youth that of mania and monomania; advancing age would be the period of melancholy; and old age, that of dementia." Whatever our view of the correctness of such a division may be, it did distinguish a specific form of mental disease affecting children. This fact alone refutes Kanner's claim that "until the beginning of the Twentieth Century no one had emphasized a specific mental ailment of childhood."

Following these two great French psychiatrists, who were the most influential of their time, similar data were gathered from all over the Continent and the British Isles. A dozen large studies might be listed, some of them of a physioneurological nature, such as Walter Dendy's *Cerebral Diseases in Childhood* (1848) or Pierre de Boismont's *On Insanity in Children* (1857). The latter employed astonishingly modern psychiatric language. The most characteristic description of juvenile psychopathology during that period was that presented by Wilhelm Griesinger in his *Pathologie und Therapie der psychischen Krankheiten* (1845). Griesinger's approach to juvenile pathology, however, was still almost the same as that of Esquirol and his contemporaries: human life was viewed with an eye to its totality. Mental pathology and abnormality must also occur during the early phases of life. Griesinger advocated the separation of age groups into prepubertal, pubertal, and post-pubertal. His view of mental abnormality in youth went considerably beyond the extreme types of mental defectives and psychotics. Using a term that might be translated as "behavior disorder," he says, "Manic states can be found in the greatest variety and gradations. They may appear as continuous habitual emotional disturbances with a resistance or quarrelling pattern, or with malicious traits. Other forms resemble the *folie raisonnate,* or moral insanity, as we observe it in adults, or finally in the form of bad character traits."

Indeed, looking on children with the eyes of adult psychiatry, Griesinger recognized the great variety of specific forms of childhood psychopathology. As is known, he was the first ego psychiatrist (his thinking in this direction had a great influence on Freud), and he viewed juvenile psychopathology predominantly in connection with ego development. There can be no doubt that the juvenile forms of insanity and psychopathology that he observed were different from adult forms. He explained this difference by pointing out that the ego in the child has not yet been completely developed and that the intellect has not yet taken on firm form. The major cause of psychopathology in childhood, he

believed, was retardation of development. This was as far as Griesinger was able to go in developing his concept. One can hardly
agree, therefore, with Dr. M. B. McMillan that this concept formed
the nucleus for child psychiatry.

An important next step was made by Henry Maudsley, whose
position as a great psychiatric teacher in Nineteenth Century Britain was comparable to Griesinger's in Middle Europe. In his
Physiology and Pathology of the Mind (1867) there is a thirty-five-
page chapter on "Insanity of Early Life." Whereas Griesinger had
been a clinician and a practitioner and expressed his views accordingly, Maudsley was a geneticist and systematizer. For this reason we have from him the first fully orchestrated presentation,
from the point of view of the mid-Nineteenth Century, of a psychopathology of the juvenile period of life. Maudsley's presentation was actually the first attempt at a classification of childhood
pathology, or to be more exact, what appeared to him the variety
of psychopathologies observable in childhood.

Maudsley's first approach was genetic. He began with the state
of existence of the child at birth and its "gradual evolution." On
this basis he tried to establish the possible pathologies. He asked,
"What are the mental derangements of the earliest human life?"
The first movements of the child are reflexes responding to impressions from sensorial perceptions. If pathologies occur in this infant stage they are convulsions or are of sensorial character. Accordingly, Maudsley designated as the first form of childhood
psychopathology what he called *sensorial insanity.*

I have specifically pointed to the genetic aspect of Maudsley's
work because it shows the basic difference between his approach
and the symptomatological approach of today's psychiatry. Maudsley's approach appears especially noteworthy in light of the fact
that we have found it so difficult, with our present approach, to establish proper insight into these earliest childhood psychopathologies. The historian, if not the present-day active child psychiatrist,
may be permitted to speculate whether this early approach of
Maudsley's is not still of considerable value in assisting the future
development of the field.

Following the child in its growth and unfolding, Maudsley tried to determine pathological patterns according to stages of develop-ment. As the child becomes more organized in his sensations, both receptive and reactive, his psychopathologies also take on new forms. Maudsley explains, "There comes method in his madness; this convulsive fury becomes more and more coordinated." Those who, like Leo Kanner, deny the earlier Nineteenth Century ori-gins of child psychiatry should take pause before this amazingly clear elaboration of a genetic pattern of childhood psychopatholo-gy.

Basically Maudsley still viewed juvenile life from a point of view abstracted from observations of adult life. Indeed this be-comes clearly evident when we follow him from his genetic to his systematic presentation of childhood psychopathology. Here are his classifications:

Monomania or partial ideational insanity
Choreic delirium or Choreic ideational insanity
Cataleptoid insanity
Epileptic insanity
Mania
Melancholia
Affective or Moral insanity
Instinctive insanity

In describing these juvenile forms of pathology, however, Maudsley almost everywhere distinguished specifically juvenile characteristics which seem not to stand behind present-day sympto-matology. For example, he identified melancholia—a somatic pic-ture applied since ancient times but today almost entirely dis-carded—with specific depressive and manic states. "The child whines and wails on all occasions and whatever impression is made upon it seems to be followed by a painful feeling. In older children the almost continuous stage of painful feeling is associ-ated with distinct delusions." As nuclear juvenile manic mani-festations, Maudsley pointed to "eccentric expressions like 'if he kicked a stone, he must return to kick it twice more; if he spat once, he must spit twice more; if he had written a word incorrectly, he must repeat the correction.' "

Those who have fought for the maintenance of a presently

acknowledged soma of manic-depressive neuroses in childhood will be interested in this impressive presentation of Maudsley's. Equally important is his insight into the background of juvenile destructiveness, which he derived from healthy selfishness in the child. He also gave a remarkable description of the psychopathology of emotions as a deviation from the healthy dualism of the normal emotional life. Although we cannot ignore the fact that Maudsley used terminology basically related to the adult for his descriptions of juvenile mental and nervous diseases, one cannot but acknowledge him as the first to attempt a systematization of the mental impairment of youth.

The dropping of almost all the concepts derived from adult psychiatry and the attemp to formulate entirely new concepts and new aspects applicable exclusively to childhood marked the third period in the development of child psychiatry. Again we must, in contrast to those who have tried to arrogate this achievement to themselves, mention the meritorious workers of the Nineteenth Century who did pioneer work in child psychiatry.

The first real demand for an independent child psychiatry goes back to 1878. It was the German psychiatrist Heinrich Schuele who formulated this demand in his *Handbuch der Geisteskrankheiten (Handbook of Mental Diseases)*. In a chapter entitled "Mental Disturbances of Childhood" he wrote, "If one is to describe these completely, one must develop an entire specialized pathology. Of greater variety, as earlier workers anticipated, abnormalities of the psychic life of the child can be specifically established, and they should not be described as poor copies *(Abklatsch)* of the psychopathologies of adults."

Twenty years before Schuele, however, there had been attempts to formulate, from careful observation, valid somatic pictures unique for childhood. For example, in Laehr's *Allgemeine Zeitschrift für Psychiatrie* (1859) there is a paper by Edward W. Guentz, *Die Wahnsinn der Schulkinder* (Insanity Among School Children), in which the writer maintains that the modernized form of school instruction then developing was causing forms of exhaustion and depression in school-aged youth which appeared to him to cause a new mental disturbance found only among the young.

According to our present diagnostic approach this juvenile pathology must be considered a kind of adolescent schizophrenia. It is precisely this pattern of adolescent psychopathology, now so well known, that can be cited as the first actually formulated and actually termed soma of child psychiatry.

Among Maudsley's successors in England, observation of what was called pubertal neurosis was already quite common, but the concept remained somewhat vague until two German psychiatrists, Karl L. Kahlbaum and Ewald Hecker, began to concern themselves with the problem. It was this concept of hebephrenia (which Kahlbaum called pubertal neurosis and about which his collaborator, Hecker, published a thirty-eight-page study) that clearly bears the traits of what we today still designate as a special form of schizophrenia. One must acknowledge the Kahlbaum-Hecker concept of hebephrenia as the first specific child psychiatric formulation.

In the following decade a dozen or more major studies of hebephrenia appeared in German psychiatric periodicals. The later demand of Schuele and others for a child psychiatry entirely separate from adult psychiatry must be considered a consequence of the preliminary efforts of Kahlbaum and Hecker.

Schuele himself had made a most intensive attempt to give the autonomous conception of mental diseases of childhood its proper place within the framework of psychiatry. "Most of the forms of adult insanity," he said, "presuppose a complete stage of personality development; for this the juvenile brain is not mature until after adolescence." He also maintained that a special symptomatology of mental diseases of childhood was difficult to present because of the meager data available. He attempted to describe such specific childhood forms of mental disease in two ways: First, as forms of deviation from normal childhood life; second, as specific deviations from adult pathological forms.

The genetic elements in childhood psychopathology appear especially important to Schuele. These elements are, on the one hand, basic factors in hampering and arresting development; on the other hand they are nuclear stages of insanity that only later come to their full unfolding. In this regard Schuele also placed special emphasis on "pubertal insanity," which in the following two decades became a specific field so that, in 1898, Walter Wille, in his *Die Psychosen des Pubertätsalters (The Psychoses of Puberty)*, could list ninety-three special studies dealing with the subject.

During this period every general psychiatric text published in the principal European countries contained at least a short chapter on the insanity or mental diseases of childhood—for instance, Rudolf Arndt's excellent text of 1883. But the definite establishment of child psychiatry as an independent field was the unique achievement of a psychiatrist who is now completely ignored. This psychiatrist is Hermann Emminghaus, who in 1887 published a 293-page book entitled *Die Psychischen Störungen des Kindesalters (Psychic Disturbances of Childhood)*, which appeared as a supplementary volume to Gerhardt's famous *Handbuch für Kinderkrankheiten*.

Emminghaus was born in Weimar, Germany, in 1845. He studied at Göttingen, Vienna, and Leipzig, took his M.D. degree at Jena, and established himself at Würzburg in 1880. In 1886 he accepted a post as a professor of psychiatry and director of the University Institute and Clinic of Dorpart in the Baltics. In 1896 he assumed a similar post at Freiburg; he died in Freiburg in 1904.

Emminghaus had an independent mind and was fired with a desire to ease the lot of the insane. He wrote several books on general psychopathology and psychotherapy, and in addition to the volume with which we are now concerned, he wrote one in 1882 on juvenile problems in his field, *Forensic Problems of Children and Minors*.

His *Psychic Disturbances of Childhood* is the first and one of the very few attempts made up to the present time to give a systematic and complete presentation of child psychiatry. Because of the obscurity into which Emminghaus' work has fallen and the originality of his system of child psychiatry, we would like to offer a detailed presentation of his pioneering book.

The introduction contains a thorough discussion of the differences in pediatrics, general psychiatry and child psychiatry, with mental diseases in children described as incommensurable with those of adults, and an appeal for a clear distinction of scientific

study in the two fields. Of the greatest importance also is Emminghaus' application of the idea, found in psychological psychiatrists
from Paracelsus to Heinroth, that the therapist should allow the
healthy nature of the patient to be the prime helper. The best
therapeutic helper of the child as a growing and incomplete being,
Emminghaus emphasizes, is his own nature and power of growth.
Since in Emminghaus' day there was not yet the distinction between psychosis and neurosis that exists today, he applied to practically all mental and psychic disorder the term "psychosis." Because the psychic life of the child is not completely developed, it
appears to be especially difficult to get a clear and definite picture
of various diseases. Emminghaus therefore proposes a typology
arranged according to age groups with five-year divisions. He
makes further separation between immaturity and a too-early ma-
turity. Again, he distinguishes between total and localized disturbances and stationary and acute conditions.

At the end of the introduction there is a twelve-page "History
of Childhood Psychoses," which is the most thorough and objective history of child psychiatry yet attempted. It begins with
Haslam and Rush and ends with Maudsley, whom Emminghaus
calls the first real child psychiatrist.

The book begins, after this introduction, with a "General
Etiology," which offers first a statistical study (mainly limited to
Germany) of the occurrence of mental abnormalities in childhood,
the various types found, and distribution according to sexual and
hereditary factors. There follows a discussion of genetic conditions. Besides congenital causes, Emminghaus enumerates the main
physical causes of psychic abnormality: retarded physical development, pathology of the nervous system, brain injury, exposure to
heat, diseases of organs near the brain, such as the ear and the
nose, cardiac and digestive ailments, common and typhoid fever,
malaria and various kinds of poisoning. Next are enumerated the
psychological causes: fright, anxiety, fear, worry, grief and sorrow.
A long paragraph discusses mental epidemics among children and
juvenile imitation of mental illness. To make the survey complete, Emminghaus sums up the social causes: bad home conditions, inappropriate or defective education, and most serious, false

school placement, classroom overcrowding and mental overburdening of the child; finally, punishment and physical restraint, unhealthy sexual stimulation and masturbation.

The second part of the book deals with "General Symptomatology." Here Emminghaus does not simply sum up somatic pictures, but presents the psychic diseases of children as deviations from normal functioning. He first presents major deviations of the emotions and feelings of childhood, enumerating hypersensitivity, pain and anxiety of various types, embarrassment and insecurity, restlessness and depressive states. Next follow pathological gaiety and excitement, emotional instability and unhealthy emotional mobility. An unusually detailed treatment is given certain pathological forms of behavior which later were generally labeled "hysteria." These include enjoyment of pain, perverted feelings such as happiness over injury and suffering of others, enjoyment of destruction and fright. There follows a section on pathological deviation in thinking and imagination. Emminghaus treats here deviation in perception and limitation of intellectual functions, pathological increase and decrease of memory, unreal and fantastic imaginings, lack of ability for abstraction and abstract thinking, special difficulties in memorizing and recounting, hallucinations and illusions, compulsive thinking, phobias about certain thoughts and perceptions, pathological questioning, brooding, precociousness, flight of ideas, incoherent thinking and megalomania.

The third section of this part of his book is devoted to pathological deviations in desires and strivings. Here Emminghaus considers misdirection of desires, destructive desires, collectivitis, lack of desire and aversion, soiling and defacing, perverted and delinquent striving, lying, stealing and pyromania, cruelty, compulsive actions and *pavor nocturnus*. At the end of this section Emminghaus discusses what he calls complex psychopathologies. These might today be classified as the most serious forms of restless behavior disorders—delirium, fury and panic.

The largest portion of the book, "Special Pathology of Childhood Psychoses," treats, in the fashion of present-day symptomatological psychiatry, specific somatic pictures. A first somatic picture Emminghaus calls infantile *neurasthenia cerebralis,* which is of special interest because it not only disproves Kanner's contention that Emminghaus simply applied adult psychiatric concepts to juvenile conditions, but shows quite the opposite; namely that Emminghaus struggled to formulate usable concepts of child psychiatry.

Throughout this chapter Emminghaus offers numerous references, of which a number are inserted under the chapter title. Checking these, we find, for instance, that one citing the well-known psychiatrist Heinrich Laehr leads us to a report of a meeting of the Psychiatric Society of Berlin. It contains an appeal for a collaboration of education and psychiatry because of the recognition of special mental ailments in children. Checking a reference to the English alienist Charles West, we find another to a number of cases which Emminghaus reprints, illustrating a certain condition for which West had no name, merely calling it a certain kind of mental disturbance. Another reference leads us to the long paper by E. W. Guentz mentioned above. In it Guentz discusses a number of cases of a recently observed new kind of mental illness, described as exhaustion of the brain and nervous system. Another author, Uffelmann, speaks of "mental atony." Finally, there is a reference to the well-known neurologist Albert Ehlenburg, who wrote a long treatise on various conditions which he sums up as "cerebral irritation." All these authors were speaking about a similar or identical abnormal mental condition, but it is Emminghaus who finally names it, in a chapter of ten pages, *neurasthenia cerebralis.* This is what we would today call "the nervous child"—a child nervously exhausted by strain, oversensitive, with various kinds of psychosomatic symptoms, schizoid traits and other symptoms which are today placed under different headings. It was a first attempt to formulate a new child psychiatric concept.

Of course not all the somatic pictures offered by Emminghaus are new, either in name or content. This would have made the understanding and application of his results more difficult to his contemporaries. There is, for instance, the picture of a *dementia acuta,* a condition that others, like Krafft-Ebbing had considered a psychopathology found mainly among juveniles. Emminghaus takes this concept over in the same form. He acts differently, however, in his approach to what has commonly been designated as melancholia. Here he specified the concept of what the Germans have called *Schwermut,* or what we would call depressive states. He distinguishes four basic forms of melancholia in childhood, one of which is juvenile suicide.

Quite different is the treatment of a group of pathologies which he sums up under the previously much-used title of mania. His definition, however, is considerably different from all former ones. A manic child is one with excessive energy who develops into an abnormal behavior pattern of routinized character composed of flights of ideas and changes of mood. In more serious forms the condition may lead to exaltation and continuous rage. Emminghaus of course uses the somatic concept of paranoia, which in his time was solidly established, but again he works out a specific juvenile aspect which is completely different from the adult form that one finds exhaustively treated in every psychiatric textbook of that time. Finally, there are chapters on idiocy and epilepsy which even Kanner has retained in his textbook.

Historically, perhaps the most important chapter of the entire book is the one that contains Emminghaus' attack against the cruel punitive treatment of children whom we would today call pathological liars and thieves. He here introduces a new and important soma, *Gemüts-Entartung,* which conveys the meaning of moral psychopathology. The concept that the insane are not criminals but sick individuals, which at the beginning of the Nineteenth Century, through Pinel and Reil, had started to become part of our humanized knowledge, was only slowly carried over into the educational field by recognition of the fact that the misbehaving and delinquent child is sick rather than morally bad. For the first time we find here definitely projected the idea of applying psychotherapy instead of punishment.

Of special interest for our evaluation of Emminghaus' early attempt at formulating a system of child psychiatry is his chapter on childhood hysteria. As we know, this syndrome was approaching the crest of its use as a major tool in evaluating psychological abnormality in children in Emminghaus' time. While even highly esteemed workers like Edward Henoch took what might appear to us today a one-sided stand, Emminghaus not only brilliantly evaluates both the validity and misuse of the syndrome, but provides a survey which with few exceptions is still acceptable today.

Considering Emminghaus' child psychiatry as a whole, it may be said that there is hardly a more recent book that in so balanced and complete a way presents a blueprint for the future development of the field. The entire field of child psychiatry is still in its beginning, even the newest books are characterized by immaturity and incompleteness. Emminghaus' mature and nuclear early attempt ought not to be left out of the picture or forgotten.

While we do not deny the eminence of Kanner's role in the psychiatric work of this century, and especially of his textbook *Child Psychiatry*, we cannot accept his presentation of the early history of the field. For the sake of historical truth I should like especially to comment on his statement about Emminghaus, referred to above: "whom [Emminghaus] behavior disorders in children interested only as seemed to fit diagnosis in accordance with classifications devised for adults."

In other words, child psychiatry was only a mimicry of adult psychiatry. The mass of facts we have presented in this chapter show this to be far from the truth. Moreover, the proof Kanner offers in support of his theories on the development of child psychiatry are somewhat unsatisfactory. For instance, as an example of a child psychiatry which simply applied adult psychiatric concepts, he points to Theodore Ziehen's small book, *Die Geisteskrankheiten des Kindesalters (Mental Diseases in Childhood)*, of 1902. This is the poorest example Kanner could have chosen. Ziehen, who was a biologist and neuropsychiatrist, had no justification for giving his book the title it bears. The book is not at all a coverage of the total, or even the wider, field of mental illness in children. Of its 216 pages, 180 are devoted to a highly detailed treatment of imbecility, and in the remainder of the book Ziehen discusses what he calls *dementia paralytica* in children. Kanner states that the Swiss psychiatrist Moritz Tramer was the first to use the term *child psychiatry* in 1933. It must be pointed out that since 1925 the Frenchman Georges Heuyer had conducted in Paris an institute called *Clinique Neuropsychiatrique Infantile.* Earlier authors, if they did not specifically use the term child psychiatry, used terms of their time which expressed the same idea. Wilhelm Strohmayer wrote in 1910 about *abnorme Kinderseelenkunde.* Emminghaus continuously spoke of *Kinderpsychosen,* and even Schuele in 1878 spoke distinctly of *die Formen des kindlichen Irreseins.*

Of all the dubious statements Kanner has made, however, those referring to Kraepelin and Bleuler are the most questionable. Almost every professional worker has had occasion to familiarize himself with the contents of the standard works of these two authors. Kanner writes, "Neither Kraepelin's monumental work nor Bleuler's classical textbook had anything to say about the psychopathologies of childhood." A glance at the subject index of Bleuler's *Lehrbuch der Psychiatrie* will guide the reader to discussions of childhood hysterias, childhood paralysis, etc. At various other places in the book there are references to juvenile forms of psychopathology. In the first volume of Kraepelin's monumental work, his *Psychiatry,* there is a lengthy discussion of basic genetic problems of child psychiatry in which Emminghaus and Hecker, among others, are mentioned. Those who are familiar with Kraepelin's ingenious mind and the thoroughness with which he thought things through must expect to find somewhere an adequate presentation of psychopathological childhood problems. Indeed, his *Compendium der Psychiatrie* contains, in the chapter on *"Lebensalter,"* a five-page discussion of the basic aspects of child psychiatry which appears to be the most farsighted and lucid presentation ever offered, even in this country. One cannot but recognize Kraepelin's statements as the classical presentation of what child psychiatry as a specific field ought to be.

Future workers with a desire to gain wider and deeper knowledge will realize that they can learn much from those Nineteenth Century workers who with such astonishing breadth of vision started the development of child psychiatry.

Chapter 22

PREDECESSORS OF MORTON PRINCE'S DISSOCIATION CONCEPT

IN his short biography, Merrill Moore justifiably designates Morton Prince as America's most highly reputed psychiatrist. This reputation rests mainly on the wide acknowledgment accorded Prince's studies in the dissociation of personality or double personality and consciousness. This work placed Prince next to Kraepelin and Bleuler in laying the ground for the study of schizophrenia, the somatological work which during the past fifty years has hardly advanced beyond what was accomplished by these three men.

The main point of Prince's study was that the usual normal unified consciousness of the personality can "disintegrate so that a second personality may come into being, designatable as 'double,' " and that this second consciousness may alternate with the first." This falling into parts of the unified consciousness is a pathology. Prince's merit is considered to lie in the fact that he was the first to describe this aspect of the somatology of schizophrenia, or *dementia praecox*.

We frequently find, in turning over the literature of the past carefully, that such "firsts" have been considered by people who in full or nuclear form presented the facts now considered new, or who speculated about them. Of those who anticipated Prince in the area of the so-called double consciousness, the most impressive were two British physicians of the 1840's, Sir Henry Holland and Dr. Arthur Ladbroke Wigan.

Holland, a fashionable court physician of his time, presented, in his *Medical Notes and Reflections* (1842), which appeared in many editions, a chapter on "The Brain as a Double Organ." He here expressed vexation about the functioning of the two cerebral hemispheres. He speculated, "Aberrations of the mind called insanity may be due to incongruous action of this double structure. In consequence there could be two states of consciousness side by

182

side or following one another according to changes of conditions. He pointed to cases of hysteria in which there have appeared two minds and "a sort of double-leading with oneself." He considered the term "double consciousness" for such states permissible, and he referred to a case reported by Herbert Mayo in his *Outlines of Human Physiology* (1837) in which a girl is described, almost identical with Morton Prince's Miss Beauchamp, who experienced fits lasting up to three days from which she awakened as a different person, not remembering the previous state.

A more impressive presentation of earlier observations of dual consciousness came from a contemporary and countryman of Holland, Arthur Ladbroke Wigan. History has treated this important man rather strangely. Although referred to in contemporary literature as ingenious and celebrated, nothing about his life has come down to us except the date of his death (December 7, 1847).

Dr. Wigan wrote two books, several pamphlets, and numerous letters to *The Lancet*. His major book, which was much discussed over half a century, was entitled *Duality of the Mind* (1844). In it he tried to prove the thesis that the two hemispheres of the brain are two completely separate organs functioning independently side by side, whose collaborating function resembles somewhat that of the eyes, giving self-control and security to man's mental functioning. Most mental diseases, Dr. Wigan believed, resulted from the nonfunctioning of one or both of the cerebral hemispheres or their malfunctioning or contradictory activity. Wigan elaborated this idea for most of the neurology and neuropsychiatry of his day. In some of his keen speculations he reached far beyond his time and into the basic concepts of the present century.

He had astonishing foresight of later insights into the constitution of the nervous system. He says, "The right brain [the right hemisphere] has no command over the right leg nor the left brain [left hemisphere] over the left leg; whenever the right brain is paralyzed, there is no power whatsoever to move the left limb, yet the left brain moves the right as well as ever. Consequently, the brains [right and left hemispheres] are capable of independent action. . . . I hope that I have proved a great many things besides the alternate influence of the two brains on muscular motion."

Among Wigan's amazing observations is the first actual inductive description of the schizophrenic thought process, which he presents in four pages, and from which I quote a brief passage, "Bring the tea—tea comes from China—wall of China—wall, mur, muraille—difference in French—French habits—habit, coat, long-tailed coat for soldiers—jackets. . . ."

This certainly seems identical with Bleuler's first descriptions.

Probably the most impressive reach of Wigan's thought into Twentieth Century psychiatry is his anticipation of Prince's dissociation concept, shown in the following passage: "We have examples of persons who from some hitherto unexplained cause, fall suddenly into, and remain for a time, in a state of existence resembling somnambulism, from which, after many hours, they gradually awake—having no recollection of anything that has occurred in the preceding state—although, during its continuance they had read, written and conversed, and done many other acts implying an exercise, however limited, of the understanding. . . . They now pursue their ordinary business and avocations in the usual manner, perhaps for weeks, when suddenly the somnambulistic state recurs, during which all that had happened in the previous attack comes vividly before them, and they remember it as perfectly as if that disordered state were the regular habitual mode of existence of the individual—the healthy state and its events being now as entirely forgotten as were the disordered ones during the healthy state. Thus it passes on for many months, or even years. This is what is called *double consciousness*—the person being in a manner two individuals, as far as sensation and sense of personal identity are concerned."

Besides the dual state which Wigan designated as somnambulistic, he further described one in which a falling into an infantile state alternated with adult consciousness, a form seldom reported but probably not too rare in our time.

There are of course basic divergences between the theoretical concepts that Dr. Wigan applied to his cases and what modern academic neurology and psychiatry cherishes. There are naturally also basic differences in theories and conclusions as between Wigan and Morton Prince. This is to be expected. The astonishing thing is the manner in which the facts were observed and presented prior to the mid-1800's, and this certainly deserves to be lifted out of the forgotten past and brought to historical acknowledgment. The historian may of course also be puzzled by the fact that the life and work of such an outstanding scientist as Arthur Ladbroke Wigan has been lost in the past, but this is a riddle we shall hardly be able to solve.

Chapter 23

PIERRE JANET:
THE PSYCHOLOGICAL PSYCHIATRIST

PIERRE JANET (1859-1947) lived a long, dynamic life. At eighty-seven, shortly before his death, he addressed an international scientific congress.

Born into a Parisian academic family, his education was guided by his uncle, the philosopher Paul Janet, whose achievements were more acknowledged in his own time than they have been by history. The uncle induced his nephew, who was more inclined toward natural sciences, to choose philosophy as his profession, and at twenty-two the young Janet was professor of philosophy at the Le Havre Lycée.

But his love for sciences prevailed. He joined the wave of interest in parapsychology—with its pathological implications from somnambulism to hysteria—that occupied the French mental scientists at that time. Pursuing the same theme that C. G. Jung had chosen for his academic thesis, "Psychology and Pathology of the so-called Occult Phenomena," Janet was warmly received and was permitted to conduct research at a local institution for the insane. He ought a scientifically sound basis to explain the mass of parapsychological facts mixed with foolishness, swindle and insanity. It was not long before he crossed the path of the psychiatric master, Charcot, who recognized his brilliance.

Charcot not only called Janet to Paris, where he opened his hospital to him, but even established a special psychological laboratory for him at the hospital at Salpêtière. It was not until he was thirty-five that Janet took his medical finals. A few years after Charcot's death in 1893, he became his own master, and in 1895 was appointed professor psychology at the Collège de France. He remained at Salpêtière and held his post at the Collège until his retirement.

Beginning with *Automatisme Psychologique* in 1889, Janet issued scientific publications in an unceasing stream. *Automatisme*

186

Psychologique, his Ph.D. thesis, established him firmly in the psychiatric field. The concepts of this book, prepared with such academic care, are almost identical with Freud's early theories on hysteria. The Breuer-Freud publication, *The Psychic Mechanism of Hysteric Phenomena,* appeared in 1893. Both Janet and Freud were searching for those "automatisms" at the basis of hysterical actions. In pointing this out himself, Janet accused Freud of having taken his basic concept from the Salpêtière laboratory and changing it into what he (Janet) rejected as pansexism and the "superficial use of clinical observations of limited validity to form an enormous one-sided medical system."

There is no doubt that Janet's influence on the development of modern psychotherapy was as great as Charcot's. Alfred Adler says without reservation in his *Neurotic Constitution,* "Janet's emphasis on the neurotic *sentiment d' uncompletude* is so wholly in harmony with the results offered by me that I am justified in seeing in my work an extension of this most important fact of mental life in neurotics."

During sixty years of search Janet developed his own system of psychopathology on the basis of what he later designated "conduct" theory. His aim was to "describe all mental disorders solely in terms of action and conduct." This conduct theory might have been of great importance to American psychiatrists since it represents a special type of behaviorism and was the only behaviorist psychiatry of consequence; Janet, however, preferred to restrict the term *behavior* to animals and to use the term *conduct* for human behavior. It is this differentiation that seems to account for his not having been accepted by American behaviorist psychiatrists, although he lectured extensively in the United States. Compared with Adolf Meyer's neuropsychiatry and Freud's libidism his concepts were not physiologically oriented enough.

Indeed, Janet's conduct psychiatry is, like MacDougall's propensity psychology, almost autonomously psychological. Its basis is the *force psychique* (psychic energy), which varies between *force et faiblesse* (strength and weakness), thus creating the multitude of pathologies. Their balance and adjustment originate psychotherapy. The simplicity of the concept has attracted as many as it has repelled. William Brown, the British middle-of-the-road psychiatrist, once said that this common-sense theory should be the most acceptable and usable for the ordinary physician. This statement has often been repeated, but has not brought wider acceptance to Janet, probably because, aside from the simple basic theory, the variations and especially the practical applications require more than prefabricated routine prescriptions. Even the simple variations of psychic weakness, from psychoasthenia to exhaustion and hysteria, require an intimacy and insight that cannot be gained theoretically. Janet himself repeatedly emphasized how much psychotherapy—and especially communicating it to students—is an art. Indeed, his techniques of both diagnosis and therapy could never be learned from his books alone. His personalized teaching was, I believe, one of his most essential contributions to psychiatry.

When I went to Paris to study Janet's techniques, I was directed to familiarize myself with the inmates and their living quarters. Coming from Kraepelin and Zurich, I was startled by the setup. I found housed together many persecutionistic patients who fired one another emotionally with fantastic tales. When I asked Janet what his therapeutic approach here was, I received the strange reply, "I believe these people, until it is proven to me that what they tell is untrue." I had just faced a young man who avoided stepping into any shadow because, in shadows roamed Napoleon, who wanted to draft him into the army. Beside him was a woman of past seventy who feared persecution from the mayor of Paris, who wanted to make love to her. I found it difficult to see any truth in such fixed ideas. Janet noticed my perplexity at his oracular words. He came over to me and said, "You see, these people are persecuted by something, and you must investigate carefully to get to the root." What he wanted to make me see was that one ought not discard persecutional fantasies as ridiculous or view them only symptomatically; one ought to take them seriously and analyze them, until the causal conditions were revealed. I have never forgotten Janet's wise word about persecutions, nor the many others which were a major factor in his relations with his students. They represented a Socratic art which I have never experienced from any other prominent teacher of psychiatry. In Janet's case it was inseparable from his concept of psychiatry.

Except for Wilhelm Wundt, hardly anyone in the field of psychology has unfolded his theory so universally as has Pierre Janet. Anyone familiar with his printed works and who has glanced over the list of his courses at the Collège will find hardly a field of application of psychology or psychiatry that he did not attempt to cover. When I saw him for the last time at the Tercentenary Celebration at Harvard in 1936, he asked me if I had read his latest book. I had to confess that, for lack of time, I had not. "There are still more than a dozen books I would like to write," he exclaimed. There was no end to the aspects of his field that he wanted to investigate.

But he was fully aware that writing in itself was not the major thing: The major thing was personal transmission of what he had to communicate. I remember his constant advice to students: "Read it and let's talk about it." In the spirited chapter he has contributed to Murchison's *History of Psychology in Autobiography*, he rejected what he called subjectivism in psychology, that is, elaborating on one's own psychological experiences. He strove for something different, but not only for the so-called objectivity of controlled experimental psychology. He had a wider concept which he called *nonpersonal psychology*. This he expressed again and again in the maxim, "To really understand and to be fully understood."

Chapter 24

AN IDEOLOGICAL INTERPRETATION OF
FREUD'S DEVELOPMENT VERSUS
THE FREUD MYTHOLOGIES

D URING the last few decades disciples of Sigmund Freud have issued a number of biographical studies. To the historian who attempts to be objective and critical, most of them appear to be more the products of a subjective, idealizing hero worship than scientific biography. A painting or sculpture of Sigmund Freud, each differing in its personal conception by the particular artist who conceives it, can be an individualized presentation which everyone accepts with ease. A biography, however, should remain in the sphere of established facts, well documented. With this last criterion in mind, objections have been voiced in an increasing degree against the three-volume biography of Freud by Ernest Jones. Those advanced by Iago Galdston in a recent paper, "Freud and Romantic Medicine," are the strongest yet uttered and the most justified.

Galdston points out that generally in studying Freud there has been "too little concern with the philosophical and historical implications." As an example he points to the role the biologist Wilhelm Fliess is supposed to have played in Freud's intellectual development, a fact to which the Jones biography has given thirty pages. However, Galdston does not get far with his attempt to correct Jones without falling into a similar error, when he writes, "Who was Wilhelm Fliess? Little was known about him before the Fliess letters came to light." This may be true for those who limit themselves exclusively to the reading of the master's works and the Freudian literature, or for those who do not care to familiarize themselves with the cultural and ideological background out of which Freud grew. Fliess was far from being an unknown man in his time. He was not, in fact, a kind of out-of-timer whom one could justifiably label a late adherent of the "Romantic school of medicine."

190

Anyone who lived on the European continent during the first quarter of this century knows Fliess, who must be counted among the twelve most discussed scientists of his generation (not excluding Spengler and Einstein). In his own biological field Fliess was at least as much discussed as Hans Driesch. As regards his major concepts, Fliess did not stand alone. Anyone who is familiar with the ideological concepts of that period knows that Fliess, along with a large number of other workers, was occupied with the categorical concept of *periodicity*.

Periodicity was represented in almost every field of science, the cultural as well as the natural. For instance, there was the author of the universal historical and cultural periodicity concept advanced so intensively by Oswald Spengler in *Decline of the West*. There also was Heinrich Wölfflin, who presented a periodicity theory in the field of history of the arts, and there was Fritz Strich who did the same in the field of literature. There was, furthermore, the Baron von Eckartshausen who applied the same principle to ethnology and anthropology. In the field of human development and education, Oswald Kroh and Charlotte Buehler, with her study of the course of human life, made intensive use of periodicity concepts. Felix Krueger of the Leipzig school of Gestalt psychology represented this concept in the psychology of man, and David Katz did the same in the field of psychology of animals.

In Vienna, in the circle nearest to Freud, there worked two rather radical periodicitists. Herman Swoboda and Otto Weininger. Nowhere in the writings or the trains of thought of Freud can one find a trace of influence either from the Viennese workers or from Fliess. Jones himself reports that Freud made ironical remarks about Fliess' ideas of tracing human life with mathematical concepts. It seems therefore rather absurd to link Fliess' major work, *Der Ablauf des Lebens (The Course of Life)*, with anything in Freud's work. Nor can one find any proof that could support the idea of connecting Freud with the Romantic school of medicine, as Galdston's construction arbitrarily does via Fliess' theories. Both these claims are nothing more nor less than mythology.

Let us first trace the relationship between Freud and Fliess, so far as we are able to establish it from the documents left to us. They consist primarily of letters written by Freud to Fliess and utterances from both these men preserved in various ways after their relationship had ceased.

Let us first ask: Who was this Wilhelm Fliess to whom Freud was so much attracted in his thoughts and ideas that he felt the urge to have an intensive correspondence with him?

Fliess was a biologist, who, among other things, was studying the relationship between the mucus membral zones and who discovered an intimate relationship between the nose and the female sex organs. This, indeed, was a realm which interested Freud greatly, and his later concept of the erogenous zones doubtlessly developed from the interchange of thoughts on this subject with Wilhelm Fliess. This was *not,* however, the Fliess of the periodicity concepts, but the early Fliess. It was not the Fliess who became widely known through his periodicity studies of the course of human life.

Freud and Fliess broke off their relationship just in those years in which Fliess started to work on his mathematical ideas of periodicity, and one may wonder whether this change of interest in Fliess may not have been the undercurrent which estranged the two men. Therefore, those who have exploited this early relationship between Freud and Fliess have not only greatly overemphasized it, they have done it on the wrong grounds. There cannot be any doubt that Fliess' influence upon Freud was much less than has been maintained by Jones.

Freud always carried on an intensive correspondence with quite a number of people. If one could study and compare letters he wrote to others during these years of his relationship to Fliess, one doubtlessly would find that Freud was equally or more intensively occupied with other concepts beside that of development at that time. However, as pointed out previously, since Freud's relationship with Fliess had ended before the latter's book on periodicity appeared, Galdston's theory of Freud's link to Romantic medicine is actually too negligible to discuss. Nevertheless, since the concept of the Romantic school of medicine has become popular with certain American medical and psychiatric writers, I feel justified in bending a little backward to try to establish some objective insight into this entire matter.

The popularization of the concept of Romantic medicine goes back to a German author, Werner Leibbrand, who has specialized in the construction of several such dubious and fantastic theories. Realizing the growing interest in this rather queer idea, Henry Sigrist, during his Leipzig years, induced one of his collaborators, Ernest Hirschfeld, to write a critical study on Romantic medicine. This appeared in Sigrist's yearbook *Kyklos*.

Originally the concept *Romantik* had been the name for a middle European period of literature. Workers in the history of culture—Wölfflin as well as Strich—warned against the application of such concepts as *Renaissance, Baroque,* or *Romantic* to other periods. Based on the same reasoning, Hirschfeld pointed out that there could not be a Romantic kind of medicine. Those who called be called Romantics were medical men living at the time of the Romantic literary period. Their contact with the members of the Romantic school was mainly in regard to philosophical concepts.

It was almost exclusively the philosopher Schelling whose ideas on nature became the object for speculation by a number of pure scientists and medical men. Hirschfeld therefore points out that Romantic medicine was a question which concerned one generation only and that all that was produced was eventually eliminated by history, because the ideas perished when they came under attack in various controversies. Finally, Hirschfeld makes this important comment: He points out that all those who could be termed Schelling adherents in the field of medicine belong to a small number of South German universities, all of which were Roman Catholic institutions. Furthermore, if one studies in detail the works of such medical writers as Lorenz Oken, Ignaz Doellinger, I. Nepomuk Ringseis, D. G. Kieser, J. M. Leupoldt and H. von Schubert, it can easily be seen that their philosophical background was much less that of Schelling than of the neo-Thomism.

Actually it is hard to understand how anyone can make even out of a periodicity student and mathematician like Fliess a believer in the Romantic school. It was no less than the unromantic thinker Immanuel Kant who formulated the basic scientific concept that any science contained as much objectivity as it contained mathematics. No member of the real Romantic school would have agreed to that. Furthermore, the attempt to use mathematics for calculations about the course of human life was not new. As early as 1811 a German statistician by the name of Wilhelm Butte had written a book on *Arithmetic of Human Life*. Fliess himself was the same type of completely unromantic thinker. He emphasized this rather clearly in giving his book, *Der Ablauf des Lebens,* the subtitle, *"Grundlegung einer exakten Biologie"* ("Fundamentals of an Exact Biology"). As an additional argument concerning Fliess' Romanticism, Galdston points to the concept of polarity. Again he seems to have completely misunderstood this in terming it a Romantic concept. It was none less than the leading classical poet and philosopher Friedrich Schiller who was the first to formulate such polarity in naive and sentimental poetry.

If we want to be ideologically sound, to sum up the entire matter, we cannot but shelve the entire concept of Romantic medicine as regards Fliess and Sigmund Freud.

The Freud mythologists have tried to paint a picture of his life, especially his youth, which would make it appear quite tragic and dramatic, but this is far from the facts. In realizing what they are, one much defend Freud against those Freudians who actually minimize the stature of their master. Galdston, for instance, says he relies on Jones' presentation as regards "Freud's childhood and young manhood." On the basis of this he writes, "Freud was poor." And a little later, "Before Freud turned to the treatment of nervous and mental diseases he ventured into a number of fields, seeking in each to make a name for himself. He experimented with pharmacological products, he worked in physiology, embryology, in neuroanatomy, dabbled in children's diseases, and tried his skill as a medical compiler, translator and author." Certainly this is less than a truthful picture.

Anyone who wants to express such a judgment should consult more accurate facts and materials. First of all, let us consider Freud's poverty. He was not more badly off than 90 per cent of all academic and government workers in Middle Europe, who had to live on a very small salary indeed until they reached the higher ranks in their profession and had well-paid positions. Nearly everyone had to try to find ways of supplementing his wages, especially those in the academic group to which Freud belonged. Some taught in high schools, some were journalists, some private tutors, others worked in industry. There was nothing unusual in the breadwinning activities of Freud. To maintain that he was "dabbling" in this or that scientific field is highly unjustified.

There exist two autobiographies by Freud. The first is the *History of the Psychoanalytical Movement,* written in 1914; the second is the *Autobiography,* which appeared in the *Selbstdarstellungen der Medicine* (Autobiographies by Medical Men) written in 1925. We know that the former was a kind of defensive writing in Freud's attempt to hold on to the crown of his movement after the breaking away of the Zürich School. This was a critical period of tremendous strain. We know that the entire relationship with the Zürich psychiatrist had been a misrelationship. As little as Bleuler understood Freud, so little did Freud understand Jung. Each group came from a completely different background. This came to the fore more and more as collaboration was attempted. In the next chapter I will present the real facts about this complete incompatibility of temperaments. Looking at these struggles we cannot expect impartiality from Freud, especially if one takes his personal traits into account. Therefore, the objectivity of his *History of the Psychoanalytical Movement* frequently has been considered questionable.

The situation is quite different so far as the *Autobiography* is concerned. It is an excellent objective presentation of Freud's early development. Several reliable authors have checked its contents. The first one was Trygve Braatøy, a Norwegian. His almost completely unknown booklet was titled *Hinsides Freud (Beyond Freud).* I have a report that when it was translated to Freud he designated it as the best presentation of him as yet written. There have also been two serious studies of Freud's early development. One is by R. Brun, issued in Switzerland, and the other is by Smith Ely Jelliffe. Jelliffe has done an amazing job of throwing light into each and every phase of the early history of Freud's professional life. This research verifies the correctness of Freud's own presentation of his mental development, as given in the *Autobiography*.

The objective historian and especially the ideologist can follow Freud in his presentation without difficulty, because it shows clearly and positively the logical way in which Freud developed. I would like to present here in a few sentences Freud's development to eliminate the major distortions produced by the mythologists. There was little choice for a young student of medicine, so each of them had to make a serious study of physiology. Vienna's Medical School at that time had one physiologist who was considered one of the most outstanding scholars of his time— Ernest Bruecke. Freud worked for some years in the Bruecke Laboratory. Since specialization was necessary, he chose for himself neurophysiology. In other words he took the practical course that anyone had to take whose aim was an academic career. It must be emphasized that Freud already had turned to neurology during the time he spent in the Bruecke Laboratory. It was in consequence of this early decision that he was determined to further his development by attaching himself professionally to the neurologist of the Vienna Medical School, Theodor Meynert.

Too much has been said about the frustrating personal influence of Meynert upon Freud. We must not forget that it was Meynert who made Freud an academic lecturer and gave him in this way his first scientific wings. The controversy which arose between the older teacher and the young scientist grew out of different ideological concepts, and not because Meynert was a cruel autocrat. In his day he was one of the most outspoken representatives of the structural school of neurology. In the decade during which Freud came to Meynert, his school was about to exhaust its theoretical possibilities and was geared to run into a dead-end alley. This was the basis of the conflict, because Freud seemed to have felt rather strongly that the Meynert neurology was facing a blank wall. He himself seemingly never had actually presented or subscribed to this losing concept of structuralism.

I have already pointed out that Freud had never belonged to

the periodicity school. He actually belonged in the school of dynamic and genetic thinking, which he knew from the work of Ernst Haeckel. Freud's interest in the problems of the psychological complex, his attempts to trace the commencement of neuroses in childhood experiences and his intensive interest in the psychology of normal and abnormal behavior of childhood, about which he wrote again and again up to the second decade of this century, are specific examples of such dynamic and genetic thinking. It was in fact at that time that neurologists like Robert Bing, Kurt Goldstein, members of the French school of neurology and Americans like Edmund Conklin turned neurology into a dynamic science.

A quarter of a century before, Freud, greatly oppressed by the task to solve these problems by himself, was going through those years which probably were his own most dynamic ones. He turned, as did almost everyone who felt himself scientifically progressive in this line of work, to France. His turning to Charcot was not a fanciful step, but a rather logical one. The Freud mythologists have called Freud's early work in neurology a "venture," but it was Meynert's neurology which did not give Freud a sound working basis for his own search, and to pursue its dynamic aspects he went to the French neurologists and later into psychiatric psychoanalysis.

In the same way it is most unjustified and unjust to call Freud's work in child neurology "dabbling in children's diseases." Because of his genetic interests it was necessary for him to be increasingly interested in child neurology. For this reason he was offered by the Vienna pediatrician Kassowitz work in child neurology in the pediatric department. Freud himself mentions some papers written on children's neurological problems in publications dating from this time.

It is equally unjustified to suspect that only a commercial impulse underlay Freud's translation of Charcot's major book. It was certainly Freud's conviction that this work ought to be known to the German-speaking followers of this field. We know how unfortunate his attempt to present Charcot's concept was for himself, in the rather backward school of Vienna, inclined toward the structural philosophical concepts. Those Freud mythologists who wish to make a martyr out of him because he was denounced after his famous lecture do it on the wrong grounds. There was no suspicion of martyrism in the conviction of Freud regarding the corrections of Charcot's dynamic neuropsychiatry. He was ahead of his time in believing in it, but we know by now that he was right. (Even if this author has never been a conventional follower and disciple of Freud and still believes that the Master erred basically in important issues, he cannot but underline the logical trend in Freud's thinking, especially in this early period.) One can only have the highest admiration for Freud for sticking to his guns when he was convinced of the truth of certain scientific ideas, even if this meant a serious setback in his chosen career.

A third aspect for us to consider, and one no less important than the previous two, is that of the actual history of the basic Freudian concepts. We can envision any important man's ideas if we see him clearly in relation to the development of the years before he began his work and later the period in which he himself grew. So it is with Freud. We shall be able to determine more definitely and decisively what his contributions are if we know what parts of them were the results of previous workers' studies and what actually are his own contribution. Of course, we meet again and again Freudian fanatics who have tried to prove that the entire history of psychiatry leads up to him as its summit. In the course of our study, however, we have found that Freud's major thoughts grew, as we might say, through the centuries from nuclear concepts far back in time. We have found that Georg Ernest Stahl said passions which have not been given a chance to live themselves out are in danger of causing hysteria. We have pointed out Tissot's anticipations of Freudian concepts as well as Reil's long exposé on the danger of suppression. From there on one can trace certain Freudian concepts everywhere in a kind of prenatal form until Freud himself gave them the formulation which is now world-famous.

In his attempt to construct a "romantic dream-bridge" between the unreal Romantic medicine followers and Freud, Galdston points to Heinrich von Schubert's *Symbolik des Traumes,* where among a dozen other motivations for dream contents we find wish fulfillment. The paradox is that Schubert's book is not listed by Freud in his long bibliography in his *Traum-Deutung.* We feel that a longer discussion about the *why* of this fact is not worthwhile, since if one consults the only historical critical presentation of the dream theories we yet have, by Wolf von Siebenthal, he will be astonished to find how many before Freud have felt that dreams fulfill a dreamer's wish.

We must tackle the study of history in a quite different way than the Freud mythologists if we want to carry it on as a legitimate science.

Chapter 25

CARL GUSTAV JUNG:
DEFENDER OF FREUD AND THE JEWS

D URING recent years a wave of misinformation concerning certain periods in the early development of modern analytical psychiatry and psychology has swept through professional periodicals and popular informative literature. Since these publications have received a great deal of attention in professional circles, it seems important to correct the information which they conveyed. This present chapter—a chapter of European psychiatric history under the Nazi yoke—is intended to be a historical report based upon published material available in the libraries of the United States, with the exception of some quotations from personal letters by Carl Gustav Jung. The authors of the misstatements this chapter aims to refute will not be mentioned here, although their assertions will be included.

This report concerns mainly the Swiss psychiatrist Carl Gustav Jung, whose role in the development of modern psychiatry is generally recognized as highly important—even if one notes that dogmatic and fanatical representatives of other schools have repeatedly attempted to minimize his importance. Academic recognition does not always constitute the perfect criterion for scientific achievement, but it may be emphasized that Jung has received more honor in this country than any other non-American psychiatrist, including Sigmund Freud. Although most of the attacks upon Jung's name have come from fanatic followers of Freud, a correct evaluation of Jung's role in the development of psychoanalysis is of greater importance for an objective understanding of the history of the psychoanalytic movement than that of any other person. This is particularly true if the historic perspective is continued beyond the point where Freud closed his own chronicle, that is, up to the years when psychotherapy was threatened in Europe by the outbreak of the Nazi movement, or until about 1935.

It seems important at the beginning of this report to emphasize

200

that its author is not a member of the association of the pupils of C. G. Jung, nor has Dr. Jung himself been consulted with in regard to the historic facts described here. The author has undertaken this writing on his personal initiative, because he believes that it is important for American psychotherapists to have objective information concerning certain momentous developments in their science.

It has been repeatedly asserted that Jung started out as a disciple of Sigmund Freud and subsequently became a traitor to his master. Freud himself—in his brief *History of the Psychoanalytic Movement,* which he wrote shortly after the separation between himself and the Zürich psychiatrists, Bleuler and Jung, and which he doubtless undertook as a justification to his more faithful pupils and himself of the break with the Swiss—wrote a significant objective report of the beginning of their relationship. We learn that Jung belonged to the Zürich school of psychiatry and that the first contact with Freud had been made by the head of the school, Eugen Bleuler, during 1907; that it was Jung's invitation which brought together Zürich and Vienna to the first Psychoanalytic Congress in Salzburg (1908); and that Freud and Bleuler joined as editors *(Herausgeber)* of the *"Jahrbücher für Psychoanalytische und Psychopathologische Forschungen,"* for which Jung took over the task of managing editor *(Schriftleiter)* in 1909. Freud also emphasizes the importance of the work Jung had already done before he came in touch with him. Very correctly, he points out that it was the problem of the complex theory which offered Jung the point of contact with him. Their break and the controversy in which Freud presents a highly subjective personal opinion in reference to the early history of his movement will be discussed later.

Jung's own writings mirror authentically and unambiguously how he stood and how he developed in regard to Freud. His first larger publication is a monograph of 122 pages, *Zur Psychologie und Pathologie sogenannter occulter Phaenomene (On the Psychology and Pathology of so-called Occult Phenomena),* which he used as required publication for his qualification as *Privat-dozent* (free lecturer) at the University of Zürich. Here we see him struggle with the same problem which every sincere research worker at that time tried to solve: the problem of hysteria. We see him, together with Freud and his contemporaries of that period, as a student of the French school of psychiatry of Binet, Janet and Charcot. He tried to reach understanding of such abnormal psychological factors as the so-called occult experiences through their parallel to similar experiences expressed by the mentally ill. We find him twice in one sentence mentioning Freud, whose *"Studien über Hysterie"* (published together with Breuer) and *"Die Traumdeutung"* seemed to have attracted him considerably. This was in 1902.

We have already learned from Freud himself that Jung belonged to a certain school of abnormal psychology known widely as the Zürich School. Eugen Bleuler, known for his famous textbook of psychiatry and his research in the field of schizophrenia, was the head of this school. Jung was a senior member of the group. Together with another member, Riklin, he was occupied in an intensive research into associations, which under the title of *"Diagnostische Associations Studien,"* appeared in the *Journal für Psychologie und Neurologie* in successive volumes from Number three to Number nine. Later, this became the basis for the entire school of associative criminological testing. Jung must be considered the founder of this method. Before the first of these diagnostic studies appeared, Bleuler wrote an introduction in which he emphasized that this work continued the tradition of the research of Wundt, Kraepelin and Aschaffenburg. A search was in progress for the unveiling of nonconscious elements, pointing in the same direction in which Freud was advancing but using other means, that of the association experiment. The meeting of the Zürich and Freudian groups was the meeting of searchers for the same goal who hoped to use techniques in common, since they had a common aim. However, as they became acquainted with each other, they not only discovered that their views on techniques did not coincide, but that their aims did not either. Therefore, after a short union, they resumed divergent paths. This was the nature of the relationship between Freud and Jung as the present writer believes it appears to the objective observer.

In the many years during which Jung worked on the diagnostic association studies he was deeply interested in Freud. This is impressively stated in practically every study. It was always one subject which interested Jung in connection with Freud. He hoped that Freud's method would solve this problem into which he felt the associative diagnosis did not lead deeply enough: the problem of hysteria and of the complexes. We find this stated in the section of the diagnostic association studies devoted to dream and hysteric symptoms in the following passage: "If one desires information about the more intimate experience, e.g., the complex, in a case of hysteria one is forced to reach it by a detour. Freud has converted this detour into a method: This is psychoanalysis." Surely one of the simplest and at the same time most impressive descriptions of the essential contests of psychoanalysis. However, when Jung, in the same year, presented a review of Freud's theory of hysteria before a professional congress, he expressed the fact very clearly that he was not a completely uncritical adherent of Freud's views.

> Freud has never developed a complete theory of hysteria but has merely attempted from time to time to formulate the theoretical results of his experience. However, what Freud has formulated theoretically must be acknowledged as a working hypothesis which adapts itself everywhere to experience. Therefore we cannot speak of a comprehensive theory of hysteria by Freud at the present moment, but of a variety of experiences which show certain common traits.

The year before, Jung had published his important book, *The Psychology of Dementia Praecox,* which was again chiefly a contribution in the field of research of his own Zürich School, and which, he emphasized, was based upon his diagnostic association studies. In its introduction, we find a very clear statement of his attitude toward Freud.

> My readings brought Freud to my attention. It so happened that I first read the *Interpretation of Dreams,* but I have also studied the rest of his writings. I can assure everyone that at first I naturally made to myself all the objections which have been made against Freud in the literature. However, I said to myself, that only those could refute Freud who have applied the psychoanalytical method extensively and who have searched as Freud searches.

Justice toward Freud does not imply, as many fear, an uncondi-
tioned surrender to a dogmatic concept; one can very well preserve
an independent judgment. If, for instance, I agree to Freud's theory
of the complex mechanism, of the dream, and of hysteria, this by no
means implies that I acknowledge the exclusive role which Freud
evidently attributes to the juvenile sexual trauma; just as I do not
place sexuality in general so predominantly in the foreground, or
even ascribe to it the psychological universality which Freud seems
to postulate for it, impressed by the powerful role which sexuality
evidently plays in the psyche. As regards Freud's therapy, it is at best
one amongst other possible procedures and probably does not always
fulfill the theoretical expectations.

Here then, we see, a definite line was drawn, before the actual
cooperation began, between acknowledgment and rejection of
Freud's major concepts.

Wherever we investigate Jung's later writings, we shall find no
change in his standpoint toward Freud as just outlined. Since many
attempts have been made to use an alleged negative attitude of
Jung toward Freud as an argument, let us quote a few sentences
from Jung's address before the meeting of the International Association of Psychotherapists at Bad Nauheim, in 1934, a meeting
which will interest us still more later on, for at this time, German
Nazism raged against the Jews and among them particularly
against Freud. Before a German assembly in a German town,
Jung said the following.

Without the existence of the complexes the unconscious would be—
as it was for Wundt—nothing but the residue of obscure representations. Through his investigations of these dark areas Freud became
the discoverer of the psychological unconscious. . . . As a logical out-
come, the first medical theory of the unconscious was the theory of
repression postulated by Freud, which was based upon purely empirical presuppositions, without taking into account the philosophical
works concerning the unconscious by Leibnitz, Kant, Schelling and
Carus, up to Eduard von Hartmann.

After this period of over twenty-five years, Jung therefore gave
to Freud the same acknowledgment as he had done on the eve of
his cooperation with "the psychoanalytic master from Vienna." In
1929, Jung wrote a short article (which is reprinted in his American book, *Modern Man in Search of a Soul*) on "The Freud-Jung

Contrast." At the end he says, "The contrast between Freud and myself goes back to essential differences in our basic assumptions." These basic assumptions, as they are enumerated in this article, are exactly the same as those expressed in the excerpt already quoted from the introduction to his *Psychology of Dementia Praecox,* written in 1906.

Let us now follow the history of scientific and personal relationships. In his *Psychology of Dementia Praecox,* Jung had offered a very positive contribution to the concept of schizophrenia, which was one of the scientific concerns of the Zürich group, especially of its leader, Bleuler. It was Jung himself, at the Salzburg meeting in 1908, who had suggested the cooperation of his group with the group of Freud. In 1909 Jung took up the task of acting as managing editor of the *Jahrbücher,* as we have mentioned, while Bleuler and Freud signed as editors, thus confirming the definite union of their two groups.

In the first volume one finds Freud publishing his famous treatise on infantile sexuality. To this, Jung adds *"Die Bedeutung des Vaters für das Schicksal des Einzelnen,"* which was followed in the next volume by his paper, *"Über Konflikte der kindlichen Seele."* If we compare the relationship between Jung's schizophrenia study and Bleuler's work on this problem on the one hand, with the relationship between Freud's writings on juvenile problems and these two contributions by Jung on the same subject, we discover the two attitudes are diametrically opposed. The relationship with Bleuler is characterized by an affirmative elaboration and an addition; whereas, in regard to Freud, Jung introduces a differing and critical viewpoint.

Nobody could consider these first real contributions to the joint work of the two groups as the work of a follower and pupil of Freud. We also know that in other ways the cooperation between the groups was not too smooth. Bleuler had been severely attacked in academic circles for his association with a man like Freud, who was considered a scientific outlaw. Bleuler responded with several articles, reaffirming his acknowledgment of Freud and of psychoanalysis. The most impressive of these appeared in the second volume of the *Jahrbücher.* Whoever reads this paper today will feel that Bleuler never had arrived at a deeper or more comprehensive inner relationship to Freud's conceptions. Conversely, his own ideas on autism, which occupied him at that time and of which the most important appeared in the same periodical, never had any acknowledgment in the more intimate circle around Freud.

The discrepancy between Jung and the entire Zürich conceptions on the one side and Freud on the other appears even more markedly in the largest literary contribution which Jung made during the cooperation of the two groups—in the subsequent two volumes of the *Jahrbücher*. This contribution contained his ideas on the libido concept of Freud. It was later published (1912) in one volume under the title *Wandlungen und Symbole der Libido*. We are told that Freud seriously opposed the publication of these studies as a separate monograph of the *Jahrbücher*. As is well known, the concept of the libido, to which he had given a very clear and precisely formulated description in his *Drei Abhandlungen*, was for Freud a most fundamental one.

Jung has reprinted in his American book, *Psychology of the Unconscious* (1937), the most essential part of his *Psychologie der Dementia Praecox*. From this we learn how he attempted to transform the Freudian concept according to his own thinking and that of the Zürich School. We read on page 144 of *Psychology of the Unconscious* as follows: "For a long time the theory of libido seemed to me inapplicable for *dementia praecox*. With increasing experience in analytical work, however, I became aware of a gradual change in my conception of libido. In place of the descriptive definition of the 'Three Contributions' (Freud's *Drei Abhandlungen*) there gradually grew up a genetic definition of the libido, which rendered it possible for me to replace the expression *psychic energy* by the term *libido*."

In continuation of this different concept Jung developed a theory of the libido which is completely at variance with that of Freud. In view of this fact, it is not surprising that on the first excuse, a break occurred in their personal relations.

In 1909, Freud and Jung, together with a number of international authorities in psychology, psychiatry and education, had been invited by Stanley Hall to celebrate the twentieth anniversary of Clark University by a series of lectures and by receiving honorary degrees. We are told that during the long sea voyage, when Freud and Jung had ample time to discuss and to work out problems of psychoanalysis in personal discussion, the differences of scientific opinion and of basic philosophical concepts became glaringly evident; a break almost occurred at the time. In the *History of the Psychoanalytic Movement,* however, Freud relates that it took three more years before the final break at a meeting in Munich in the fall of 1913.

According to Freud's account, Jung presided in an "unamiable and incorrect fashion" and "accepted the presidency of the International Psychoanalytic Association again, although two-fifths of the members present refused him support." Freud adds, "We took leave of one another without feeling the need to meet again."

To the present writer, it would seem that Jung's consent to continue as the president of the International Association expressed his desire to uphold and save the relationship and the collaboration, while Freud, angry and disappointed that events did not develop according to his wishes, pushed toward the break. Consequently, we witness in the same year—after the publication of five volumes—the resignation of Bleuler and Jung from the editorship and managing editorship of the *Jahrbücher.* From the fact that his note of resignation says he is leaving for "personal reasons," one can infer that it was Freud's personal attitude which forced the resignation, and that both sides would have been willing to continue if objective reason had been the main consideration. With the next volume, the *Jahrbücher* ceased to appear, thus ending the literary expression of the short collaboration of the Vienna and the Zürich groups.

Freud spoke harsh words about Jung in his *History of the Psychoanalytic Movement,* from which we quote here: "Jung, by his modification of psychoanalysis, has furnished us a counterpart of Lichtenberg's famous knife. He has changed the hilt and has inserted a new blade into it, and because the same trademark is engraved upon it, we are required to regard the instrument as the former one."

We find similar expressions wherever Freud comes to speak

about Jung, often indeed in an unjust manner. He had expected a pupil who completely accepted his theories. Jung, on his side, never desired or committed himself to such a complex allegiance, and he maintained a more objective and unbroken acknowledgment to Freud. He has never spoken of Freud in such impassioned negative terms as the latter did about Jung. In the controversy over the psychoanalysis of Freud and his own—which he termed *analytical psychology*—he always tried to keep the debate on the level of a scientific discussion or an explanatory description. He always acknowledged Freud's basic importance and historic role. No one could express this more valiantly than did Jung in his speech on Freud on the occasion of the aforementioned Nauheim meeting after the Nazi purge. This speech is indeed, the present writer thinks, the expression of one of the most knightly and courageous attitudes in the records of present-day science.

During the Twentieth Century, psychiatry and psychotherapy have just begun to outgrow their children's shoes. Previously, no definite line or pattern had been discernible in the development of "scientific help to the sick soul." During the last two decades of the past century, the most advanced and intensive work of this kind had been done in France. No one who was interested in the advances in the field could fail to study the results obtained by the doctors of the mind of Nancy and Paris. This work earned for itself a certain international reputation, but no national or international organization was connected with it. There were intelligent and successful workers elsewhere, too, who even created scientific schools for themselves, such as Lombroso in Italy, Bleuler in Zürich or Kraepelin in Munich.

With the start of the new century a fundamental change occurred. A strong demand arose for organization in psychotherapy. We must emphasize that it was around Freud and his psychoanalytical teaching that the first real international organization grew. Soon after the International Psychoanalytical Association had been started, the students around Alfred Adler—who like Jung had for a short while attempted an association with Freud—organized themselves into a similar group which, after some changes, became the International Individual Psychological Association. Not long after Jung had left the post of an alienist in the Zürich Psychiatric State Hospital, the *Burghoelzli*, students from all over the globe congregated around him and founded a similar international organization.

This was rather a new pattern in psychotherapeutic work. Of course the old academic neurological and psychiatric medical associations existed, but they had no specific aims to differentiate them from any other academic association, whether made up of philosophers or entomologists. Naturally, these psychotherapeutic international groupings, each around its own teacher, comprised only a small proportion of the entire professional group of psychiatrists, which has been rapidly growing since the end of the past century.

Among the latter, a good many were interested in one or the other of these three organized schools without feeling inclined to commit themselves to any one of them. There were also several rather distinguished teachers in psychotherapy who had their own theories and concepts and were unwilling to associate themselves with any group with a one-man leadership. There were Dubois and Forel, for instance, in Switzerland, Steckel in Vienna, Van der Horst and Bowman in Holland, Joergensen, Bjerre, Gadelius and Voght in Scandinavia, and there were a number of Germans like J. H. Schultz, Ernst Kretschmer, Arthur Kronfeld, and especially, Robert Sommer.

In the wider circle of academic workers in abnormal psychology, Sommer had a role similar to that of Adolf Meyer here in America. Although he had never written a large textbook defining his own basic psychiatric or psychotherapeutic concepts, he wrote a great number of shorter papers and booklets which contained communications which aroused the greatest attention and discussion. He had a great many independent pupils and a still greater number of friends. No professional worker, including Freud himself, exercised a greater influence in middle European psychiatric circles than did Robert Sommer.

Perhaps as a result of the organization of the pupils of the three individualistic leaders, perhaps because it was the trend of the time, an impulse arose in the middle 1920's to organize the independent workers in an association on an international level. During 1926 and 1927, discussions were held which centered around Robert Sommer, and in 1928, an *Allgemeine Ärztliche Gesellschaft für Psychotherapie* was founded with Robert Sommer as president. This society created as its organ an *Allgemeine Ärztliche Zeitschrift für Psychotherapie und Psychische Hygiene,* of which Sommer was the editor, while Wladimir Eliasberg and Rudolf Allers were nominated managing editors. After a further year and a half, that is, at the beginning of the third year of the new organization, the title of the publication was changed and Dr. Eliasberg's connection as managing editor ended. Sommer was then joined by Ernst Kretschmer as editor. Arthur Kronfeld and J. H. Schultz were appointed managing editors together with Allers, who was named the review editor. The new journal, under the title of *Zentralblatt für Psychotherapie,* grew rapidly until it became the most widely read and most progressive psychotherapeutic periodical in Europe. Hand in hand with the growth of the journal, the society rapidly became an acknowledged group which drew membership from all the countries of middle and northern Europe. A number of the more independent members of Freud's and Adler's societies also joined the *Allgemeine Ärztliche Gesellschaft.* Freud and Adler themselves appear never to have belonged to it. Jung must have been a member, since he is reported to have been vice president *(2. Vorsitzender)* in 1933. Considerable interest in Jung evidently existed among the members of the society, since in 1932 one of Jung's pupils reported on one of the series of seminar lectures which Jung gave for the members of his own organization.

Jung had come to hold a central position in mid-European psychotherapy when, in 1933, the Nazi purge destroyed much of the collaboration which in manifold ways had been built up during the previous twenty years. The first effect was the elimination, as a result of Nazi anti-Semitism, of the work done by Jewish scientists. The organizations of Freud's and Adler's pupils were dissolved and their members were expelled from the German national sphere. At the same time all Jewish members of the staff of the *Zentralblatt* had to resign. One should note here that it had been due mainly to Arthur Kronfeld's effort that the *Zentralblatt* had grown to a periodical of such extensive influence. At the same time, Rudolf Allers, who belonged to an extremely religious Roman Catholic group, also resigned from the editorial board. All Jewish members of the *Allgemeine Ärztliche Gesellschaft für Psychotherapie* were dismissed from the organization. Many inaccurate and untruthful statements have been made about the events of these fateful months. They convey a distorted and misleading picture. I am basing this report strictly upon the information provided by the *Zentralblatt*, of which the complete set of issues is available in the Library of the New York Academy of Medicine.

As mentioned before, the *Allgemeine Ärztliche Gesellschaft* existed as an international organization in which psychotherapists from all countries from Czechoslovakia to Holland and Belgium and from Norway to Hungary were united. Nazism would never permit such an organization to continue, since all international relations were ordered to be severed. The only possibility of organization under the Nazi rule was to be found in every country a national *Ärztliche Gesellschaft*. Permission was obtained for these individual national societies to cooperate—not in an "international" —but, according to a newly created German term, in an *übernationale Gesellschaft* which can best be translated as a "supernational" society. This actually meant an association of the various societies. If this was to survive, then any trouble with the Nazi authorities had to be avoided. Ernst Kretschmer, who had been the last president of the former international society for the year 1932-1933, resigned. Those who became blinded and embittered by their hatred of the National Socialist excesses, in reviewing the events have deeply resented the fact that at this point the aged director of a mental hospital of the Ruhr district, Dr. U. H. Goering, should have been elected president of the German psychotherapeutic society. He had never played any significant role in this field, but had derived his prestige only from being a relative of Hermann Goering. It is evident from the report on the events as given in the *Zentralblatt** that it was a matter of expediency to make Dr. Goering the *Führer* of German psychotherapy as a person capable of maintaining contact with the Nazi government.

---

* *6* (3):142, 1933.

Carl Gustav Jung never was a member of the German "Nazified" *Allgemeine Ärztliche Gesellschaft für Psychotherapie*. Under the new setup, he had become a member of the Swiss *Allgemeine Ärztliche Gesellschaft,* which was organized as a national group like the Dutch and the Scandinavian psychotherapists. However, as we read on the same page of the *Zentralblatt* from which we quoted before, Dr. Jung, who had been the vice president of the former international society from 1932-33, was asked to become the president of the association of national societies—the Überstaatliche *Ärztliche Gesellschaft für Psychotherapie,* which had taken the place of the international society. The report, which was written by the secretary of the German society, says, "On account of his acceptance of the presidency on June 21st, 1933, we owe to Dr. C. G. Jung the survival of our scientific society and of the *Zentralblatt."*

Because of the great decrease in membership it would have been impossible for the relatively small German group to support the *Zentralblatt,* of which Jung at the same time assumed the editorship. Again, it must be emphasized that the choice of a non-German, a member of the Swiss people (who at that time were already extremely anti-Nazi), was motivated by the desire to prevent the whole psychotherapeutic society from falling under the influence of National Socialism. Here again, all subsequent reports regarding the attempts to nazify psychotherapeutic work in Europe are completely false and misleading. At the first meeting of the new association of national therapeutic societies which occurred in May, 1934, the report of which can be found in the *Zentralblatt,** Jung himself told of the difficulties which arose in Switzerland when upon request of the German society he agreed to take over the presidency of the *Überstaatlichen* society. He had accepted it at a personal sacrifice which he had been willing to make.

Before we continue the report of the history of this period, we consider it necessary to insert some more general statements concerning Jung's fundamental opinions and concepts. This should lead toward a better understanding of his actions and of the ori-

---

* 7 (3):130, 1934.

gins of certain misstatements which have been circulated in regard to those actions. In this connection we will also consider some of the facts, many of them brought to light in the biography by Jones, about Freud's character and attitudes, which will further our understanding of the relationship.

The most severe and at the same time the most unjust accusation ever levelled at Jung is that he had a share in the horrors of anti-Semitism which have swept across the civilized world. This accusation originates in a sentence which Freud wrote in the already mentioned *History of the Psychoanalytic Movement:* "He [Jung] also seemed prepared to enter into friendly relations with me, and to give up, for my sake, certain race prejudices which he had so far permitted himself to indulge."

I have read through all of Jung's writings prior to the date of Freud's statement and instead of discovering any statement which might be interpreted as anti-Semitic, I have found no allusions to any Jewish factors and no derogatory remarks regarding other "racial" groups. In this statement, Freud has revealed the Achilles heel of his character structure, a vulnerable spot of a dangerous nature.

Fate and character had made Freud highly sensitive to any tendencies that might be thought to be anti-Semitic. I do not wish to join those who have tried to analyze Freud's character and who have dwelt upon assumed weaknesses in his personality. I am here interested only in establishing some enlightening historical facts from documents which we may take as authentic. The main source is the three-volume biography by Jones. Although, as we have said, there has been some more than justified objection to major parts of the episodic contents of the work, there are letters and impressions covering decades of personal relationship which are in the range of acceptable historical information.

Jones' statement that Freud had "the common Jewish sensitiveness to the slightest hint of anti-Semitism" and that he made "very few friends who were not Jews" appears to offer some ground for a reevaluation of the charge of anti-Semitism made against Jung.

For most people, especially Americans, anti-Semitism is mainly linked with Hitler and the Nazi movement. Hardly anything is known of the widespread racial animosity that had existed since the middle of the Nineteenth Century. Freud himself reports that as a young man his father had been pushed off the sidewalk—an offense commonly committed by the Nazis against Jews. It has been emphasized that Freud's father had been ruined financially and driven from the small Moravian town where he lived by anti-Semitism. In the Jewish quarter of Vienna where the family finally settled, Sigmund Freud grew up in an atmosphere of pronounced Jewish-consciousness which was accompanied by an attitude of suspiciousness toward the outer social world and a tendency to see any expression of animosity as an expression of anti-Semitism.

Throughout the Freud biography, Jones reports incidents relating to this experience of Freud's which extended from personal attacks to professional relations. Jones reports that "it was the anti-Semitic attitude in official quarters" that held back for so many years Freud's academic advance to a professorship. Recently, however, a well-documented paper by Dr. J. Gicklhorn has brought to light the fact that it was not only racial animosity against Freud, but Freud's refusal to register *(venea legendi)* as a private docent in psychiatry that apparently was also a serious obstacle to his academic advancement.

Racial considerations were of course involved in the formation of Freud's scientific circle and its development into the psychoanalytic movement. The original group of Vienna collaborators was entirely Jewish. When information about Freud's work spread beyond Austria, the majority of those who associated themselves with him were professional workers of Jewish descent. When, suddenly, an acknowledged non-Jewish and non-Austrian group indicated its willingness to join the nucleus in Vienna, Freud wrote to his collaborator, Karl Abraham, "After all, our Aryan comrades are quite indispensable to us; otherwise, psychoanalysis would fall a victim to anti-Semitism."

This letter was written in 1908. The break with Jung and the accusation against him of anti-Semitism did not occur until 1914. One becomes aware what that sentence in the Abraham letter means: It expressed Freud's consciousness of anti-Semitism. Freud was well aware that the Swiss psychiatrists were far from being anti-Semitic.

Nothing illustrates this attitude of Freud's more impressively than what Ernest Jones himself reports about Abraham and his role in the relationship between Freud and Jung and in respect to the Vienna and Zurich psychoanalytical groups. Dr. Abraham had been working for three years as a psychiatrist under Bleuler and Jung in Zurich, but had become "disconcerted at what he called the tendency to occultism, astrology, and mysticism," and had disagreed about certain scientific concepts. There had always been, both before and during Abraham's time, persons of Jewish descent among the members of the Zurich group, and whatever criticisms Abraham did make, there is nowhere to be found a word about anti-Semitism. Abraham had studied Freud's books since 1904. In 1907, after he had left Zurich to become a practitioner in Berlin, he had been in personal contact with Freud. An intensive correspondence and personal relationship developed which lasted over a long period and about which Jones reports in considerable detail.

When the difficulties of weaving the Zurich and Vienna groups together became more and more evident, the discussion between Freud and Abraham mirrored the essential features of the problems. Jones reports* the increasing antipathy between the Viennese and the Swiss, which on the Viennese side appeared to be the jealousy of the new "Gentile adherents."† Abraham confesses his own "animosity against Bleuler and Jung,"‡ which Freud felt he had to smooth over after an open scientific clash between Abraham and Jung during the Salzburg Congress in April of 1908.* On May 9, 1908, Freud wrote the following most significant paragraph in a letter to Abraham.

> Be tolerant and don't forget that really it is easier for you to follow my thoughts than for Jung, since to begin with, you are completely independent, and racial relationship brings you closer to my intellec-

---

* *II:34.*
† *II:43.*
‡ *II:49.*
* *II:40-48.*

tual constitution, whereas he [Jung], being a Christian and son of a pastor, can only find his way to me against great inner resistance. His adherence is therefore all the more valuable. I was almost going to say it was only his emergence on the scene that has removed from psychoanalysis the danger of becoming a Jewish national affair.

In another letter of December 26, 1908, Freud added the following.

We Jews have an easier time, having no mystical element. . . . I surmise that the repressed anti-Semitism of the Swiss, from which I am to be spared, has been directed against you in increasing force. My own opinion is that we Jews, if we want to cooperate with other people, have to develop a little masochism and be prepared to endure a certain amount of injustice.

It was Freud's own unfortunate disposition which here broke through: Any negative attitude on the part of a non-Jew against a Jew had to be, basically, anti-Semitic. Because Abraham disagreed with the Zurich psychiatrists in regard to the concept of schizophrenia, there had to be anti-Semitism at work on the part of the latter. When, because of a disagreement regarding the libido concept, Jung contradicted Freud, again it had to be anti-Semitism that created the disagreement on theoretical concepts.

The most significant statement for us in the Freud letters to Abraham is that in which Freud says that Abraham's racial relationship brings him closer to his (Freud's) intellectual constitution. This, we repeat, was said in 1908. When Jung, in an attempt to create an objective basis of discussion, spoke of a "factual difference between Germanic and Jewish psychology."* this was angrily denounced as anti-Semitism and Nazi sympathy. In fact, twenty-eight years earlier, Freud himself, with the purpose of making a young Jewish friend comfortable in an intellectual contradiction in a scientific argument with non-Jewish colleagues, had expressed the same idea of a difference in "intellectual constitution" (and what is this if not psychology?) between racial groups. It was Freud also who used the term "Aryan" in professional psychiatric discussion at a time when nobody had the slightest idea that a quarter of a century later this word would become the carrier of

---

* *Zentralblatt für Psychotherapie*, 7:9ff., 1934.

Nazi anti-Semitism. It was not Jung but Freud who, because of his unfortunate early experiences and the impairment of his career, was burdened with sentiments of racial controversy.

Jung always had and continued to have until the end of his life a considerable number of Jewish pupils. Not long before the anti-Semitic wave in Europe rose to its National Socialist height, he said in a lecture to the Swiss Protestant clergymen,[†] "I have treated many hundred of patients, the larger number being Protestants, a smaller number Jews, and not more than five or six believing Catholics." No convinced anti-Semite would write such a sentence.

In his attitude regarding racial and collective problems, Jung has been tragically misinterpreted because the basic concepts governing his motivations have been misunderstood. No one who has accused Jung of Fascist tendencies and of anti-Semitism has grasped what he said and meant. These persons have not confronted themselves with the same demand Jung made of himself when he encountered Freud, "to search as Freud searched." Only he who fully understands Jung would have the right to contradict him.

Jung's psychology is a differential, comparative psychology, a *verstehende Psychologie* in German, an expression which is difficult to translate. Jung is interested in the differentiation of structural and functional manifestations of the psyche and their causation. This has made him the exponent of psychotypology, which has won him his fame. However, his differential viewpoint does not stop at character and personality differentiation, but goes on to typological expressions as they appear in a social, cultural, and finally, anthropological, psychological aspect.

Jung strives to find clear and understandable descriptions of the expressions of the various human families on this earth. He is not a believer in the exclusively physical differentiation of man, or the purely biological reality of man. Humanity's religions and all cultural expressions are as real for him as are our eyes or any part of our physical anatomies. He therefore asks himself about the *how* and *why* of each specific form and content of these cultural

---

† Reprinted in JUNG, CARL G.: *Modern Man in Search of a Soul.* New York, Harcourt, p. 264.

realities. Jung believes that the collective powers which make up our social and cultural life are much stronger than many of the attitudes which express the individual configuration. He sees these collective patterns survive even though the individual may perish, and he sees these superindividual patterns inherited as psychological traits, just as we observe in ourselves inherited similarities from the physiognomies of our parents or grandparents. Jung has acquired a deep knowledge of the various types of this collective language, which assumes its own shape in symbolic and formal expressions. He has set for himself as the major therapeutic task that of assisting the individual to achieve a positive relationship with these collective forces, which, he holds, have a basic tendency to overpower the individual existence. Many of these conflicts exist on a subconscious level or in the realm of our irrational and emotional lives. The one effective means for their control is to lift them to the level of conscious experience. This does not mean rationalization, but rather awareness of their existence and of their symbolic manifestations.

To raise to a conscious level all discussions which are kindled by collective and individual emotional tensions—for instance, hate between racial or other human groups—would form the only basis for overcoming them or for paving the way toward a positive mutual understanding. Finally, there is still another postulate: The competent worker in the field of psychotherapy does not regard any life situation with either dogma or hypothesis, but accepts it as it presents itself when help is desired or administered, making the best use of the prevailing circumstances and preventing their deterioration. The foregoing remarks on Freud's character and this brief summary of some concepts of Jung is intended to assist in understanding the events which are to be described in the chronicle of 1933 and 1934, especially 1934.

Let us first consider these events by using the material which has formed the basis of the accusations concerning Jung's alleged Fascistic and anti-Semitic attitude. These quotations deserve a thorough discussion and need to be put in the right light. Finally, excerpts from a letter written by Jung to a Jewish friend in the spring of 1934 will be presented to demonstrate clearly his personal interpretation of the occurrences of those tragic months.

One recalls that the *Allgemeine Ärztliche Gesellschaft* and the *Zentralblatt* were founded because a large number of psychotherapists did not wish to be members of any of the psychiatric groups headed by one leader, but preferred a general organization. When, in 1933, Jung was asked to help save this international group and its journal by becoming president of the international association of national psychotherapeutic societies, the request came at a moment when it would have been senseless to launch an intensive attack upon anti-Semitism. During the preceding period, psychotherapy had become largely identified by the lay public with Freudianism, which was now being denounced by the Nazi propagandists as a prototype of Jewish psychology. In the true interest of the Jews, it would have been unwise to make a frontal attack against the German psyche, which was seething with hatred. To achieve any positive result, it was imperative to approach the question rationally and carefully.

How did Jung attempt to solve this obviously explosive problem? When taking over the editorship of the *Zentralblatt* he wrote a one-page announcement in which he said the following.

> Although psychotherapy as a science has nothing to do with politics, fate has ordained that I take over the editorship of the *Zentralblatt* at a moment which is characterized by a confusion of theories and standpoints in psychotherapy not unlike that which has hitherto prevailed in politics. One-sided viewpoints, which cannot be brought to agreement, have gained too great an influence not only on specific medical concepts but also on the psychological opinions of many educated laymen. The ensuing contradictions were still further increased when my completely different conceptions became known; and this, to such a degree, that the phrase "confusion of the minds," seems to be the only applicable one. It will therefore be the most distinguished task of the *Zentralblatt* to create a general attitude which will do justice to the basic facts of the human psyche to a higher degree than has hitherto prevailed, by means of an impartial appreciation of all objective contributions. The factually existing differences between the Germanic and Jewish psychologies should no longer remain blurred— to present them clearly is an aim from which science can but derive benefit. There exists in psychology, more than in any other science, a kind of "personal denominator," the disregard of which falsifies the results of practice and theory. I wish to state emphatically that this does not imply a depreciation of the Semitic psychology, just as a discussion of the distinctive psychology of the Far Eastern peoples does not imply a depreciation of the Chinese.

By attempting to raise the emotions underlying anti-Semitism to a higher level, Jung tried to give to the psychotherapeutic groups the basis of an existence despite the fanaticism of the Nazis. We know that he succeeded at least in the first rounds of the fight. His demand for an acknowledgment of all factual contributions to psychotherapy, in which he himself undertook the defense of Freud, subsequently aroused considerable antagonism on the part of National Socialism. This finally forced Jung to give up his efforts.

Unfortunately Jung's first attempts were as violently misunderstood by the Jewish side as they were by the personal enemies who used his statements against him. A Jewish periodical in Switzerland accused him of identifying the Jews with Mongolian hordes! The intolerance expressed in such a distortion is the equivalent of the intolerance of the anti-Semitic standpoint. Neither of these hostile viewpoints recognizes the higher objectivity which characterizes Jung's own viewpoints and action. Furthermore, if such a distortion warranted a reply, one might add that Jung has been a great admirer of Chinese religion and culture, as proved by his editorship of and commentaries on the *Tibetan Book of the Dead* and the *Secret of the Golden Flower*.

But a second step remained to be taken. This step was to make the psychotherapist aware of the subconscious and collective psychological background of National Socialism and to try to understand the role of anti-Semitism as a powerful weapon in its hands. Jung has not explicitly stated the following maxim, but it speaks through each of his lines: If you want to render help under such threatening conditions, you must first understand their cause. In the next issue of the *Zentralblatt** he wrote a long paper entitled *"Zur gegenwaertigen Lage der Psychotherapie"* ("On the Present Situation of Psychotherapy"). Here we will quote from it, in careful translation, the pages which have been widely circulated in misleading abbreviations and translations, and from which extracts have been pieced together in a fashion which distorts their meaning. In the first seven pages Jung discusses mainly Freud's

---

* 7 (1 and 2).

and Adler's concepts of psychotherapy, maintaining that they have developed therapeutic techniques which could be used in a routine manner, but not a therapeutic concept which would take care of the sick person as a total personality, and, at the same time emphasize the responsibility of the therapist, whose own attitude and background—in short, whose own personality—represent integral elements in his task of helping.

All these reflections lead us back to the attitude of the physician and to the need of a critique of the subjective premises. A *Weltanschauung* must not be uncritically applied to the concept of the neuroses, as happens for instance in the case of the Freudian concept of the unconscious or its materialistic prejudice in regard to the religious function of the soul. The psychotherapist should no longer indulge in the delusion that the treatment of the neuroses demands nothing more than the knowledge of a technique; he needs to understand very clearly that the psychological treatment of a patient constitutes a relationship which involves the physician as much as the patient. True psychological treatment can only be individual. Therefore, even the best technique possesses only relative value. Greater significance accrues to the physician's own general attitude, of which he himself must be sufficiently aware, in order not to destroy the particular values—whatever they may consist of—in the patient entrusted to his care. If Alfred Adler should request an analytic treatment from his old teacher Freud, Freud would have to accommodate himself to seeing Adler's special psychology and even acknowledge its collective right of existence. For there are countless persons who have the psychology of the frustrated son. If, on the other hand, I were to analyze Freud, I would be doing him a great and irreparable wrong if I did not take fully into account the historic reality of the nursery, the importance of the emotional entanglements within the family chronicle, the bitterness and seriousness of early acquired resentments and their compensatory concomitants of (unfortunately) unfulfillable wish fantasies, and if I did not accept their existence as an accomplished fact. Freud would certainly not be satisfied if I were to tell him that resentments are nothing but a "substitute" *(Ersatz)* for neglecting to love one's neighbor, or something of the sort. True as this statement may be in other cases, it would be inaccurate here, even if I should succeed in convincing Freud of the truth of my idea. Doubtless, Freud means what he says, therefore he must be accepted as the person who says such things. Only then is his individual case accepted, and, with him, are recognized those others whose psychology is similarly constituted. Now, insofar as one can hardly assume that Freud and Adler are universally valid representatives of European humanity, there exists for myself the immediate hope that I, too, possess a specific psychology and with me all those who similarly cannot subscribe to the primacy of infantile-perverse wish-fantasies or to that of the urge to power. It is self-evident that this must not be a matter of naive self-deception, but rather an opportunity for critical self-observation in the light of these negative psychologies which no psychotherapist should forego. Freud and Adler have seen very clearly the shadow which accompanies everyone. The Jews have this peculiarity in common with women: Being physically the weaker they have to aim at the chinks in their opponent's armor, and since this technique has been enforced upon them during a history of many centuries, the Jews themselves are best covered at the spots where others are most vulnerable. In consequence of their more than twice as ancient culture they are vastly more conscious of human weaknesses and inferiorities and therefore much less vulnerable in this respect than we are ourselves. They also owe to the experience of ancient culture the ability to live consciously in benevolent, friendly and tolerant neighborhood with their own defects (Untugenden), while we are still too young to have no illusions about ourselves. Moreover we have been called upon by fate still to create culture (for we are in need of it), to which end so-called illusions in the shape of one-sided ideals, convictions, plans, etc., are essential. The Jew as a member of a race whose culture is about 3,000 years old, like the educated Chinese, is psychologically conscious in wider areas than we are. Consequently it is less dangerous, generally speaking, for the Jew to devaluate his unconscious. The Aryan unconscious, on the other hand, contains tensions and creative germs of an as yet unfulfilled future which one may not devaluate as nursery romanticism without endangering the soul. The still young Germanic peoples are entirely able to produce new forms of culture, and this future still lies in the darkness of the unconscious of each individual, as a germ laden with energy, capable of a mighty blaze. The Jew, as relatively a nomad, never has produced and presumably never will produce a culture of his own, since all his instincts and gifts require a more or less civilized host-people for their development. Therefore the Jewish race as a whole has, according to my experience, an unconscious which can only conditionally be compared to the Aryan. Aside from certain creative individuals, the average Jew is already much too conscious and differentiated to be pregnant with the tensions of the unborn future. The Aryan unconscious has a higher potential than the Jewish; that is the advantage and the disadvantage of a youthfulness not yet fully estranged from barbarism. In my opinion, it has been a great mistake of all previous medical psychology to apply Jewish categories, which are not even binding for all Jews, indiscriminately to Christian Germans or Slavs. In so doing, medical psychology has declared the most precious secret of the Germanic peoples—the creatively prophetic depths of soul—to be childishly banal morass, while for decades my warning voice has been suspected of anti-Semitism. The source of this suspicion is Freud. He did not know the Germanic soul any more than did all his Germanic imitators. Has the mighty apparition of National Socialism, which the whole world watches with astonished eyes, taught them something better? Where was the unheard-of tension and energy when there was as yet no National Socialism? It lay hidden in the Germanic soul, in that profound depth which is everything else except the garbage bin of unreliable childish wishes and unresolved family resentments. A movement which seizes a whole people has ripened in every individual, too. It is for this reason that I say that the Germanic unconscious contains tensions and possibilities which medical psychology must consider in its evaluation of the unconscious. It does not deal with neuroses but with human beings, and it is truly the fortunate privilege of a medical psychology that not only is it permitted to *treat the whole person;* it even needs to do so. Therefore its framework must be widened to reveal to the eye of the physician not only the diseased aberrations of a disturbed psychological development, but also the constructive and creatively active forces of the soul, not only an obscure section but the significant whole.

Neurosis, namely, is by no means something merely negative, it is also positive. Only a soulless rationalism could overlook, and has overlooked, this fact, supported by the narrowness of a merely material *Weltanschauung.* In reality, the neurosis contains the patient's soul, or at least an essential part of it and if, according to rationalistic intention, the neurosis could be extracted like a diseased tooth, the patient would have gained nothing but would have lost something very essential, namely, as much as a thinker who has lost doubt about his conclusions, or a moral man who has lost his temptations, or a brave man who has lost his fear. To lose a neurosis means to become unsubstantial, indeed life loses its point and so its meaning. It would be no cure but an amputation; and it is a deceptive consolation if thereupon "psychoanalysis" assures us that nothing has been lost except the infantile paradise with its (perverse) wish-chimeras. One has lost much more, for in reality there is embedded in the neurosis a piece of still undeveloped personality, without which the human being is condemned to resignation, bitterness and other antagonisms to life. The psychology of neuroses which sees only the negative, empties out the baby with the bath, in that it neglects the meaning and value of the "infantile," i.e., the creative fantasy. Often the efforts of this psychology consist essentially in an attempt to find out how one could explain—anything at all—downward, and actually there is nothing incapable of an obscene caricature. This possibility never proves, however, that the symptom or symbol explained in this way actually has this meaning, it only proves the dirty adolescent fantasy of the interpreter.

I cannot avoid mentioning how often it happens that otherwise serious physicians, in complete disregard of all the fundamental tenets of scientific conscience explain psychological material by means of subjective conjectures—conjectures of which one can really make nothing, except that they are attempts to find that particular obscene witticism through which the material under investigation could be in some way related to an anal, urethral or other sexual abnormality. The poison of a devaluating interpretation has infiltrated the very marrow of these people, so that they can no longer think at all except in the infantile perverse jargon of certain cases of neuroses which are characterized by the special features of Freudian psychology. It is really too grotesque that the physician himself falls into that way of thinking which he rightly objects to as infantile in others, and therefore would like to cure. It is certainly much easier to make conjectures over the heads of other people, than to discover what the patient's empirical material means in itself. After all, one must assume that the patient comes to the doctor to free himself of his pathological modes of thought and of approach and, therefore, one might well assume—as is moreover the case in all modern medicine—that in the syndrome itself are also contained the healing tendencies of the diseased system. But if the physician's thoughts overtly or silently are as negative and devaluating as the patient's, and are equally desirous of pulling everything and anything into the infantile perverse morass of an obscene wit-psychology, one must not be surprised if the latter's soul becomes a barren waste and he compensates for this barrenness by an incurable intellectualism.

No one with any objectivity can maintain that we are here confronted with a document of anti-Semitic character or one which registers consent to, or admiration for National Socialism. In the accusations made against Jung the following expression in particular has been used as a weapon of attack: ". . . the mighty apparition of National Socialism which the whole world watches with astonished eyes, . . ." or, in the original German: ". . . *die gewaltige Erscheinung des Nationalsozialismus, auf den die ganze Welt mit erstaunten Augen blickt. . . .*"

There are two points in this sentence which need to be interpreted in their original meaning. The first is that the word *gewaltig* has a somewhat different connotation in Swiss usage than it has in German. Jung has frequently used the word—we would like to refer the reader to a context already presented in this chapter, where he speaks of the *gewaltige* (powerful) role which sexuality plays in the human psyche. In the German language, as it is understod by those who have exploited this sentence, one would hardly place sexuality and a political uprising on the same level. The Swiss dialectic version of German uses the word in a more dynamic sense and with greater frequency to describe an impressive event.*

The second point concerns the expression "with astonished eyes." Those who interpret these words as admiration of Nazism are motivated by the undercurrent of their own negative emotions, the projection of which makes them incapable of evaluating fairly any objective statement, which they can only perceive as an emotionally loaded one in a positive or a negative sense. Anyone among us today, opening an illustrated magazine of 1934 showing the massing of regiments and their flags on an occasion such as a Nürnberg meeting, must agree that this was an astonishing display, unexpected in its forcefulness, especially to those who spent their lives at a distance of several hundred miles. One can be astonished by certain phenomena without sympathizing with them; and one can be deeply disturbed by them and yet prefer not to express one's own negative feelings—in order to preserve one's own plans for helping others against new outbreaks of violence.

One must remember what position Jung occupied at that time, when he had to write for and to keep alive a publication printed for German doctors in Germany itself. Fanatics may often look upon cleverness with suspicion, but the question is whether this cleverness achieves the positive help for which it aims. Not one action can be found which could be interpreted in any way as showing that Jung had any part in National Socialist acts and plans, either in Switzerland or in Germany. On the other hand,

---

* For an analogy, consider such differences in British English and American English as the usages of "bloody" and "bitch"; or note that a British (or German) "billion" is a thousand times the size of an American billion. One might also recall the colloquial American—particularly adolescent American—habit of applying "terrific" to anything from a new movie start to a thunderstorm.

we have positive proof of the opposite, particularly where he opposed the anti-Semitism and the plans for anti-Semitic action made by the Nazis.

There is one point which must still be reported here in detail. From the days when Jewish psychiatrists in Germany were disqualified, Jung made every attempt to help them, as he fought against anti-Semitism in general whenever it was possible to do so without endangering his own moves to help. Anyone who, like the present author, has tried to learn from Dr. Jung must have been struck by the fine distinctions expressed through his actions and in the restraint imposed upon the spoken word.

We have already reported Jung's fine and gallant attitude during the first meeting of the international association of the national groups of psychotherapists in Bad Nauheim in central Germany in May of 1934, when he chose as the topic of his address the "Theory of Complexes," in which he paid homage to Freud, who was then the target of Nazi hatred. I recall how, on the following day, the German Press raged against Jung and carefully registered the number of times Jung had pronounced the hated name of Freud. There would certainly have been no reason to expose oneself in this manner during these weeks of the most fanatical outburst of anti-Semitism if one had wished to ingratiate himself with the National Socialist regime and its leaders.

During those same weeks, Jung undertook something which he would not have been able to do openly without destroying its success. He had caused a kind of amendment to be added to the rules of the international association of the national groups of psychotherapists. This amendment was not communicated in an official manner through the *Zentralblatt,* but was circulated quietly alongside one issue of the journal. The communication reads:

> During the last Congress of the *Überstaatliche allgemeine Ärztliche Gesellschaft für Psychotherapie* it was decided, to constitute the society in the form of national groups. Consequently, national groups have now been founded or are in process of formation in the various countries which were represented at the Congress [Denmark, Germany, Holland, Sweden and Switzerland]. The conditions of membership in these national groups vary according to local by-laws. On account of the political circumstances in various regions, and because of the

lack of national groups in certain countries, making it impossible for individuals to join their respective groups, it has been decided that membership in any national group is on a purely voluntary basis, in other words individual membership can be achieved directly in the *Überstaatliche allgemeine Ärztliche Gesellschaft für Psychotherapie* without the intermediary of a national group. The *Überstaatliche Gesellschaft* is politically and confessionally neutral. Those wishing to become members in it, are asked to communicate with the office of the secretary general of the *Überstaatliche Gesellschaft* represented by Dr. W. Cimbal in Altona, or with the business manager of the president, Dr. C. A. Meier, Burghoelzli, Zürich. The organ of the society is the *Zentralblatt für Psychotherapie. . . .* We therefore politely invite you to join the *Überstaatliche allgemeine Ärztliche Gesellschaft für Psychotherapie*.

Zürich-Küsnacht   Dr. C. G. Jung.

What Jung has done here was actually to find means of reviving under the nose of the Nazis the old "international society" by making it possible for anyone to become a member of the international association. At the same time something else was achieved, of which no mention was made, but which I, living at that time in Europe, knew was the main reason for this arrangement. This is corroborated by Jung's own report in the letter which will be reprinted later in this chapter. German Jewish psychotherapists, who were not allowed to join the German or any other national organization, were thus enabled to become members of the supernational association.

One more deduction can be made from this announcement. The denationalized psychotherapists wishing to join the international group could make their application through the business manager of the German "Nazified" group. If this group was willing to lend its services against the Nazi Order, then the entire psychotherapeutic association, including the German national group, must have been strongly anti-Nazi.

This was actually so, as I can assert from personal knowledge of the circumstances. Jung did not "play along with the Nazis," as has more than once been charged. Instead, he fought in a clever way, and the only possible way, against them, adjusting himself to the given conditions so he could extend his help.

Here is another refutation of the charge of anti-Semitism against

Jung: The first book he published after the Nazi rise is his volume, *Wirklichkeit der Seele*. The book has 409 pages. Of these, fifty are given over to a long study by a Jewish pupil of Dr. Jung, Hugo Rosenthal, entitled *"Der Typengegensatz in der jüdischen Religions-Geschichte"* ("The Typological Opposites in the History of the Jewish Religion"). Certainly this also was not an action which could have been intended to win him sympathy and friendship from the Nazis, and it was not meant to do so. Its meaning will become clear from the letter which will be presented.

Of course, persons with hate-inflated emotions may accept the presentation given here and yet may find the proof inadequate. However, the presentation here is made for sound and humanly adjusted minds and not for psychopathological personalities.

It now remains to follow the events which led to Dr. Jung's eventual resignation from cooperation with the *Überstaatliche Gesellschaft* and consequently from any contact with the then-existing German organizations.

To give a reasonable start to the collaboration within the framework of national groups set up by stipulation of the Nazi government, a first series of issues of the *Zentralblatt* was planned and executed, each issue undertaken by one of the national groups. The first one was a German issue, followed by Swiss, Dutch and Scandinavian numbers. Soon, however, regular publications became the rule once more.

Considerable distrust on the part of German officialdom appears to have existed concerning the psychotherapeutic organization; distrust however, which did not find sufficient grounds for interfering with its existence. However, a year later, we see Dr. Goering appearing as co-editor with Dr. Jung, while Dr. Cimbal retired in favor of a man who seems to have appeared more trustworthy to the Nazi authorities. This was in 1936. A neurologist and psychiatrist about whose political attitudes I have been unable to obtain sure information, Dr. von Weizsaecker, was added to the editorial board. This arrangement, however, only lasted for two more years. From 1937 onward, Jung's name was retained only more or less pro forma as a co-editor of the *Zentralblatt*.

Following is the letter written by Jung during May of the fateful year, 1934, to a Jewish pupil and friend who at that time still lived on the other side of the Atlantic, but who is now a practicing medical psychotherapist in this country. The recipient of this long letter has kindly agreed to have it reprinted in part. All and any passages of a personal nature have been omitted as well as those not essential to the task which this reprinting serves. Because the wording of such pronouncements is of basic importance, it is first reproduced in German, with an English translation also supplied.

. . . Es scheinen ja amüsante Gerüchte über mich ausgestreut zu werden. Die einzige Tatsächlichkeit, die hinter all diesem blöden Geschwätz liegt, ist, dass ich als Ehrenvorsitzender der Internationalen Gesellschaft für Psychotherapie diese nicht im Stiche lassen konnte, im Moment als Kretschmer zurücktrat. Ich bin von den deutschen Aertzten dringend ersucht worden, diese Stellung beizubehalten und habe in der Folge dasgetan, was jeder an meiner Stelle getan hätte, nämlich meine Pflicht gegenüber dem Internationalen Verein. Diese bestand wesentlich darin, die Rahmenorganisation zu halten und die deutsche in diese Organisation einzugliedern. Dies ist nun im letzen Nauheimer Kongress gelungen, und es ist auch die erfreuliche Tatsache zu verzeichnen, dass auf meinen Vorschlag ein besonderer Paragraph angenommen wurde, der es nun den deutschen jüdischen Aertzten ermöglicht, als Einzelmitglieder dem internationalen Verband beizutreten. Damit sind sie vollberechtigte Mitglieder geworden.

Auf die übrigen Gerüchte brauche ich wohl kaum einzugehen. Es ist eine glatte Lüge zu behaupten ich hätte gesagt, die Juden seien in der Analyse unehrlich. Die Leute müssen mich doch für reichlich dumm halten, wenn sie meinen, dass ich so etwas idiotisches behaupten könne. Ebenso habe ich weder im Rundfunk noch sonst irgenwie Hitler angesprochen oder irgend etwas in politischer Hinsicht gesagt.

Was nun meine Ansicht anbetrifft, dass die Juden voraussichtlich keine eigene Kulturform erzeugen, so beruht diese Ansicht, 1. auf historischen Tatsachen, 2. auf der anderen Tatsache, dass die eignetliche kulturelle Leistung des Juden sich am deutlichsten entfaltet innerhalb einer Wirtskultur, wo der Jude sehr oft zum eigentlichen Kulturträger wird, oder zu deren Promotor. Diese Aufgabe ist so eigenartig und anspruchsvoll, dass man kaum absehen könnte, wieso daneben erst noch eine individuelle jüdische Kultur entstehen könnte. Da nun in Palästina tatsächlich sehr eingenartige Verhältnisse vorliegen, so habe ich ein vorsichtiges 'voraussichtlich' in meinen Satz eingeführt. Ich möchte keineswegs die Möglichkeit bestreiten, dass dort etwas eigenartiges entsteht, aber ich weiss es bis jetzt noch nicht. Ich kann schlechterdings in dieser Ansicht nichts antisemitisches entdecken. . . .

. . . Der jüdische Christuscomplex ist eine sehr beachtenswerte Angelegenheit. Wie Sie wissen, stimme ich Ihnen in dieser Hinischt durchaus zu. Die Existenz dieses Complexes bedingt eine etwas hysterisierte allegemeine Geisteshaltung, die mir besonders jetzt bei der gegenwärtigen antichristlichen Hetze gegen mich, deutlich geworden ist. Die blosse Tatsache, dass ich von einer Differenz zwischen jüdischer und christlicher Psychologie spreche, genügt schon, um jeden das Vorurteil vorbringen zu lassen, ich sei ein 'Antisemit.' Oder wie "z. B. das Schweizerische Israelitische Wochenblatt" meint: mit meiner Behauptung, dass ich ebensowenig ein Antisemit wie ein Antichinese sei, wolle ich die Juden einer mongolischen Horde vergleichen. Diese Empfindlichkeit ist einfach krankhaft und macht jede Diskussion beinahe unmöglich. Schon Freud hat mich, wie Sie wissen, des Antisemitismus angeklagt, weil ich seinen seelenlosen Materialismus nicht billigen konnte. Mit dieser Bereitwilligkeit überall Antisemitismus zu wittern, beschwört der Jude direkt Antisemitismus herauf. Ich sehe nicht ein, warum der Jude nicht ebensogut wie ein sogenannter Christ annehmen kann, man kritisiert ihn persoenlich, wenn man eine Meinung über ihm hat. Warum muss denn immer gleich angenommen werden, dass man das jüdische Volk damit verdammen wolle? Der Einzelne ist doch nicht das Volk? Ich halte dies für eine unzulässige Art, den Gegner mundtot zu machen. Ich bin mit meinen jüdischen Patienten oder Kollegen in der grossen Mehrzahl der Fälle sehr gut ausgekommen. Dass ich an Einzelnen Kritik üben musste, das kommt auch bei anderen Leuten vor, wird aber vom diesen nicht darauf bezogen, dass sie Engländer, Amerikaner oder Franzosen seien. Allerdings gibt es da eine Ausnahme, die ich erwähnen will, das sind die Deutschen. Es ist mir naemlich mehr als einmal passiert, dass wenn ich einen einzelnen Deutschen kritisierte, er flugs auf die Idee verfiel, ich sei ein Deutschenhasser. Es ist aber zu billig, wenn man seine eigene Minderwertigkeit hinter einen politischen Vorurteil verbergen will . . .

. . . Sie wissen doch zur Genüge, wie sehr ich den Menschen als Persönlichkeit nehme und mich bestrebe, ihn aus seinen Kollektivbedingungen herauszuheben und zu einem Individuum zu machen. Es ist ja, wie Sie ebenfalls wissen, nur möglich, wenn er seine Besonderheit, die ihm durch das Schicksal aufgenötigt ist, erkennt. Keiner der ein Jude ist, kann zum Menschen werden, ohne dass er weiss, dass er ein Jude ist, denn das ist die Basis von der er ein höheres Menschentum erreichen kann. Das gilt für alle Nationen und Rassen. Der Nationalismus, so unsympathisch er auch ist, ist darum eine

Conditio sine qua non, nur darf der Einzelne nicht darin stecken bleiben. Aber als Massenpartikel soll er sich auch nicht darüber erheben. Als Mensch bin ich ein Europaeer, als Massenatom bin ich ein schweizerischer Spiessbürger, wohnhaft Seestrasse 228 Küssnacht bei Zürich. . . .

Zum Schluss möchte ich Ihnen noch mitteilen, dass mein neues Buch "Wirklichkeit der Seele" erschienen ist, worin ich einen jüdischen Autor über alttestamentliche Psychologie aufgenommen habe, um die National-sozialisten zu ärgern, und alle diejenigen Juden, die mich als Antisemiten verschrieen haben. Das Nächste was jetzt erfunden werden wird, ist, dass ich an einer kompletten Standpunktslosigkeit leide und weder ein Antisemit bin noch ein Nazi. Wir leben in einer Zeit, die von Narrheit überströmt. *"Quem Deus vult perdere primus dementat."*

Mit den besten Grüssen, Ihr
C. G. Jung,
et semper idem.

The Translation

. . . it appears that amusing rumors are being spread about me. The only unquestionable fact which lies behind all this stupid gossip is that having been elected honorary chairman *(Ehrenvorsitzender)* of the International Society for Psychotherapy. I could not desert the society at the moment when Kretschmer resigned. I have been urgently requested by the German physicians to retain this position and have consequently done what anyone else would have done in my situation, namely, my duty toward the International Society. This consisted in the main in preserving the supernational society *(Rahmenorganisation)* and in affiliating to it the German society. This was accomplished at the last Nauheim Congress. We can also register the satisfying fact that at my suggestion a special paragraph has been adopted to the effect that German Jewish physicians can individually join the international organisation. They have thus become full members with equal rights.

I need hardly mention the other rumors. It is a downright lie to quote me as having said that Jews are dishonest in analysis. Anyone who believes that I could say anything so idiotic must think me extraordinarily stupid. Neither have I addressed Hitler over the radio or in any other manner, nor have I expressed anything in regard to politics. In regard to my opinion that the Jews probably do not create their own forms of culture, this opinion rests upon (1) historical facts, (2) the fact that the specific cultural contribution of the Jew achieves its clearest results within the circle of a host culture, where the Jew frequently becomes the very carrier of this culture or its promoter. This task is in itself so specific and so demanding that it is hardly to be conceived that any individual Jewish culture could arise alongside it. Since Palestine actually presents very peculiar conditions [The recipient of this letter was at that time living in Palestine], I have cautiously inserted the word "probably" *(voraussichtlich)* into my sentence. I would in no wise deny the possibility that something specific is being created there, but so far I do not know it. I cannot discover anything anti-Semitic in this opinion. . . .

. . . The Jewish Christ complex is a very remarkable affair. As you know I completely agree with you in this respect. The existence of this complex makes for a somewhat hystericised general attitude of mind *(Geisteshaltung)* which has become especially clear to me in the course of the present anti-Christian attacks upon myself. The mere fact that I speak of a difference between Jewish and Christian psychology suffices to allow anyone to voice the prejudice that I am an anti-Semite. Or, in the opinion of the Swiss Israelitic Weekly, my assertion that I am as little an anti-Semite as an anti-Chinese proves my intention to compare the Jews with a Mongolian horde. This hypersensitivity is simply pathological and makes every discussion almost impossible. As you know, Freud previously accused me of anti-Semitism because I could not countenance his soulless materialism. The Jew truly solicits anti-Semitism with his readiness to scent out anti-Semitism everywhere. I cannot see why the Jew, like any so-called Christian, is incapable of assuming that he is being personally criticized when one has an opinion about him. Why must it always be assumed that one wants to condemn the Jewish people? Surely the individual is not the people? I regard this as an inadmissible manner of silencing one's adversary. In the great majority of cases, I have got along very well with my Jewish patients and colleagues. It happens in the cases of other people, too, that I have to criticize the individual; but they do not ascribe it to the fact that they are English, American or French. However, there does exist one exception worth mentioning in this respect, and that is the German. It has happened to me more than once that when I criticized a German he immediately concluded that I am a hater of Germans. It is really too cheap to try to hide one's own inferiority behind a political prejudice. . . .

. . . You know well enough to what extent I approach the human being as a personality and how I endeavor to lift him out of his collective conditioning and to make him into an individual. This, as you know, is only possible if he acknowledges his peculiar features *(Besonderheit)* which have been forced upon him by fate. No one who is a Jew can become a human being without knowing that he is a Jew, since this is the basis from which he must reach out toward a higher humanity *(Menschentum)*. This holds good for all nations and races. Nationalism is therefore a *"sine qua non"*—no matter how objectionable it may appear—but the individual must not remain stuck in it. On the other hand, insofar as he is a particle of the mass of the people, he must not elevate himself above it, either. As a human individual I am a European, as an atom of the masses I am a Swiss bourgeois, domiciled at 228, Seestrasse, Küsnacht near Zürich....

Finally I want to inform you that my new book, *Wirklichkeit der Seele*, has appeared. I have included in it a Jewish author on the "Psychology of the Old Testament" in order to annoy the Nazis and all those Jews who have decried me as an anti-Semite. The next thing they are going to invent about me now is that I suffer from a complete absence of convictions and that I am neither an anti-Semite nor a Nazi. We happen to live in a period which overflows with lunacy. *"Quem deus perdere vult primum dementat."*

With kindest regards,
Yours,
C. G. Jung,
et semper idem.

Chapter 26

CARL GUSTAV JUNG AND AMERICAN ACADEMIC PSYCHOLOGY

IN the second volume of the *Psychological Bulletin* of 1905, the Baltimore psychiatrist Adolph Meyer, reviewing the first volume of C. G. Jung's *Diagnostic Association Studies,* wrote, "This remarkable piece of work and its continuation are no doubt the best single contribution to psychopathology during the past year."

Born and educated in Switzerland, Meyer apparently understood the essence of Jung's study. In the next (third) volume of the *Bulletin,* another unnamed American reviewer discussed the continuation of the *Diagnostic Association Studies* with a completely different result: "We will have to admit frankly that our mind is less adapted to this type of work than Jung's; it would be foolish to be sensitive about admissions of personal differences; and the psychology of the subject must be supplymented by the psychology of the experimenter."

These remarks referred to the early work of Jung, which admittedly still stood on the ground of academic experimental psychology, and one cannot but agree that no one among Jung's later critics has formulated as sincere and objective a critical stand. When, later, Jung's characteristic major psychological works appeared, American psychology found it difficult *not* to reject them as mysticism and as "religious and metaphysical speculation, not at all scientifically acceptable." However, the monumental eighteen-volume edition of Jung's work now being published in this country puts before American psychology the peculiar task of finding some kind of objective position. William Douglas, a specialist in the psychology of religion, wrote a general evaluation of the seven volumes published up to that time. Dr. Douglas has made a highly commendable attempt to bring Jung closer to American academic psychology, but one cannot but gain the impression that he only speaks *about* Jung and does not open the road to a real understanding. He refers to the introverted Oriental and stops with Henry Murry's suggestion to "feel and think at once." His highest acknowledgment is, "If you have wrestled with Jung you are never the same again."

When Jung's scientific development did, for a few years, run parallel to Freud's, he felt obliged to help make the Vienna master acceptable to his hostile contemporaries. The basic element in Jung's psychological approach is to be found in the statement he wrote again and again: "To understand Freud one must learn to think as Freud thinks." He called this *"verstehende"* (search-for-understanding-and-empathy) psychology. This understanding involves, in the view of the reviewer quoted above, an understanding of the personal differences and psychology of the experimenter.

Psychology, like the other fields of human scientific endeavor, is based on the experience of certainty. When Descartes had established the personal experience of certainty in his *cogito ergo sum,* and Kant had postulated the concept of a specific certainty as a principle of all scientific endeavor in his demand that acceptable scientific standards be based only upon a mathematical certainty, modern scientific autonomy challenged this unjustified generalization. We now accept the fact that the entire world of the living, which we study by the aid of the sciences of biology and physiology, has its own laws which go far beyond those presented by the mathematical sciences. This means that biology also has a different concept of certainty. Coming back to psychology, we find that the majority of its representatives, and especially those of the American behaviorist school, consider psychological facts as merely being expressions of physiological functions which they wish to establish scientifically by a methodology and a certainty concept derived from physiology. Psychology, in other words, is regarded as a biological science. Thus, to speak of an autonomous psychology is considered a dubious undertaking, and an attempt to establish a purely psychological experience is considered introspective, unscientific subjectivism.

From the point of view of theoretical general psychology, Jung's major contribution is that he has attempted to establish such a scientific autonomous psychology based on a concept of the psyche as a dynamic, self-contained energy system which, so far as it is conscious, can be experienced by almost everyone who has been trained in objective psychological observation. Starting with his *Diagnostic Association Studies,* Jung attempted to develop such an objective method of psychological observation. Just as the eye must be trained to observe through the microscope or to read X-ray films, the method of experimental observation, as adopted from physiology and considered as the objective basis of academic psychology, can be applied to introspective self-observation. The observer need simply make himself aware of the psychological attitude with which he observes and apply this to his personal psychological experience. From this there develops a new, purely psychological sense of certainty, an autonomous psychological one. Jung has in his writings shown various ways of achieving this experience, and Douglas, who has experienced the change, says that one is "never the same" after such training.

Henry Murry's explanation (quoted by Douglas) that the experience amounts to a combination of thinking and feeling has only limited validity, since there are also other approaches. Jung himself has repeatedly referred to the central element of his psychology and psychotherapy as aimed at individuation. The autonomous psychological certainty experience is introductory to this. The majority of Jung's writings, including those that have been labeled metaphysical and mythological fantasies, become experienceable in their psychological reality after this introductory experience is achieved.

Finally, it may be added that such an objectivized introspective psychology is well able to distinguish between autonomous psychological certainty experiences and what William James, at the end of his *Variety of Religious Experience,* called the experience of God, which is indeed a metaphysical experience.

Chapter 27

THE FRAGMENT OF A GIGANTIC
PSYCHOLOGY

WITH the passing of Carl Gustav Jung on June 16, 1961, the curtain of history fell on a period extending over three-quarters of a century, during which the most outstanding and influential world concept received its orientation from insight into the reality of man's soul. Although Freud, Adler, and Jung, and most of those who joined them in the new approach, were first of all professional mental healers, or psychiatrists, it can now be seen historically that their attempt aimed to transform the physical and physiological conception of the world, built up during the preceding three hundred years, into an autonomous orientation deriving from a point of view centered in man's inner life.

Although there has been an astonishing amount of writing regarding this new psychological concept, it must be conceded that almost all that has been presented by way of basic orientation has come from Freud, Adler and Jung, the principal founders of the concept, and that no signs are evident that the concept will be carried much beyond what they have achieved. In fact, in the narrower field of psychiatry we are already witnessing in the present decade a swing back to a neurophysiological point of view. Still less can we see any definite promise that the psychological orientation will be revived in the foreseeable future.

During the first decade of the development of this new concept, workers in the field—almost all of them Freudians—and Freud himself created the impression that Sigmund Freud was the sole originator and that the others, especially C. G. Jung, were dissenters and traitors. This contention has been intensively opposed. Now, after half a century, the clouds of emotional attachment have been cleared from the historical horizon and a more objective view is possible.

There can be no doubt that in the beginning Jung was considerably influenced by Freud. In his doctoral thesis of 1902, he referred in several places to Freud's *Interpretation of Dreams*. In 1904, the year in which *The Psychopathology of Everyday Life* appeared, he wrote* in a reply to a critic an as-yet-never-quoted sentence: *"Die Analyse des Krankheitsbildes lehnt sich nicht an franzoesische Autoren sonder an die Freudische Hysterie-Forschung an"* ("My analysis of illness rests not on French authors but on Freud's research in hysteria").

But this is as far as it went. If one studies Jung's first major work, his *Diagnostic Association Studies,* one cannot but recognize that here is a scientific mind completely different from Freud's, working from different basic approaches and with different aims. If one follows the workings of this mind over the decade of relationship with Freud, one must also recognize, as I have already indicated, that it was directed toward clarifying differences and not toward submission to the other's wider concepts. When this difference was ultimately clearly defined in Jung's book, *Transformations and Symbols of the Libido* (which appeared in English as *The Psychology of the Unconscious),* it signaled the start of the final break. Freud stigmatized the break by personal accusations. Jung's way was always to avoid personal attacks. When the break between the Vienna and the Zurich group came, Jung had announced his resignation as editor of the jointly published journal simply as due to "personal reasons."

Because of his tendency to withhold personal information, it is not easy to draw a picture of Jung's personality, but history seems to demand to know more about a man's origins and motives than the man is sometimes willing to reveal of his own volition. From the few biographical sketches we have of Jung, we receive the impression that the functioning of his personality and his passage through the earthly life were smooth as compared with the stormy events of Freud's life. To one who was privileged to obtain a more intimate view, however, it is apparent that Jung's personality and activities were not without profound contradictions.

He was born into a middle-class Swiss clergyman's family, but

---

* Hysterical Misreading. *Arch Ges Psychol, II*:347, 1904.

most of his adult life was lived as a well-to-do aristocrat. Those who knew him during the first decade of this century thought him the perfect type of a psychiatric institutionalist and academician, but this soon changed, and he remained for most of his life a practitioner and professional writer, returning only during the later decades to limited academic teaching in a chair especially created for him.

From his work one must receive the impression that to him nothing was more essential than group formations and man's collective relationships, yet he never achieved the creation of a collective movement based on his philosophy of life, and in fact he made no serious attempt in this direction. In is hard to imagine a more cosmopolitan thinker than Jung, yet he has again and again been accused of racist and Nazi tendencies and attacked for being anti-Jewish-minded. This author can state from personal experience that Jung did his utmost, both personally and financially, to help Jewish colleagues who were victims of Nazi oppression.

No one, not even Wundt, has more profoundly probed the realm of man's psychological experience than has Jung in his works. Jung, however, never attempted a systematic presentation of his work. All of his works are of a problematic nature, and many of his books are collections of short problematic papers. In one of the most impressive discussions I had with him, to which I shall refer later, he said, "There is nothing more difficult than to think any problem really through to its end." This is characteristic of Jung's thinking, in which every problem contains the nucleus of at least two new ones.

Accordingly, Jung's psychology has grown out of an unfolding problematic. We see him starting out from what seems to be the psychological or psychopathological problematic of the turn of this century. Every where in Europe—in France, Italy, England, middle Europe and Scandinavia—as well as on this side of the Atlantic, the professionals were occupied with the problematic of a super- or subconsciousness and its detrimental influence on the status of the human consciousness itself. Late in life Jung occupied himself with this problem of the simultaneous occurrence of similar problems in unrelated spheres of mankind's experience, and he designated this phenomenon, which others had called *Zeit-Geist,* as *synchronicity.*

Jung's initial tackling of this problematic in his doctoral theses of 1902 *(Psychology and Pathology of so-called Occult Phenomena)* shows that he had a quite different and much wider view of these problems than Freud ever had. The entire study was more the asking of questions than an answer to one. Jung was very dissatisfied with the customary method of inventorizing consciousness. He presented his own attempt at a new method in an extensive research project which was published some years later as *Diagnostic Association Studies.* Although, as I have indicated in the foregoing chapter, Jung has again and again been accused of unscientific mysticism, it has always been his aim to develop exact scientific methods in whatever field of human experience he was working.

The early *Diagnostic Association Studies* was still entirely in the realm of contemporary psychology, and it received the highest acknowledgement. As practically everyone knows, these early tests devised by Jung have become the basis for broadly applied testing methods in psychopathology and criminology. Unfortunately, the translators of the American Edition of the early works of Jung were not able to transcribe the terminology in which Jung was thinking at that time into the professional language of the American psychologists of today, making it almost impossible to understand the texts.

At the time that Jung was occupied with his association studies he had already realized that they would not lead completely satisfactorily to the revealing of the causal background of conscious factors which were themselves unexplainable. It was at this point that Jung had hoped to find in Freud's psychoanalytical method the key that would open the closed door. The importance of Freud's psychoanalytical method was always acknowledged by Jung, but Freud had more than this method. He had an underlying predominantly biogenetic theory—his libido concept. In *Wandlungen und Symbole der Libido (Transformations and Symbols of the Libido),* published in 1912, Jung definitely formulated the difference between his and Freud's basic concepts. It was this difference that caused the break between them. Already in this book there is clearly contained, in nuclear form, Jung's own psychology.

Jung had on various occasions described his psychology under the three major aspects of *Erlebnis-, Verstehende-* and *Komplex-Psychologie* (self-experience, understanding, and complex psychology).

The aspect of self-experience has to do with the most basic factors: The human psyche is not a secondary sphere of reality compared with the outer world or the body; it is as real as the latter. To experience the psyche in this way, another kind of experiencing is necessary from that applied by our present experimentally oriented psychology. Jung rejects the differentiation of introspective and experimentational verification. Self-experience psychology is an objectivized self-observation, as objective as any other scientific method. Self-experience psychology widens the sphere of psychology to the infinite on the one hand, and on the other it establishes an autonomous psychological energy concept, the first postulation of which is the individual psyche as a closed energy system. For most American psychologists, Jung's self-experience psychology is incomprehensible.

The understanding aspect of Jung's psychology is that of an increased empathy which does not describe and explain only, but rather analyzes the inner dynamics and the causes of psychological factors and events. At the time when Jung was defending Freud against his critics, he demanded that one first be able to "think as Freud thinks" before rejecting him. Jung's understanding, illustrated in this attitude, has become the basis for his frequently acknowledged sensitive approach to psychopathology, as well as to the formulation of his typology. It has been, finally, the basis of the attempt to understand the forces empowering Nazism and the characteristics of the Jewish mentality that arouse anti-Semitism. Both of these attempts to help by finding ways to understand have been misunderstood and condemned.

Jung's complex psychology grows out of the aspects of self-experience and understanding. The self-experience theory opened the way to a multitude of psychological facets which were applied not only to the differential details of his typology but to the differential aspect that has been frequently denounced as mysticism. The latter comprises his concept of the shadow, of *animus* and *anima,* of introvert and extrovert, and so forth. From Jung's theory of complex psychology result, further, his concepts of the subconscious, the archetypes and the collective subconscious. To see Jung as a reviver of antique, primitive and medieval religious concepts because he studied and wrote widely on the subject, for instance, of alchemy, is to misunderstand him. These studies were presented for comparative and explanatory purposes. Jung saw, in his self-experience and complex psychology psychological factors similar to those at issue in the anthropological and religious spheres, and he tried to make himself understood by applying them in an analogical way. This historical method is not new: The Freudians applied it in their Oedipus complex, and it has been used in every phase of anthropological interpretation.

Jung has been most unfortunately misunderstood by those who accused him of wanting to revive religion to replace modern scientific experience. Jung, in fact, only pointed out that religion is a basic form of human experience not properly understood even by the many persons who are consciously or unconsciously deeply involved in it. Jung saw it as a major task of his psychological approach to clarify this involvement and thereby try to solve the severe psychological and psychopathological problems connected with religious involvement. He never preached any religion, but one is made soundly aware of the real role of religion by applying his concepts. Recently I met a prominent Indian at an event at the United Nations. He expressed the opinion that too much is said about religious freedom in America, where, he said, there is actually less religious freedom than anywhere else in the world. In his own way, this Easterner was expressing Jung's view that collective powers impose taboos that hamper the individual in achieving insight into decisive factors of his very existence and in achieving self-control. Indeed, Jung emphasized that mental health depends on psychological awareness of and independence from collective subduing powers. All of American communal life suffers most seriously from the lack of this awareness and independence.

Jung's work proceeded along two lines which, in one sense, are deeply connected, and in another, are far apart in aim. The one was that of the psychiatrist and psychological healer, the other that of the psychological educator, or as we might call it on this side of the ocean, the mental hygienist. At about the time that he broke with Freud, Jung also separated himself, although not as dramatically, from his teacher and friend, Eugen Bleuler. Bleuler had achieved his fame with his remarkable phenomenological description of psychopathological somatic pictures. Against this Jung contended that psychopathology should be viewed first and last as a deviation of a normal psyche, a pathological process in which cause, beginning and end should be viewed always in the singularity as they appear in an individual patient.

Originally much involved in Bleuler's schizophrenia researches, Jung later more and more enlarged his horizon. He once told me, "There should be a system of deviations from the normal, which alone could give a proper basis to psychiatry." It is most unfortunate that he never presented such a system of psychopathology.

Jung apparently considered the second of his psychological tasks, the educational, as the more important. The major part of his writing was devoted to education in psychology. He once explained to me that he believed his most important insight was his recognition of modern man's need of proper psychological education. At the center of all major religions, including early Christianity, is the care and development of the individual's mind and psyche and their guidance through life. Modern religion has little concern for these matters, and this is a major reason for the confusion and mental pathology of modern man.

Jung saw as the great task of modern psychology—scientific in the sense he understood it—the development and guidance of man's mind and psyche. At the center of this approach to mental health was Jung's concept of *individuation*. What to earlier religions were maturation and initiation procedures and rites, Jung formulated as a process of self-development and completion of the regulating of the individual's relationship to his collective ties. On thus completing the development of one's personality also depends, of course, the individual's mental health. Because of the similarity of this individuation psychology to the initiation procedures of earlier periods, it appears justified, as has been done, to describe Jung's psychology as a modern initiation psychology.

Although Jung wrote more than fifty books and several hundred papers, one cannot get over a feeling of incompleteness in this gigantic life work. The reason for this is that Jung never drew together the major aspects of his teaching. In this connection, an account of my last personal meeting with him in Europe is relevant.

The meeting occurred in the fall of 1935, just prior to my final departure for this country. I was then employed in the capacity of editor by the publisher of most of Jung's work, who had begun the publication of a library of the basic philosophies of the major scientific fields. Included in the planned volumes was one on psychology, which we felt only Jung should write. Besides, this would provide the occasion, finally, for Jung to write a systematic presentation of his psychology, which most of those who followed his thinking felt was sorely needed.

I was given the task of convincing Jung, if possible, to agree to the plan. Time was limited. Jung was then at his country place on upper Zurich Lake. He agreed to a conference, and I was asked to meet him at the nearest railroad station. The day of the meeting was a day of Swiss "land-rain," and it was decided that instead of my going to the country place we would have our conference over a glass of wine in the railroad restaurant.

I was well prepared in my mind for my diplomatic mission. I entered upon a long introduction and went into great detail about the need for the book. Jung listened attentively in his kindly way, asking one-word questions here and there while he drew geometric figures on the white marble table between us. When I thought I had completed my plea, I waited in silence. From the increasing strain visible in Jung's face I knew that he was moved by my urging and concerned as to his answer. He spoke for more than half an hour. He emphasized how slowly he had proceeded to formulate his concepts, how long it had taken to work out this or that aspect, how little he had actually completed, and how much was still to be done. With an almost pained expression, he finally rose saying, "I am sorry I cannot do what you ask. To complete this psychology would take more than a lifetime." He drew his raincoat tightly around his shoulders and walked away into the rainy night. Jung died in the summer of 1961, eighty-five years old. He had left no systematic presentation of his work, only a gigantic fragment.

Chapter 28

WILLIAM ALANSON WHITE:
THE FORGOTTEN GIANT OF AMERICAN
PSYCHIATRY

THERE now exists a William A. White Institute, William A. White Lectures and the William A. White Foundation; but who is this William Alanson White, who died just twenty years ago, and what is it that he did? Hardly anyone knows. Even if his scientific twin brother, Smith Ely Jelliffe, wrote in an obituary note that White was "the outstanding all-around leader in psychiatry in this country," scarcely one of his two dozen books and almost 250 scientific papers is still read. His basic text, *Outlines of Psychiatry,* which had fourteen editions during the author's lifetime, can be found piled in second-hand bookstores. It takes long searching to find his name quoted in any of the major books on psychiatry published since 1945.

What is the reason for this phenomenon? Someone with superficial knowledge of psychiatry's development during the last half-century may ask if White was an adversary of the Freudian boom that swept over this country like a duststorm, blinding many professional eyes to any academic or non-Freudian views. White, however, was not an antipsychoanalyst. On the contrary, he founded and edited the *Psychoanalytic Review.* In addition to introducing DuBois' and Bleuler's works to this country, he acted as the eager promoter of Freud and Adler and some of Freud's immediate students. He even endorsed Freud for the Nobel Prize. However, as the obituary pages in the *Psychoanalytic Review* report, White came into psychoanalysis not by any direct Freudian way, but via the Zurich school. Although he undoubtedly had thoroughly absorbed Freud's theories into his psychiatric thinking, he did not associate with those orthodox Freudian groups which became leaders of psychoanalysis in this country in the 1920's and '30's.

It is common knowledge that a few years before White's early death, a group was organized which later called itself the White Institute of Psychiatry. Its leader was Harry Stack Sullivan. Sullivan was a man who apparently had a considerable following, or else his intellectual production, mainly sets of lectures, would not have been published by his friends as late as half a dozen years after his death.

If one examines Sullivan's set of five memorial lectures, given in 1939 at the Institute, looking for quotations from his teacher, W. A. White, one observes with some astonishment that only in the beginning and final sections of the first lecture does he quote him. White is nowhere else mentioned. If, however, one examines some of Sullivan's writings more thoroughly—for instance, his major work, *The Interpersonal Theory of Psychiatry*—one finds that it is actually only a variation on White's basic concepts. Chapter by chapter one notices that it is based upon White's *Introduction to the Study of the Mind*—without any mention of this, however.

We are not so much interested in this fact, though, since it seems rather doubtful that many readers would have gone back to White's writings. It is factually more interesting that Sullivan's presentation of White's ideas became popular, while the actual originator's books dropped into the world of the forgotten.

It remains for historical inclination to discover why White's psychiatric thought did not take root in American psychiatry's general development. White's neglect in this seems joined to that of another psychiatric writer, Boris Sidis. Sidis was personally connected with White and seems to be similarly wiped off the slate of American psychiatric history. If White's long set of writings is visualized, one element comes forward which seems to separate him from the majority of present-day psychiatrists. This is his middle-of-the-road attitude, which coordinated various schools of his time.

He was not a dogmatic follower of Freud, Adler or Jung, not to mention Adolf Meyer, but accepted certain aspects of each's theory—a rare attitude indeed in the last twenty-five years. He also did not fall into line with the stereotyped ways of writing which cover and paralyze most of psychiatry as well as the field of medicine. He wrote in a simple, almost unscientific style which, outside of certain necessary terminology, is understandable to any lay reader, as White once mentioned he had intended. Jelliffe, closer than anyone to White, pointed out in a memorial article that he actually started out with Kraepelian psychiatric thought in his first edition of *Outlines of Psychiatry* (1907), but that he changed over the years. Indeed, if we view the various editions up to the fourteenth (1935), we will see an assimilation of various Freudian and other outlooks.

To this author, the lack of interest in White's psychiatric thinking by the following generation seems to be caused by his applying concepts that are quite far from the mainstream of current theoretical interests. This includes, for example, the concept of totality that he assimilated specifically from the Zurich school's psychological viewpoints. In what is probably his most mature book, *Introduction to the Study of the Mind,* he demands that totalistic thought should be applied everywhere. The individual should be seen as a physio-psychic unit; the psyche is again a unit in itself. In addition, experiences with the outer world should be correlated as a unit.

In this attempt at coordination he not only desired to correlate Freudian psychoanalysis with academic psychiatry, but also attempted to tie together the British aspect of mental science and medical psychology with the pragmatic and behavioristic thought that was a specifically American tradition. There was a wide difference, for example, in this respect, from Adolf Meyer's much more simple, seemingly practical physiological or biological psychiatry.

White's influence during his life resulted from his personally fascinating way of presenting his thoughts to his large group of pupils. He was a much sought-after speaker, but after his death his writing proved to be a hardly understandable scientific language. One who makes the effort to read White's books, however, will be astonished at his broad outlook and his penetrating insight. In his autobiography, in one of his far-seeing insights, White correctly said of himself, "My initiative kept me forging ahead all the time, and tended not only to keep me perhaps abreast of the times, but a little ahead of them, which is always a dangerous position to occupy."

This dangerous position made him too-soon forgotten, but for the sake of psychiatry's progress we can only hope that the next generation will rediscover William Alanson White.

NAME INDEX

A

Abraham, Karl, 214 ff.
Ackerknecht, Erwin H., 16
Adler, Alfred, 187, 208 ff., 221, 237, 246 ff.
Aetius, 82
Allers, Rudolf, 210 ff.
Arndt, Rudolf, 69, 175
Aschaffenburg, Gustav, 202
Achner, Bernhard, 15, 21
Augustin, Friederich L., 68
Aurelian, 81
Avincenna, 81

B

Beauchamp, Miss, 183
Bellini, Lorenzo, 81 ff.
Beneke, Friederich Eduard, 4, 134-153
Benedikt, Moriz, 68
Beyerholm, Otto, 16, 133
Bing, Robert, 197
Binet, Alfred, 202
Bini, L., 67-69
Bjerre, Poul, 209
✓ Bleuler, Eugen, 5, 87, 160 ff., 181, 182 ff., 200-233, 243, 246
Boerhaave, Hermann, 81, 138
Boismont, Pierre de, 170
Boor, Wolfgang de, 158 ff.
Braceland, Francis J., v-viii
Braatoy, Trygve, 195
Bresler, Johannes, 155
Breuer, Joseph, 187, 202
Brown, William, 188
Bruecke, Ernst, 196
Brun, R., 195
Buehler, Charlotte, 191
Butte, Wilhelm, 194

C

Carus, C. G., 12, 204
Cerletti, Ugo, 67-69

Charcot

Charcot, Jean M., 5, 186 ff., 197 ff., 202
Cheyne, George, 58-66
Chiarugi, Vincenzo, vii, 75-85
Christoffel, Hans, 31
Cimbal, Walter, 227 ff.
Conklin, Edmund, 197
Conolly, John, 13
Crutcher, Roberta, 168
Cullen, William, 81, 83

D

Damerow, Heinrich, vi, 5, 7, 15-27
Danz, Ferdinand Georg, 126
Dendy, Walter, 170
Descartes, Renatus, 235
Dewey, John, 162
Doellinger, Ignaz, 193
Douglas, Willam, 234 ff.
Driesch, Hans, 191
Dubois, Paul Ch., 209, 246
Duchenne, G. B. C., 68

E

Eckartshausen, Baron von, 191
Ehlenburg, Albert, 178
Einstein, Albert, 191
Eliasberg, Wladimir, 210
Emminghaus, Herman, 175 ff., 178
Esquirol, Jean Etienne D., 169
Ettmueller, Christian fr.B., 81

F

Fabrius Cunetator, 109
Fernel, Jean, 81
Feuchtersleben, Ernst von, 13
Fichte, Johann Gottlieb, 11, 113
Flemming, K. F., 13
Fliess, Wilhelm, 190-199
Fontana, Felice, 45
Forel, Auguste, 209
Fothergill, Anthony, 131
Franklin, Benjamin, 133

Freud, Sigmund, v, vii, 3, 5, 43, 52, 56, 70-74, 94, 131, 134 ff., 187 ff., 190-199, 200-245, 246 ff.
Friedreich, Johann Baptist, v, vi, x, 4 ff., 16 ff., 76, 122 ff., 133, 137, 164

G

Galdston, Iago, 16, 190-199
Galenus, 24, 73, 82
Gadelius, Bror, 209
Gerhard, Paul, 175
Gicklhorn, J., 214
Goering, Herman, 211
Goering, V. H., 211 ff., 228
Goethe, Johann W., 42, 137
Goldstein, Kurt, 197
Goodman, Nathan G., 132
Gregor, Albert, 97
Griesinger, Wilhelm, 5, 7, 42, 75, 170 ff.
Guentz, Edward W., 173, 178

H

Haeckel, Ernst, 6, 197
Haeser, Heinrich, 12
Hall, Stanley, 206 ff.
Haller, Albert von, 71, 81
Hartmann, Eduard von, 204
Haslam, John, 75, 138, 169, 176
Hauser, Kaspar, 168
Hecker, Eduard, 163, 174, 181
Hegel, Georg Wilh. Frd., 4, 5, 6, 11, 113, 136 ff., 157
Heinroth, Johann Chr., v, vi, vii, x, 4 ff., 16 ff., 31, 42, 76, 90, 106-130, 133, 138, 139, 150, 152, 168, 176
Henoch, Edward, 180
Herbart, Johann Fried., 138 ff.
Herz, Marcus, 138
Heuyer, Georges, 180
Hippocrates, 10, 24, 41, 82 ff., 131
Hirsch, August, 12
Hirschfeld, Ernest, 193
Hitler, Adolf, 213, 229, 231
Hoeffding, Harold, 7
Hoffbauer, Johann Chr., 86, 138
Hoffmann, Friederich, 81
Holland, Sir Henry, 182

Horst, Ludwig v. d., 209
Humboldt, Wilhelm v., 10, 121

I

Ideler, Karl W., 41
Isensee, Emil, 12
Itard, Jean, 168

J

Jacobi, Jolande, 15
Jallabert, Louis J., 67
James, William, 236
Janet, Paul, 186
Janet, Pierre, vii, 22, 186-189, 202
Jelliffe, Smith Ely, ii, 195 ff., 246 ff.
Joergensen, Carl, 209
Jones, Ernest, 190 ff., 213 ff.
Jung, Carl Gustav, v, vii, ix, 15, 19, 42 ff., 134, 140, 186, 200-245, 247

K

Kahlbaum, Karl Ludwig, 154-167, 174
Kant, Emanuel, 6, 137, 138, 157, 194, 204, 235
Kassowitz, Max, 197
Katz, David, 191
Kieser, D. G., 193
Kirchhoff, Theodor, 13, 16, 41 ff., 77, 86, 97, 157
Kirkbridge, Thomas, 112
Kornfeld, S., 16, 68
Kraepelin, Emil, x, 5, 77, 87, 158, 160 ff., 181, 182, 188, 202, 208, 248
Krafft-Ebbing, Richard, 178
Kretschmer, Ernest, 95, 158, 209 ff., 229, 231
Kroh, Oswald, 191
Kronfeld, Arthur, 209 ff.

L

Laehr, Heinrich, v, 14, 173, 178
Langermann, Johann Gottfr., 42
Laseque, Ernst Charles, 13
Leibbrand, Werner, 193
Leibnitz, Gottfried Wilh., 204
Lentz, F., vi, 13, 14
LeRoy, J. B., 67

Leupoldt, J. M., 193
Lichtenberg, Georg Chris., 207
Linné, Karl von, 81 ff.
Lombroso, Cesare, ix, 208
Lorry, Charles, 81
Lowrey, Lawson George, 180

M

Macbride, David, 81
MacDougall, William, 187
Maudsley, Henry, 5, 7, 171 ff., 176
Mayo, Herbert, 183
McMillan, M. B., 171
Meier, O. A., 227
Meyer, Adolf, 187, 234, 247 ff.
Meynert, Theodor, 196 ff.
Mobius, P. J., ix
Moore, Merrill, 182
Monro, Alexander, II, 44, 45
Mora, George, 77 ff.
Murchison, Karl, 189
Murry, Henry, 235 ff.

N

Neumann, Heinrich, 12, 13, 122, 138, 139,
    161
Nollet, Abbe, 67

O

Oken, Lorenz, 193

P

Paracelsus, Theophrastus, v, vi, 15-27,
    29 ff., 41 ff., 72, 79, 131, 176
Perfect, William, 169
Petzold, Ingeborg, 98
Pinel, Philippe, vii, 75-85, 133, 168 ff.,
    179
Pitcairn, David, 58
Plater, Felix, vi, 28-40, 159
Prince, Morton, 87, 182-185

R

Reil, Johann Christ., 4, 7, 12, 42, 86-105
Ringeis, I. Nepomuk, 193
Riklin, Fr., 202
Rosenkranz, Karl, 157 ff.

Rosenthal, Hugo, 228
Rush, Benjamin, 91, 106, 112, 121, 131-
    133, 168 ff., 176

S

Savanorola, Giovanni M., 81 ff.
Sauvage, Boissier de, 81
Scheidemantel, C. G., vi, 46-57, 68
Schelling, Friedrich v., ii, 193, 204
Schenk von Grafenberg, J., 82
Schiller, Friedrich v., 194
Schleiermacher, Friedrich, 136
Schopenhauer, Arthur, 136
Schubert, H. von, 193, 199
Schuele, Heinrich, 13, 77, 173 ff., 181
Schultz, J. H., 209 ff.
Semelaigne, Rene, 13
Semon, Rudolph, 161
Sidis, Boris, 247
Sibenthal, Wolf von, 199
Sigrist, Henry, 193
Socrates, 26
Sommer, Robert, 112, 209 ff.
Spengler, Oswald, 191 ff.
Sprengel, Kurt, 10
Stahl, Georg Ernst, vi, 41-43, 72, 138, 198
Steckel, Wilhelm, 209
Strich, Fritz, 191
Strohmayer, Wilhelm, 181
Sudhoff, Karl, 15
Sullivan, Harry St., 246 ff.
Swoboda, Herman, 191
Sydenham, Thomas, 131

T

Tertullian, 82
Tissot, Simon A., vi, 49, 66, 70-74, 92, 102
Tramer, Moritz, 180
Trotter, Thomas, 62-66
Tuke, Daniel H., 133

U

Uffelmann, Julius, 178

V

Vogel, R. A., 81
Voght, Ragnar, 209

W

Weininger, Otto, 191
Weizsaeker, Victor von, 228
West, Charles, 178
White, William A., viii, 246-248
Whytt, Robert, 60-66
Wigan, Arthur L., 182-185
Wilmsen, Friedrich Philip, 136

Willis, L. T., 81 ff.
Woelfflin, Henrich, 191
Wundt, Wilhelm, 189, 202, 204, 239

Z

Ziehen, Theodor, 155, 180
Zilboorg, Gregory, 76
Zindel, Nicholas, 73

SUBJECT INDEX

A

Aggritude, 26
Alchemy, ix, 17, 18, 23, 41
Alinatio, 34 ff.
Ambition, 53
Amensia, 80 ff., 83
Anatomy, 29, 30
Animus, 41 ff.
Anthropology, 28 ff., 122, 191
Anthropomorphic, 28 ff.
Anti-Semitism, 210, 233, 239
Arrogance, 53
Aryan, 216, 222 ff.
Autonomism, 7, 8, 187 ff.
Automatisme Psychologique, 186 ff.

B

Bedlam, 91
Bicetre, 91, 169
Blood-letting, 25, 131
Blood-purifying, 25

C

Calvinism, 74
Catalepsy, 172
Catatonia, 155 ff.
Causality, 24
Chemotherapy, 25, 150
Child-Psychiatry, 4, 155-164, 168-181
Chinese, 219 ff.
Chorea, 172
Classical Period, 6
Classify, 95
Clergy, 124, 126-130, 136
Complex, 134
Consciousness, 140, 148
Consciousness, Double, 184
Consteneatio, 34 ff.
Convulsion, 34, 50, 105, 111
Cosmocentric, 28 ff.
Cox Rocking Chair, 114, 132

Criminal, 122
Custodial, 112

D

Daemonicis, 26
Daydreaming, 103
De Animi Morbis, 42
Deductive, 106, 163
Delirium Tremens, 150
Dementia, 169
Dementia Acuta, 178
Dementia Praecox, 87, 161 ff., 182 ff.
Depression, 25, 50
Diagnosis, 203
Dialectic Principle, 45
Diastrephia, 162
Diopathic, 42
Dietetik, 102 ff.
Direct Psychic Method, 112
Dissociation, 182-185
Dolor, 33 ff.
Dream, 203
Dysphrenia, 161 ff.
Dysthymia, 162

E

Ego-Psychiatry, 5 ff.
Electroshock, vi, 67-69
Endemic, 101
English Malady, 58-69
Epidemic, 101
Epilepsy, 34, 150, 162, 172, 179
Ethical Pathology, 156
Etiology, 156, 176
Exorcism, 31
Experiment, 44 ff., 67-69
Experimental Convulsion 67-69
Experimental Psychology, 189
Eyesight, 68

F

Facultas Incognita, 61
Falling Sickness, 20

253

Female, 116
Female Sex, 192
Foramen Monroe, 44
Fear, 50 ff.
Fieber-Lehre, 97 ff.
Floride, 156
Folie Raisonante, 170
Force et Faibless Theory, 187

G

Gemein-Gefuehl, 87 ff., 99 ff.
Germanic, 225 ff.
Gestalt-Psychology, 7
Grief, 55

H

Hebephrenia, 155 ff., 174
Heuristic, 107 ff., 114
Hippocratic Oath, 121
Holism, 43
Homesickness, 53, 111, 151
Hope, 52, 56
Humanitarism, vi, 6, 217
Hydrotherapy, 25
Hypochondriac, 151
Hysteria, 50, 73, 181

I

Ideopathic, 101
Imbecility, 78, 83 ff., 141 ff., 147
Imprudentia, 34
Indignation, 51 ff.
Individual Psychology, 48
Individuation, 243
Inductive, 106
Insani, 18, 23
Insanity, Affective, 172
Insanity, Instinctive, 172
Insanity, Moral, 170
Insanity, Pubertal, 175
Insanity, Sensorial, 171
Insomnia, 117
Intelligence, 103
Isolation, 114

J

Joy, 52, 56
Jews, Jewish, 204-233

Juvenile, 155 ff.
Juvenile Psychopathology, 156 ff., 170 ff.

K

Kahlbaum's Pedagogicum, 155-167

L

Laesio, 33 ff.
Lunatici, 18, 23, 26
Libido, Freud's, 187 ff.
Libido, Jung's, 238 ff.
Lie, The, 122
Longing, 53
Love, 52, 56

M

Man—a Machine, 41
Madness, 87
Male, 116
Mania, 20, 21, 35, 80 ff., 83 ff., 109, 147, 169, 172
Manic Depressive, 173
Medical Pedagogy, 156
Melancholici, 23
Melancholy, 18, 20, 23, 24, 25, 50, 80 ff., 118 ff., 147, 151, 169, 172
Melancholy Attonia, 165
Mens, 34 ff.
Mental Hygiene, 58
Mental Retardation, 34, 168, 171
Micro-Cosmic, 79
Mind-Body Relations, 47
Mnemonism, 5
Mongoloid, 169
Monomania, 169, 172
Morbus, 26
Motus, 41
Music-Therapy, 92

N

Nazism, 200-233, 239
Nerve-Fluid, 47
Nervenarzt, 14
Nervensaft, 122
Neurastenia Cerebralis, 177 ff.
Neuro-Drug, 44
Neurology, 29, 67-69, 70, 77, 169
Nightmare, 105

Non-Stimulation, 151
Nosology, 76, 78

O

Obsession, 18, 24, 26, 35
Observation, 29 ff.
Onanism, 71 ff.
Opium, 44 ff.
Oddness, 87 ff.
Oedipus Complex, 242
Orphancy, 156
Organon, 118
Overstimulation, 34, 144, 147 ff., 151

P

Palliative Treatment, 112, 117
Paralysis, 50, 104, 111, 181
Parnoia, 83, 87, 162
Passion, 48 ff., 54 ff.
Pathology, 12, 102 ff., 116
Patient-Centered, 26
Pauperization, 156
Pauperization, Physical, 156
Pazzia, 78
Pediatry, 169
Periodicity, 191-199
Personality, 117
Phenomenology, 79, 136-163, 139 ff., 152
Physis, 41
Physio-Therapy, 150
Praxis Medica, 33 ff.
Pharmacology, 8, 114
Phlebotomy, 112, 114
Physically Sick, 108
Physical Treatment, 117
Plagiary, x, 17
Pleuralism, 20
Pragmatism, 138
Presbyterian, 131
Preservation, 26
Pre-Freudian, 134 ff.
Preventive, 25 ff.
Prophylactic, 25
Protestant, 123, 217
Protopathic, 101
Psychiatrist, 121-125, 126-130
Psychiatry, Unilateral, 161
Psychic, 143

Psychic overheating, 143
Psychic space, 143
Psychism, 4 ff., 16
Psycho-Analysis, 42, 48, 146
Psychological Medicine, 125
Psychology, 3, 30 ff., 42 ff., 46-57, 72, 76, 99, 137 ff., 235
Psychology, Complex, 241
Psychologie Naturwissenchaftliche, 164
Psychology, Nonpersonal, 189
Psychosomatic, 42, 46-57
Psychotherapy, 95 ff., 102, 106-120, 115, 118, 151
Pubertal Neurosis, 174
Punishment, 114

Q

Quaker, 131

R

Rage, 55
Realism, 41
Religion, 113
Rhapsodies, 90 ff.
Rockefeller Fellow, vii
Roman Catholicism, 31, 74, 193, 211, 217
Romanticism, 16, 41, 46-57, 190-199
Rush Restraining Chair, 132

S

Salpêtrière, 186
Sauvage de L'Aveyron, 168
Scare, 55
Schizophrenia, 89, 163 ff., 174, 182 ff., 184, 205, 216, 243
Schizophrenia, Adolescent, 174
School of French, x, 197
School of Freud, 147
School of Gestalt of Leipzig, 191
School of Romantic, 190-199
School of Romantic Literature, 193-199
School, Somatic Medicine, 164
School, Vienna, 3, 196 ff.
School, Zuerich, vii, x, 188, 195, 202-225
Schub, 166
Semiotik, 126-130
Sense-Perception, 141

Sexology, 73
Shock, 50
Slave, 222
Sleepwalking, 25
Smallpox, 70
Social Psychiatry, 58
Socratic Art, 188
Somatism, 4 ff., 16, 111, 122, 135, 137, 139 ff., 164, 172, 182
Somatopsychology, 42
Spirit of Life, 20 ff.
Spiritualism, 31
Sporadic, 101
Starvation, 114
Stimulation, 149
Strait-Jacket, 114
Stupidity, 142
Subconscious, 135
Suicide, 179
Suppression, 74, 135
Sympathic, 42, 101
Symtomatology, 10, 89, 101, 105, 162, 171, 177
Synchronicity, 240
Systematic, 100, 159
Systole-Diastole, 42

T

Taubsucht, 21 ff.
Temperaments, 19, 73, 116 ff.
Temperance, 50
Terminology, 154-167
Theology, 136
Theoria Medica Vera, 41-43
Therapy, 101
Thermotherapy, 25
Thomism, Neo-, 193

Torpide, 156
Totality, 7, 18, 86, 165
Traité sur les Nerves et leurs Maladies, 70 ff.
Transfusion, 25
Tranquilizer, 25
Treatment, 102, 110 ff.
Treatment, Formal, 115
Treatment, Pure psychological, 115
Turks, 52
Typology, 89

U

Ueberstaatlich, 212
Unilateral, 15, 20, 32, 42, 48, 52, 56
Unilateral pain, 16
Unitarian, 131
Unstructured, 131

V

Vanity, 53
Vecordia, 161 ff.
Vesani, 18, 23
Vesania, 161 ff.
Vascular System, 33
Vitalism, 43, 142, 144
Vitalizing, 114
Vitia Corporis, 38 ff.
Vitia Exretorum, 38 ff.
Vitium, 33 ff., 38

W

Will, 83
Witch-Burning, 31

Z

Zeit-Geist, 240